By John P. Marquand

Thirty Years

Thirty Years

by

JOHN P. MARQUAND

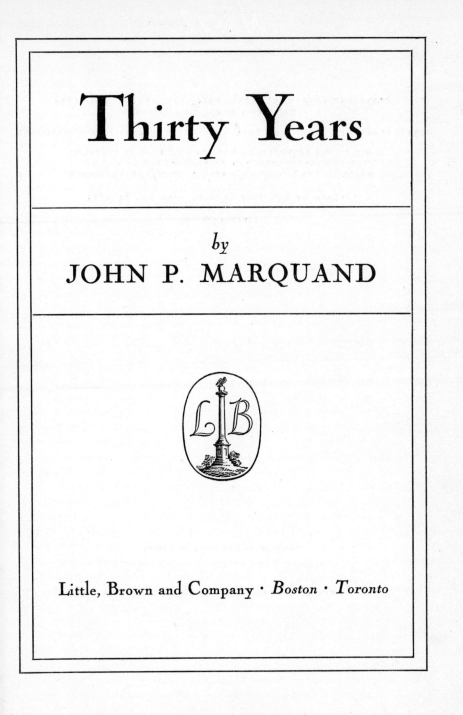

Little, Brown and Company · *Boston* · *Toronto*

Published simultaneously in Canada
by Little, Brown Company (Canada) Limited

PRINTED IN THE UNITED STATES OF AMERICA

Introduction

MR. MARQUAND and I are two of the five members of the Board of Judges of the Book-of-the-Month Club. At a recent meeting one of the novels discussed happened to deal with American Indians. I am case-hardened to the erudition of my colleagues. Nonetheless I was staggered by Mr. Marquand's revelation of his intimate familiarity with Indian life. With Harvardian casualness he finally admitted that he had once spent several weeks living with an Ojibway tribe and had even joined with modest success in its ritual dances. I look forward to solacing myself in my twilight hours with the vision of our handsomest and best-groomed novelist leaping and yelling to the tom-tom's hot beat in the company of a select group of proper Ojibways.

But I should not have been surprised, any more than I was surprised to learn from one of the stories in this collection that he once tried to buy a temple in Mongolia for one hundred dollars. Mr. Marquand does not have to draw on his unconscious for his material. He has been around others as well as inside himself. His knowledge of the garden variety of human beings is almost as extensive as his knowledge of the rarefied specimens in and about Boston. He is not ashamed of being a sharp observer, of owning a lenslike eye, a microphonic ear. As he says somewhere in this volume, "I have . . . written about a *galerie* of which I know, and I wish that all writers, young and old, would do the same."

New England of course fills the background of many of the pieces in this book. But Truk and Ascension Island are here too, and Iwo Jima and Honolulu and Mongolia and especially his beloved city of Peking as it was before the Communist *Gleichschaltung*. He is at home in the dividend-insulated beach clubs of the Bahamas, in the dormitories and on the playing fields where urchins are improbably turned into gentlemen, in the cauliflower-eared world of Damon Runyon. He knows a great deal about three wars, generals, admirals, fighting men and the military mind. More important, he has reflected upon such things and despite every temptation refused to come to rubber-stamp conclusions about them.

These stories and sketches, like those of Ring Lardner and Somerset Maugham, were written primarily for purposes of entertainment; and, again like those of Lardner and Maugham, are not, once these purposes have been attained, exhausted of interest. Most of the stories, as the author makes clear, were tailored to meet the needs of the market. The happy ending of "Golden Lads," for example, is not implicit in the tale, and the flashback, however neatly handled, is there largely to supply the standard ingredient of "action." But subtract these elements and a good deal is left: the insight into certain deep and persistent New England traits and into the tough fidelities, almost the *mystique* of Family. From "The End Game" we learn so much about Hawaii, so much about the minds of soldiers, and indeed so much about human beings that it is churlish to wave aside this beautifully woven long narrative merely because of its final and, one suspects, secretly ironical bow to the bright tin divinity of the Happy Ending.

For at least three of these tales no excuses are needed. It comforts me, for he is a mercilessly accurate judge of his own work, to note that they are also Mr. Marquand's favorites. "Lunch at Honolulu" is remarkable for the absolute rightness of its dialogue (can any contemporary American novelist other than Hemingway touch Marquand for dialogue?), the neat surgery of its satire, the absence of even a single soft sentence and the unforced compassion of its conclusion. The reader's most fervent admiration, however, will probably go out to the pair of Mulligatawny Club stories. The irony, as edged as anything in Lardner, is not corroded with bitterness. Marquand is not as intense as Lardner by any means, but in compensation he runs no risk of losing his temper. These two stories seem to me to be absolutely first-rate of their kind, merging humor and illumination, and written with a perfect control over a peculiar idiom. This idiom is that of a special class of very rich (not the *very*, very rich, who, I understand, are all quite nice people) who have everything, including absurdity and excluding charm. None of our writers seems to know this milieu as intimately as does Marquand. He has cut out for himself a specialty in which he is unrivaled. As technical feats these two stories are brilliant, for he manages to say something about the Mulligatawnymen that is both serious and funny and to do so within the stringent limitations laid down by the large-circulation magazine.

At one time Marquand thought of becoming a chemist. Actually he has very little of the scientist in his make-up — man, not nature, triggers his brain — but there is a reminiscence of the chemist in his ability to analyze out the components of a given social structure. He knows how to "place" people, without guesswork and without the unscientific interposition of his own subjectivity. Stories such as "Good Morning, Major," "Fourth Down," "Beginning Now" and "Just Break the News" are of course well-turned articles of commerce. But at the same time with what laboratory accuracy they note a hundred tiny differences of caste and class.

We like to think of ourselves as a people in process. As a whole we are that; but nevertheless there are millions of us who live by codes, inherited or invented. One of Marquand's talents is the capacity to decipher these codes, to show us clearly what is fruitful in them and what sterile. He understands the admirable loyalty, linking often with dazzling personal courage, that moves his prep-school boys and his Harvard golden lads. He understands too that this loyalty and this courage, like all virtues not mortised in philosophy, are limited because barren of attachment to a larger world. It is this understanding that makes me quarrel gently with his too-severe estimate: "Of necessity these stories lack depth and significance, qualities popular periodicals customarily avoid . . ." They are hardly masterpieces, but they are better than Marquand thinks. They are topflight entertainment; they are curiously interesting demonstrations of the growth of a professional writer; and they are, some of them, much more.

From large-circulation writing Marquand learned all it had to teach him. These are not small things, unless you consider as small things readability, clarity, pace and the restraint of the ego. When he was ready to pass beyond this point into a subtler, larger and freer air he did so. The result was *The Late George Apley* and the novels that followed.

Indeed Marquand's whole writing career may be thought of as a series of enlargements. Each of these enlargements stops short of complete escape. Thus the hallmark of his art is the tension resulting from the play between his precise memory of a smaller experience and his growing understanding of a larger one. He began as a writer of advertising copy and grew into a Pulitzer Prize winner. But he has never wished completely to disown the world of Madison Avenue, only to mature to the point where he could, contemplating it with irony and not with indignation, incorporate it into a picture with a wider frame. He loves Harvard — see "Commencement, June 11, 1953" and "The Social Future of the Harvard Man" in this collection — but the professional alumnus is fair game to his pale, uneloquent but all-observant Yankee eye. His lineage is first-grade New England but, while acknowledging the nobilities of family tradition, he has educated himself to see it in proper proportion. Nothing could be more affectionate than his charming essay "The New Look Reaches Boston"; yet he knows the hub of the universe is not located on Beacon Hill. (See the absolutely delicious foolery of the "Letter to Dr. Huntington," the kind of naughty literary pastiche you are not supposed to be capable of unless you have been to Oxford.)

Finally, he has been for most of his life a respectable member of the upper middle class and has seen no reason hotly to renounce all its values merely because that was for a time the modish thing to do. Instead he has set himself to understand, without indulgence but also without aversion, the curious tragicomedy of that class. The circumstance that its tragicomedy is, though only partially, his own infuses into his best works a certain melancholy that gives them depth. "One must have a living stake in the community," he wisely remarks, "in order to convey a deep impression of it to others."

The English critic Oliver Elton once wrote of W. M. Praed (1802–1839), an elegant writer of *vers de société:* "He has the code, the wit, the manners, the way of taking itself for granted that belongs to the caste, but is something more as well; for in him the caste turns upon itself, and describes and mocks itself, though still it knows of no other self, and refuses to mock too hard." The words do not fit Marquand too badly. But they do not fit exactly either, and that is why he is a serious writer and Praed is not. In the story "Golden Lads" he makes one of his characters remark, "I did not have that intangible radiant inheritance which makes for carelessness and joy, or that heaven-sent serenity and regardlessness of others' rights which was so beautiful yet cruel. It touched me, but I did not have it."

It touched me but I did not have it. There is the secret of Marquand's charm. It is what makes him, I think, the best novelist of social comedy now at work in our country. He is at once outsider and insider. He is the sympathetic dramatizer of that moment of doubt — the doubt as to whether outer and inner security necessarily coincide — which, though it comes to all of us, is the particular gadfly of the gentility.

Of all the writers I can think of he most resembles Thackeray. He has Thackeray's fruitfully ambivalent attitude toward his own class, his irony, his good manners, his self-doubts and much of his humor. And, in time, I think he will come to occupy a place in the American novel of the twentieth century not too unlike that of Thackeray in the English novel of the nineteenth.

CLIFTON FADIMAN

Foreword

THE RANDOM NOTES and papers in this book are not intended to be examples of the essay, formal or informal; and the short stories that have been selected make no pretense at being a prize collection. They are intended solely to represent various phases of my own development as a writer over a period of more than thirty years and, with only a few exceptions, they illustrate my experiments in the field of social satire. The collection will, I hope, be of interest to other writers, because it probably forms a sort of literary autobiography that is in many respects similar to their own.

It has been my fortune, due to economic necessity, to have been obliged to learn how to write while supporting myself and my family by what I was writing. This far from unique situation obviously has its own artistic limitations, and some of the hastily turned out results would have been better if stillborn. Nevertheless, in this connection, I am reminded of a remark attributed to Mr. Sinclair Lewis during an address to a class on the short story at Columbia University. "I am under the impression," Mr. Lewis said, "that I am speaking to students who want to write. Therefore I am asking all who hope to be writers to raise their hands." Then, looking down upon a sea of waving arms, Mr. Lewis concluded his discourse. "All right," he said, "instead of listening to me, why don't you all go home and do it?"

The longer I hear the craft of fiction discussed, the more increasingly I find myself in sympathy with this suggestion. I do not believe that anyone, however able he may be, can directly teach another individual the art of writing, because the development of literary skills and techniques, I think, rests mainly upon personal experience. Thus, few if any writers have ever appeared at the height of their varying powers without having undergone some process of initiation. Most of them have faced a discipline of having a list of periodicals, popular and otherwise, reject their earlier efforts. Others, in a higher income bracket, have been able to indulge in the luxury of destroying their less mature creations at the moment of production. Personally I have not been so fortunate as to have fallen into either of these categories. According to my best recollection, the second short story I ever offered an editor was purchased by the *Saturday Evening Post* in the summer of 1921, and for many years after this initial success I managed to dispose of all the stories I wrote to a few competing sources at gradually rising prices. Reviewing some of my efforts now, I cannot see why many of them were not rejected, but then, I can console myself with the knowledge that the Curtis and Hearst publications have never been conspicuous as charitable institutions. These facts are of interest only insofar as they show that I was caught early in the meshes of what is unkindly but accurately called "commercial writing" — a hard school and one which finally demands a broad knowledge of techniques. It is, unfortunately, a difficult school from which to graduate, particularly if one is noticed favorably by the headmasters. Consequently some of my most brilliant contemporaries are still in it, and I am one of the very few who, after taking a full course of instruction, have not remained with them. Though this is one of the few facts that lends interest to my literary career, I am still not sure whether I left of my own accord or whether I was eventually expelled for misbehavior.

I only know that I find it increasingly difficult to achieve the highly exacting demands of the popular short story. I may have lost my skill by dealing with longer forms, in which error is less disastrous, or I may finally have lost my taste for the whole business because of overindulgence. Unfortunately there is no such thing as writing acceptable fiction, or even what are called "pot-boilers," with one's tongue in one's cheek. I have no desire to apologize for any of the stories that appear here, because each was the best I could do at the time I wrote it. Many show that I strove in various ways to reconcile popular writing with art, and I often overstrained myself in the process. Of necessity these stories lack depth and significance, qualities popular periodicals customarily avoid, and almost inevitably they reach a happy ending.

Though they do not appear here in any chronological order, the date when each was written is appended, and these dates, I hope, may indicate certain stages of progress and craftsmanship. I further hope that they will show that I am able to write better now than when I started, that I am less apt to succumb to temptation and that I have partially solved through trial and error a few problems of fictional composition. In case any reader should care to go further into this thorny subject, I have added to some of these stories a few short notes of self-criticism, always with the caution that I am still far from being a master of the short story, which is a most difficult literary form to achieve, or even to define.

In spite of its many technical hazards and truly harrowing demands, the short story seems to stand in the minds of many persons who should know much better as a literary exercise for beginners which can be easily mastered. Any thoughtful professional must regard with amazement the multitude of persons who consider themselves equipped to teach and criticize the art of the short story. There is scarcely a university in this happy land that does not offer one or more courses on the subject, and these studies spill over into the love-making and soul-searching of a great many summer literary conferences. The bibliography on the writing of the short story has lately assumed enormous proportions, and in our slender magazines for writers only, whole columns of experts offer their services to disturbed short-story writers on a private consultive basis. It is small wonder, in view of this mass encouragement, that most young writers plan, as I did once, to turn out short pieces of fiction as a ready means of livelihood between their more serious bouts with composition.

It is small wonder, too, that the amount of short fiction produced annually in America is so prodigious that many anthologists are continually engaged in sorting it into attractive groups. Yet what, in the last generation, has been the net result of all this effort?

Very little, I am very much afraid. Nearly every successful writer has turned his hand to short stories at some time or other with reasonable competence, but the literary bones of many craftsmen, as potentially able as those who have succeeded, are bleaching upon the short-story reef. These are the individuals who have become so involved with short-story intricacies that they have finally ended by being unable to achieve a longer piece of work. In fact, out of all the hundreds, perhaps thousands, who are now coping with this medium, I can name only one living American who is a short-story writer par excellence. He is, of course, Mr. Hemingway. Though I am tempted to name a few candidates for second place, the effort would only cause confusion. There are a number of brilliant performers, but not one can be relied upon to be consistent — and Mr. Hemingway himself will probably be best remembered for his novels. I am not belittling the short story. It is a most intriguing form. Personally I began to bid farewell to it when I found myself writing various series of short stories involving the same characters, a method which invariably leads to longer narrative.

What, after all, is a short story? No one, as far as I know, has as yet come up with an adequate inclusive answer. Not wishing to compete with efforts of others, I shall offer nothing but an indication. A short story, if it is successful, is a narrative that fits with ease and naturalness into a narrow area that is always surrounded by a frame of conventions. The conventions that circumscribe the short story may vary in species from the depressingly commercial taboos and demands of large-circulation periodicals to the equally dogmatic fashions of the *New Yorker* or of *avant garde* publications. The final result of these conventions, whether they are vulgar or artistic, is formula, and formula only adds to the frame. It is not necessary to study these restrictions for long, whether they are of space or taste, to recognize that each is a limiting factor, although a reader should never be conscious of limits. The inevitability and the narrowness of the frame are what make the short story peculiarly difficult.

The beginner in writing especially is tempted to put either too little or too much upon his canvas and to overwrite or to underwrite in his efforts to keep his work within bounds. It will be obvious from a perusal of these stories that I have been guilty of all these errors — sometimes transparently so, and it may be that someone will profit, as I hope I have, by my mistakes. Only three stories in this volume seem to me to have the naturalness and apparent lack of effort that fulfill the requirement I have outlined for a successful short story. They are "Lunch at Honolulu," "Sun, Sea, and Sand," and "King of the Sea." The first appeared in *Harper's.* The others were ingested by the so-called "smooth" periodicals, with restrained enthusiasm, and these are the last short stories I have written.

Compared with these adroit sophisticates, many others included here have an adolescent enthusiasm and remind me of college sophomores trying frantically to please and stumbling in the process. Still,

I envy them their youth and optimism, and I wonder at my own fearless willingness in writing them. They all have one desirable element. They were intended primarily to entertain, and I hope they still achieve this purpose.

J. P. M.

Contents

A Local Flavor

Letter to Dr. Huntington

Being the refusal of Mr. Horatio Willing, author of The Late George
Apley, *to attend a small dinner given by the Boston Tavern Club to
Messrs. Kenneth Roberts, Walter Edmonds and Marquand.*

November 2, 1937

My dear Dr. Huntington:

This letter is my grateful acknowledgement of your invitation to take
part in your literary dinner of November the ninth. It is with genuine
regret that I find myself obliged to inform you that I cannot conscientiously come, since I realize that my refusal may interfere with
your plans of entertainment. I trust that you may find someone else,
possibly some English instructor, who will consent to take my place,
and thus will give the occasion the literary touch which you desire.

Fearing that you will be surprised and hurt by my refusal, I deem it
advisable to go at some length in explaining my position, both for my
peace of mind and for yours.

If it were not for my own sense of artistic integrity, which to me is
my most valued possession, I should deplore my bad taste in criticizing
as I must your selection of guests. I do so only for personal reasons and
for the additional cause that the club of which you are now secretary
exercises a definite influence on the cultural background of our community. In emphasizing the presence of these individuals at your board
you are giving them your tacit approval. In asking me to be present
you are making use of my position to emphasize this approval. I regret
that I cannot be a party to any such procedure.

Let me hasten to explain that I have nothing against Mr. Roberts or
Mr. Edmonds, and desire to cast no aspersions upon them. Their field

is the historical novel, which has been dignified by Sir Walter Scott
and our own James Fenimore Cooper.

Though I should prefer to take Mr. Cooper to bed with me rather
than either Mr. Roberts or Mr. Edmonds, I must admit that both
Roberts and Edmonds deserve recognition. It is true that, like Mr.
Marquand, they both have a taint of commercialism, although they all
seem genuine in their desire to live it down. Nevertheless they deal
candidly with history, our common mistress. Without approving their
occasional coarseness and levity, I applaud their accuracy as well as
their reasonably careful use of English. I should be pleased if you
would tell both these gentlemen privately that I should have been
glad to have shared a happy evening with them and should have been
glad to have given them the benefit of my advice. It is different with
Mr. Marquand. After the recent unfortunate experience I have had
with him in allowing him to handle my interests in the life and
letters of my friend, the late George Apley, I cannot give him my
approval.

Frankly I believe that I know him better than you do, having been
quite unpleasantly associated with him for a long period of time.
Frankly I do not think, Dr. Huntington, that he is quite the calibre
which should be emphasized by your club. It is my belief that you
would have been far safer and that the world of Boston letters would
have been better, had you invited him to a small lunch at one of the
corner tables with some of your less responsible members. If you had
wished to carry the matter further, a graceful offhand allusion by the
toastmaster, when he was speaking on some other subject, would have
been quite enough for a man who was reared in Newburyport, Massachusetts, who is in no sense a Bostonian, whose name has never appeared in the pages of the *Atlantic Monthly*, and who has supported
himself for many years by writing squibs for a superficial publication,
known as the *Saturday Evening Post*.

Since this indictment may seem severe to you, I feel it only just that
I offer certain evidence to support it. You may indeed advance the ob-
jection, I admit with a modicum of truth, that Messrs. Roberts and
Edmonds have both been contributors to this periodical, and that Mr.
Roberts indeed was nurtured for some years at its enervating bosom.
This is a temptation to which other writers have been subjected, and
once they have succumbed to it I do not believe that they are ever

afterwards quite the same. It is true that Mr. Roberts and Mr. Edmonds have both measurably succumbed, but I do not think that they have succumbed as frequently, or have tried to succumb as hard or as blatantly as Mr. Marquand.

In my opinion, and I believe that my opinion is worth something in the sounder world of letters, Mr. Marquand is in no sense a writer. He is a scrivener and copyist who battens upon the ideas of his intellectual superiors. Furthermore his rhetoric is bad; his grammar is not all that it should be; he is factually inaccurate and at all times careless. These I admit are severe indictments to use against anyone who is even on the outer fringes of that democratic brotherhood of the pen. I regret to say that I must sustain these indictments by dealing at some length with personal matters, which I both deeply regret and desire to forget as soon as possible.

I met Mr. Marquand when I was in the midst of getting in hand material for the life and letters of my friend, the late George Apley. At the time I was deep in other work, being obliged to prepare several papers for local societies of a learned and literary nature, of which I have the honour to be a member. This pressure was the only reason that I even gave a moment's attention to Mr. Marquand's gratuitously proffered suggestion and highly meretricious enthusiasm. Though I was instinctively shocked by his idea of submitting my material to the hands of a commercial Boston publisher, I finally consented in the belief I owed a personal duty to a world which now produces so little good writing and so few good books. Further, I saw myself in the position of offering to a larger audience something of my own which was worth while. I had intended turning over the letters and a few notes, as has sometimes been my practice, to a young acquaintance of mine at Harvard for a little, a very little, necessary brushing up. Instead I entrusted this superfluous task to Mr. Marquand, although of course the idea and the general conception of the work were entirely my own. The net result is the inaccurate and mangled volume known as *The Late George Apley*. I cannot decline being associated with it, but I must decline, and have declined, all responsibility.

In publishing this volume, in which I take no pride whatsoever, Mr. Marquand and those commercial printers, Little, Brown and Company, have given me no author's credit. My name does not so much as appear upon the title page. Instead, for the first time in his career, and if I have anything to do with it the last time, Mr. Marquand has obtruded himself upon serious critical attention by stepping parasitically into the shoes of an able and recognized man of letters. I shall not say what I think of this form of literary robbery, since my other achievements, under my own name, speak adequately for themselves.

Indeed, Dr. Huntington, I should be glad to dismiss this from my mind with only a shrug at turpitude, were it not for the reactions caused by Mr. Marquand's maladroitness, among my own acquaintances and among the general public. In editing my remarks and by clumsy cutting, my subject, Mr. Apley (who would have hesitated to receive Mr. Marquand in his parlor except upon some large occasion, such as a world war, or for raising money for a local charity), and I myself have been depicted in a manner which too often borders on the ridiculous. It would sometimes even seem that Mr. Marquand had consciously made an effort in perpetrating humour. This, however, I absolve him of, since he has neither the wit nor the polish to turn a humorous phrase.

The reception of this volume by the critics, touted as it was by the publishers, received more credit than it deserved, considering the form in which it was presented, but I desire to make it clear beyond all peradventure that anything good which may have been said of the book is my own work and not Mr. Marquand's, who masquerades as its author. I am not responsible, however, for the well-deserved barbs of sarcasm which have been shot against it; these are the fault of Mr. Marquand.

I should be the first to applaud the critics for their sagacity in picking out the many obvious flaws which the book contained, if it were not that I have to face my many friends and acquaintances and be twitted by them for my lack of taste, tact and general culture. Matters have long ago reached a point where I feel a sense of genuine embarrassment when I appear among persons whom I have known for a generation.

At the risk of straining your patience I shall endeavour to be more specific. A critic in one of our learned quarterlies has considered my book, not Mr. Marquand's, on terms of its merit, but has added that "now and again it lists somewhat heavily to the baroque." Though this fault is in no sense mine, it has plagued me deeply. My style and my point of view towards life have never been baroque. The same is not true of Mr. Marquand. This baroque quality which he has injected and has played upon *ad nauseam* has caused me lively humiliation. The publishers' desire for wide circulation has done the rest. Because undue emphasis was laid upon the fact that one of Mr. Apley's relatives was exhumed from the family lot in Mt. Auburn Cemetery and removed to a more suitable place — a matter which I intended to deal with in the most casual manner — I have been accused by half a dozen Bostonians as referring to the vicissitudes of one of their own relations. Because I touched very lightly and delicately upon a passing infatuation which Mr. Apley had for a young woman in South Boston, I have been accused by half a dozen families of revealing an intimate secret known only to themselves, which should have been forgotten. It is not my fault that the lives of many right-thinking people in Boston are identical. It is, however, Mr. Marquand's fault that such an obvious fact has become more obvious.

These may all seem small matters, including the fact that I was called "a stuffed owl" by the London *Morning Post*, but taken collectively indeed they are not small; collectively they have caused me mental anguish not palliated by another circumstance.

It was not until the unfortunate complication of *The Late George Apley* that my work was ever compared to that of one of my colleagues in Boston. I refer specifically to M. A. DeWolfe Howe.* It is true that this gentleman has laboured with me in the vineyard of lives and letters; it is true that he has received a greater public acclaim than I, in that he has been accorded a prize awarded by a former yellow journalist, known as the Pulitzer Prize. Although Mr. Howe is in many ways admirable and conscientious, this one event stamps him as a caterer to a more public sort of appeal than I, for one, have ever coveted. I believe conscientiously that I may tell you that I should refuse such a distinction, should it be offered me, which it has not, and I hope never will be. It is my belief, shared by many close acquaintances, that my style is considerably better than Mr. Howe's. It is my belief that I am justified in resenting this comparison, although as I say Mr. Howe is in

* The literary rumor that Mr. Howe was the model for Mr. Horatio Willing, the author of *The Late George Apley*, is one of the grossest absurdities I have ever encountered. Ironically enough I discussed the novel with Mr. Howe many times before I started writing it. Eventually Mr. Howe was kind enough to read the manuscript, and made many valuable suggestions regarding Boston and the Boston background, nearly all of which I adopted. — J. P. M.

many ways admirable and undoubtedly makes a conscientious effort to do as well as he can.

All these matters I should pass over were it not for this which I have left for the last. I have prided myself always on the use of the English language. If I have been nothing else, I have been a purist, Dr. Huntington, and now through no fault of mine the effort of a lifetime has been broken. I have been pilloried in the public press for certain grammatical lapses for which a schoolboy would be birched. I have been japed at for using the phrase "different than" and for using "who" instead of the objective "whom." It is needless to say that I have confronted Mr. Marquand and his publisher with these facts, demanding an immediate withdrawal of my book from circulation, but their answer has been unsatisfactory. Each has blamed it upon the other, but the reply of Mr. McIntyre, now the president of what was once a literate publishing house, has been the worst. He has told me that his proof room made no grammatical changes, since they considered my grammar was exactly as I had intended it. In other words, no help was given in "brushing up" my work.

Out of all these elements of clumsiness and confusion which have fallen so undeservedly on my unsuspecting head there is only one aspect in which I can take pride, in that it is a last tribute to my friend, the late George Apley. Despite the inaccuracies and innuendoes with which Mr. Marquand and certain critics have besmirched what was intended to be the career of an outstanding man, my friend, the late George Apley, has been able to rise above them. Indeed I think his character has become the greater from the contrast, so that despite Mr. Marquand, despite the japes of the small-minded, he stands as one of the best products of America. He typifies the spirit of Boston. Nay more, in doing so, he typifies a city which in my opinion changing times have rendered the only place in America fit to live in. May I add that this final and important result is my doing and in no sense Mr. Marquand's?

I might go further, but I will not, since I strive for conciseness in correspondence. If I have said enough to make you understand why I cannot be with you on the evening of the ninth, these few lines of mine have achieved their purpose. I have done enough for Mr. Marquand and a great deal too much. I hope you realize now that you are doing too much for him also, although I feel it is now too late to rectify your error. In closing, I must beg you to be more careful in the future, Dr. Huntington, and kindly convey my respectful regards and some small word of congratulation to Messrs. Roberts and Edmonds. Also, if you please, give some friendly word to M. A. DeWolfe Howe. You might tell all three that I am watching their efforts with interest, and I trust that they will all do better some time in the very near future. Please extend my regards to other members of the Tavern Club, and let us hope that we may meet on some more fortunate evening.

Respectfully yours,
HORATIO WILLING
author of *The Late George Apley*

The New Look Reaches Boston

(1953)

BOSTON, though a large city, especially when the population of its environs is included, has many small-town attributes. Everyone seems to know a little about everyone else there, and all good Bostonians are partial to local gossip and anecdote. These tales may be apochryphal but usually they rest somewhere on truth's foundation — like the time-worn one about the Beacon Street butler announcing some newspaper reporters — "A man from the *Post*, a man from the *Globe*, and a gentleman from the *Boston Evening Transcript*." There is a commonly accepted legend that Mr. Godfrey Cabot, now in his nineties, still walks each morning from his home in Cambridge to his office on State Street. This may not be so, but the idea is reassuring, because Bostonians pride themselves on being a hardy race. There is a story about one of them who, when taking a Sunday stroll over his country estate, slipped when climbing a stone wall, fell and broke his arm, and simply said, "Oh, sugar." Not very long ago when the kettle of deep fat in the kitchen of the Somerset Club burst suddenly into flames, it was reported that the firemen answering the alarm were told to use the service and not the members' entrance. It seems that actually this was a true report but one which still hurts the feelings of loyal members, because it implied exclusiveness. It should be added that these directions were given the firemen because the service entrance was the shortest way to the kitchen. Almost daily there are new additions to this wealth of Boston lore, but ancient tales are also passed on by succeeding generations. Even today you can still hear a story about old Mr. Perkins, the great merchant in the China trade, who used to have a man run ahead of his horses when he drove to his summer home in Brookline. It is said that a Boston jeweler, noticing that Mr. Perkins wore a leather thong attached to his gold watch, asked if Mr. Perkins would not like a gold watch chain, considering his position, and Mr. Perkins answered that his position was such that he could afford to wear a leather thong. But the one which I still like best of all concerns the Honorable Cameron Forbes when he was United States Ambassador to Japan. "If Cameron does not come home soon," one of his relatives is reported to have said, "he will get out of touch with Milton," referring not to the poet, but to the famous suburb of Boston.

This in a strict sense is truer than one might think, for Boston is a complex of intricately developed manners and of delicately balanced values that make it not only a city but also a state of mind which demands constant association if it is to be fully comprehended. Otherwise one does indeed get out of touch with Boston. I am acutely aware of this personally, although an orthodox Bostonian would say that I am in no position whatsoever to make any authoritative remark on the subject, since I come from Newburyport, Massachusetts, and was born in Wilmington, Delaware. He might also add that I am not even what is sometimes called a professional Bostonian, like certain enthusiastic Westerners and Jerseyites who have settled in the city limits and have carried the torch until they have out-Bostoned Boston. Nevertheless I have developed a certain superficial awareness, since most of my life has been spent shuttling in a highly schizophrenic manner between Boston and New York.

Nothing, I believe, is more spiritually difficult than an attempt to adjust oneself to the life of these two utterly divergent cities. A true Bostonian is fortunate in that he has never made such an effort. There is no necessity, because he is completely content with his environment and entirely secure in his civic integrity. A genuine Bostonian is always anxious to get home. New York, he will tell you, if you meet him on the five o'clock as it leaves the Grand Central, is not a nice place to come to but it is a very good place to get away from. Bostonians used to frequent the Hotel Belmont, presumably to be as near to the New York, New Haven, and Hartford Railroad as possible, but now that this hostelry has disappeared, a Bostonian, when in New York, is a man without a country. It is very easy and, for one who has his roots there, dangerous to get out of touch with Boston. Nevertheless, it is surprising how quickly this city reclaims an erring son, once he has returned. The more things change, as the French say, the more they remain the same things, and here perhaps the French are right.

I was in Boston last December — not one of the city's best months or one of its worst ones either. I had come there primarily to attend a dinner party on Beacon Street, but I had really come because of a deep desire to see the place again, a desire which arises often in every Boston expatriate, no matter how long he has been away. It was a cold late afternoon and the sky was the color of lead, heavy with the threat of snow, and the clouds across the Charles River Basin bore the grim afterglow of an early winter sunset. The streets and the buildings all were waiting stolidly for the approach of another hard winter. It was a long way from New York, a city which is usually successful in ignoring the onset of natural phenomena, and of the two cities Boston seemed the more indestructible. Copley Square and Commonwealth Avenue looked dingy in the dusk, and a snatch of T. S. Eliot's poem came back to me — about the readers of the *Boston Evening Transcript* swaying in the wind like a field of ripe corn, not that there was any wind, or any *Transcript* any more to be dropped on Back Bay doorsteps. There were, however, a few ashcans not yet drawn back into the basements and a few odd scraps of more modern journals near them. The lights were on in the cocktail lounge of the old Hotel Vendome, a spot once called the Nippon Room before the late unpleasantness. There was nothing new or extraordinary about any of the local sights or sounds but, combined, they had their own contagion and evoked in me a familiar emotional response. I began to wonder why I had ever left Boston, and yet at the same time I knew that I should leave it again. I had been out of touch too long to stay, but it would always call me back.

A Boston dinner party is always different from its New York counterpart, and personally, I think, in many ways superior. It is a more solid, more self-possessed social function — less hilarious, perhaps, but at the same time more friendly. A Boston host once told me of a crisis he had been obliged to face one evening. Suddenly, just before dinner was announced he observed to his horror that there was a gentleman in the drawing room whom he had completely forgotten he had invited. It was necessary to act rapidly and to add a new place and card to the table, but fortunately this guest never knew. He *never* knew. Things would have been different in New York, where everyone would have been more frank and might even have made a good joke out of the occurrence. There is something both more subtle and more brittle about New York dinner guests. The women are dressed more dash-

ingly and the men are more alert. There are more strangers at the table
from outlying parts of the country, and no one can safely predict exactly what may happen at a New York dinner. In Boston, on the contrary, everybody knows in advance, and thus everything is on a firmer
foundation. At a good Boston dinner everyone knows everyone else,
or at least who everyone is. There is not so much need for what is
called "small talk" with the ladies on one's right and left. Boston
women are less anxious and much more composed, and Boston men are
better looking than their New York opposite numbers. They are better
preserved, too, and even Harvard professors, who come to Boston dinners occasionally, have a touch of the out of doors about them.

Conversation seldom demands New York's creative invention, because it is usually about Boston or Boston personalities, and everyone
present is always aware of the city's fascination. On this December
evening the table talk was fairly general. Being close to Christmas, it
was concerned with the difficulties of the season. There was a discussion of the dubious taste displayed by Mayor Hynes, who, many
thought, had overdecorated the Common, and then naturally the subject veered to Christmas Eve on Beacon Hill. Once this had been a
strictly neighborhood affair, with open houses, candlelit windows, and
a few carol singers and bell ringers, but lately these picturesque activities had attracted crowds in such unmanageable numbers that it was
better to keep the front doors locked. One lady living on Louisburg
Square told of discovering a strange young man in her upstairs library.
She thought he must be a friend of a friend until she found him still
there and asleep when it was time to put out the candles. It appeared
that he had made a mistake and that he had thought he was in the
house next door. Then there are some good stories which can only be
heard in Boston. Recently there was a coming-out party in a garden
at Chestnut Hill. The debutante's father, who, among his other business interests, had acquired a wild animal farm in New Hampshire,
had brought a few of the animals down and had placed them in the
garden for the delectation of the company. One of the guests had gone
so far as to give a baby elephant a playful slap on the rump. He had
never slapped an elephant before and was not familiar with the durabil-
ity of a pachyderm's epidermis. As a result he broke several small blood
vessels in his right hand and was obliged to wear his arm in a sling for
several weeks.

It is often said that Boston is a man's town and that Boston men are always out several nights a week at small club dinners. A New York visitor has even been known to observe that a Boston man only asks two questions about another Boston man: What class was he in at Harvard, and What did he do in the war? Though this is an exaggeration, very little more is actually necessary here in the way of identification. That evening, when the men were alone together there was no nonsense as there would have been in New York about hurrying to join the ladies. The men all knew that the ladies were having a good time by themselves, and thus there was ample time for some solid and serious conversation. Over the brandy and coffee there was an intelligent discussion regarding the relative merits of several Boston investment trusts, as well as the tastes and eccentricities of a few trustees. It was only natural that the conversation should also linger for a while on state and local politics and on the Boston Irish, and the parking problem, and the Boston police, and all this inevitably led to further reminiscence.

It seemed to several present that Boston was not the place to live in that it used to be, not the tight little community that it was in the days of Edwin Booth and John L. Sullivan. When my father was a little boy he had climbed the fence of a Beacon Hill back yard to secure a bunch of grapes and an old lady had called to him from an open window. "Young man," she had said, "if you begin by stealing grapes, you will end by stealing Government bonds." This prophecy had not been fulfilled, but small things were growing larger and small portents were becoming ominous. Insignificant cracks in the social structure were becoming chasms now. There was a time in horse-drawn Boston when children could coast in comparative safety down Mount Vernon Street. In the winter small bridges spanned the paths of the Common for the benefit of other coasters, and there were once snowball battles between the North End and the West End. All this is over now. Boston is no longer the fine city it was once. One is forever recalling the past there while deploring what is happening now, and there has always been a great deal in Boston to deplore. Things were growing shaky back in 1910, when the Victorian era was ending, and things had grown rapidly worse ever since World War I. Admittedly we were in an era of alteration, but would anything be left of Boston Character, we were wondering, if present trends continued? It was well to consider present trends before we joined the ladies.

There is no city in this kaleidoscopic country that has not suffered its growing pains of change, but Boston, I imagine, has undergone more startling and soul-shaking upheavals than most, in spite of what untutored critics say about its static qualities. No one who even delves superficially into the record can ignore all the terrific things that have happened and are still happening there, always accompanied by the protests of an outraged citizenry. It would be possible, if one wished, to start with the making of the Back Bay from the mud flats of the Charles River, a stream which, in spite of its alterations, still separates Boston from the hazy and enigmatic reaches of Cambridge. But by now the Back Bay and all its brick and brownstone houses have become as permanent, almost, as Beacon Hill. Since that time, however, other shattering changes have been constantly on the march. As an example, there was the construction of the subway through Boston Common. To achieve this improvement it was necessary to excavate a graveyard at the edge of the Common and to re-establish many remains on top of the subway, a pious act which still stands in the minds of a few as an outstanding exhibition of civic gymnastics. Then there was the damming of the Charles River to make what is now the picturesque Basin, an encroachment on individual rights which aroused the wrath of dwellers along the water side of Beacon Street, who had enjoyed watching from their back windows the rise and fall of the tide and who were obliged to alter their household systems of drainage. Even a brief perusal of the public prints shows that some group of Boston citizens has always been protesting against something. There was, for instance, around the latter twenties, the difficulty over the erection of a large electric sign on the roof of a Park Street building that overlooked Boston Common to advertise the Chevrolet automobile. Many persons felt that the sight of it over the Parkman Bandstand and the Common's educationally labeled trees was a desecration of hallowed ground and that the electric advertisements bordering the Common on Tremont Street were quite enough. History may prove that this event was the source of a new rush of bad ideas which have yet to cease. Only a year or so ago housewives on Beacon Hill were compelled to move their Boston rockers outside their dwellings and to sit in embattled formations in order to prevent a city contractor from tearing up the bricks of their sidewalks and substituting modern unsightly concrete, and worse was soon to follow.

The recent governor of Massachusetts, the Honorable Paul A. Dever, is blamed in many quarters for the latest *bouleversements*, and with some justice — for not even James Michael Curley himself, Boston's perennial mayor as long as one can remember, and a name frequently used to frighten small Beacon Street children, has done as much to change the face of this splendid city. Under the generous and friendly Dever administration "A Great New Highway System" — as Mr. Dever has called it on hundreds of billboards, always asking the passer-by to excuse the inconvenience — is now knifing its way through Boston. Skyway ramps are arching over its ancient winding lanes, and intricate clover leaves, flanked by swimming pools and playgrounds, are appearing at unexpected points. The Esplanade along the Charles, the generous gift of Mrs. Storrow, where it was once possible to wheel babies, walk dogs, and even to sail toy boats in comparative security, now — excuse the inconvenience — has a six-lane concrete highway running through it, with underpasses, overpasses, and bridges for pedestrians. The old North End — excuse the inconvenience — where the Old North Church and the rewarding residence of the late Paul Revere, not to mention the old Copp's Hill Burying Ground, still presumably remain intact, and where one once purchased Italian goat cheeses and spaghetti dinners — now resembles the blitzed-out area of London in the vicinity of St. Paul's. Block after block, fragile shops and tenements, which frankly could not have stood up much longer anyway, have now been leveled down to rubble, so that our cradle of liberty, Faneuil Hall itself, begins to stand nakedly before the intricacies of the Great New Highway System.

Goodness only knows what has become of various corners and houses that one once used as reference points when traveling through this confusing foreign and market district, or what will happen to many more, because the Great New Highway System is not finished yet and the Massachusetts Public Works Department, like the Pentagon in Washington, only reveals its future plans to properly cleared individuals. I have not traveled through the South End recently, having for several elections voted the Republican ticket, but I hear rumors that this section of Boston too, with its fine old residential squares, is full of similar surprises, including swimming pools and roller-skating rinks. Goodness only knows where this all will end, and a few people are even wondering who will pay for it or how, but only a very few. After all, finances do not matter much in Boston any longer. The city has been so mismanaged in ordinary human memory that it has nearly always teetered with comparative safety upon the abyss of bankruptcy. Goodness only knows also how anyone, including even the local taxi drivers, who have developed the homing instinct of guided missiles, will be able to find their way through Boston when the Great New Highway System is eventually completed. Traffic now runs one way on Beacon Street and another way on Marlborough and a wholly different way on Charles. Restrictions against entering and turning now render it necessary for a normally observant driver to describe a series of decreasing circles to reach a given point. Even with the scholarly road signs of what is presently completed of the new highway system, a motorist seeking the Sumner Tunnel and East Boston frequently finds himself at Kendall Square in Cambridge. Yet, as the most mentally retarded rat eventually learns his way through a psychologist's maze, no doubt many operators of motor vehicles will do equally well. Eventually there may be valid reason to expect that the traffic which for years has overburdened Boston's equestrian streets will be sucked into these new arteries like dust through the tube of a vacuum cleaner. In fact the time may be just around the corner when one can travel through Boston without knowing one is there at all, and, curiously enough, I doubt whether Boston will greatly care.

These physical changes, imposing though they may be, are only symptoms of an era's social change. Ever since Ireland's potato famine of 1848 certain sections of Boston's population have been endeavoring, like defeated armies, to break contact with pursuing elements. Irish Bostonians have held the South End so long that they have lost their brogue and are today in many ways as aloof as the Boston Brahmins, but the Italians, who have staked their claim to the old North End, are constantly treading on their heels. Besides these larger quotas, orthodox Jewish communities, a small Chinatown, and a growing Harlem, not to mention colonies of Syrians, Poles, and Greeks, have all taken root in Boston, but no other group has yet duplicated the migrations of Boston's most publicized minority, sometimes termed "the Proper Bostonians" or "the Last Puritans."

From the earliest history of Boston to the present these individuals have been assiduously engaged in escaping from strange neighbors and, more recently, from themselves. When Bonner drew his inviting map of Boston before the middle of the eighteenth century, the Brahmins, if there were Brahmins then, dwelt in gambrel-roofed houses in the vicinity of the North End, only to move south under the pressures of business and population growth. The days of Gilbert Stuart and the China trade saw them building on Beacon Hill, and also in the region where the shopping district now flourishes, on Franklin, Summer and Winter Streets. Some of them tried Tremont Street for a while, ending by building the beautiful Colonnade Row, recalled now only in ancient prints, but their culture vanished from these districts years ago, leaving only an occasional square or church behind it. They also experimented with the South End for a while, evolving exclusive residential developments, still visible in the vicinity of Worcester Square; until eventually they were attracted to the Back Bay and began living life anew on the right and wrong sides of Commonwealth Avenue, on Newbury and Marlborough Streets and on the water and wrong sides of Beacon. It almost seemed, around the turn of the century, that polite Boston was permanently established in this area. Conservatives even began to venture from their Bulfinch fronts on Beacon Hill to settle behind the uglier but more fashionable façades of the new land beside the Public Garden. There they dwelt — and some do still — in a soberly intellectual affluence, accounts of which still linger like a happy echo in the pages of Dr. Holmes or the novels of William Dean Howells and Judge Grant and occasionally Henry James.

Space prevents any full description of their remarkable and often endearing customs. There is only room to observe that though they have long been a minority surrounded by a population as much a part of Boston as themselves, their vigor, their impeccable instinct for order and tradition, combined with their capacity for making and conserving comfortable sums of money, have always given character and tone to the whole city, an unquestioned fact tacitly admitted by the Curleys, the Devers, and the Kennedys. They have even contrived, in spite of their small numbers, to run financial State Street, and more often than not to govern the state and represent its people in the halls of Congress, and their genius has not yet evaporated. It has been assisted always by the infusion of new blood, as Mr. Howells has observed in his novel *The Rise of Silas Lapham*, depicting the career of an astute and aggressive Yankee from the wrong side of the tracks. There are plenty of Silas Laphams still, revered figures in the Chamber of Commerce, if not in the Somerset and Union clubs, but most of these somehow prefer rural life in the Newtons.

It is disturbing to report that proper Boston, so well defined and so conspicuous, is now undergoing the greatest change of all. In the last two decades, and indeed even before, proper Bostonians have been leaving Boston, and the exodus has now become so great as to remind one of Philadelphia, that strange city now almost completely devoid of proper Philadelphians.

The vacant houses and the sales signs on Commonwealth Avenue and Marlborough Street chant in a mute chorus the lament of a vanishing way of life. Few persons can afford and fewer wish to live in their grandparents' mansions now, in drafty rooms with dated heating plants and plumbing. Boston servants, whose wages plus their food frequently exceed the salary of a Harvard instructor, are neither as spry nor as hardy as they used to be, granted that their services are obtainable. Neither do their loyalties and spirit of sacrifice meet the standards which any Beacon Street housewife once felt justified in expecting. They have somehow lost that fine old pride in work which once kept the shadowy dining rooms, drawing rooms, and libraries spotless, and they show a marked distaste for cosy unheated quarters beneath the slates. For years the real value of these dwellings has dropped below what they are assessed for tax purposes. It is cheaper to leave them than remodel, and besides, Beacon Street and Commonwealth Avenue are shaken now by a roar of traffic, and parked cars are jammed all day along the curbs. It is better for the children to move to the country.

Thus many peculiar contradictions are appearing on Boston's proudest streets. First the dentists and the doctors and the osteopaths appeared, and then small apartments and larger apartment buildings, and next a few restaurants. The Slater House with its great ballroom became an eating establishment known as the Fox and Hounds, and a casket company has its offices at the far end of Commonwealth Avenue. Several imposing dwellings now house secretarial schools and colleges and academies of song and dance. Outlanders by the hundreds, according to older standards, are now quite at home on Beacon Street. It is growing increasingly difficult to reconstruct old Boston now.

The protesters against the Chevrolet sign and kindred desecrations are still calling for the moving vans, and not for any conventional trek to the now-citified suburbia of Brookline and Chestnut Hill. They are moving to more distant, less disturbed perimeters — to Concord, Dedham, Beverly Farms, and Hamilton, and even to points beyond. Incidentally, it is interesting to note that the Boston Irish too are not unsusceptible to the travel virus. Their comfortably situated lawyers, brokers, contractors, and plenty of their politicians are now living the year around in Cohasset and Scituate and other South Shore points. It is true that the breadwinners of all these solid families still spend their days in Boston offices, own Boston real estate, park their cars in front of the No Parking signs, and with their wives and children patronize Boston stores, hotels, and theaters, but they no longer live or vote there. Imperceptibly at first but with growing momentum the conservative balance and leadership of the town is disappearing to parts unknown, leaving vacuum in its place. Soon, if the trend continues, only a corporal's guard will be left behind the ancient and purpled windows of Beacon Hill and around the Public Garden. New baby carriages and new juveniles will gather in that garden soon, in the vicinity of its little lake and the bronze statue of George Washington. Dogs of a different type will follow their masters on what is left of the Esplanade. New faces by the hundreds will appear in the congregations of the Arlington Street Church, of the Church of The Advent, Emmanuel, and Trinity. It may even be that the Boston Athenaeum itself will not be immune to change.

It is all very well to remark that something has always been happening to Boston. In all probability since the days of that well-disposed Indian, the chief Shawmut, whose name still adorns a local banking house, and who had real-estate interests on Boston Neck when the first Puritans arrived, there have been individuals who have said that Boston is not what it used to be. Furthermore, of course, nothing anywhere is ever what it used to be. Nothing is easier than to lament the good old days, and most lamentations can be discounted in the name of progress. Nevertheless the fact remains that the physical face of Boston and its habits and institutions have undergone more alterations in the lifetime of its present generation than ever before in its history. Boston has been shaken by impacts that may well make strong men weep, and no one can foretell what the final result may be, but it is curious to discover that nothing of its personality has been basically altered yet. It still remains one of the few cities in America with an individuality and flavor entirely its own. It has never forgotten its past in terms of its present, and to anyone who has lived in it long enough to know its ways, Boston is still, from a prejudiced viewpoint, one of the most satisfactory cities anywhere, and one of the most beguilingly beautiful.

Volumes are written annually about the character and distinctive charm of cities, but seldom with any marked success. Character, even in an individual, is most difficult to define or translate. It is a composite of small details, each almost negligible in itself, and the complexities that make up a city's character increase in an alarming sort of geometrical progression. Any city rooted in history and playing an active part in modernity cannot help but be anything except itself, and Boston is very much itself indeed. Anyone, for example, alighting in the Back Bay Station, still with an atmosphere all its own, in spite of its fairly recent innovations, is aware at once that he is in a non-run-of-the-mill city, both from the bewilderment of strangers and from the marked conditioning of its regular inhabitants.

A Bostonian has a knack of being able to tell another Bostonian instinctively, regardless of his occupation or his bank account. They are drawn together by common knowledge and by a common attitude that may be defined as a grim sort of civic pride. They have all been molded by environment and they have all reacted to a sequence of common experience which has sharpened their capacity for adjustment until they are more at home in Boston than in any other place. In fact anyone who has lived for a while in Boston will bear the city's mark, no matter where he may go subsequently, and if he has stayed too long he will become progressively unfitted to live in any other place.

Climate, perhaps, has done more to manufacture local personality than any other force. At any rate it seems safe to state that Boston has the most variable if not the most difficult climate in the super-equatorial world. From infancy everyone in Boston has been taught to regard the thermometer with care combined with cynicism. In few other cities can the mercury rise and fall so rapidly, depending on the variability of the always-erratic winds, in winter touching readily points below zero, only to snap, in a few brief hours, upward to the fifties or sixties. During this inclement season Boston is also subjected to an unpredictable series of snowstorms ending in rain or sleet, followed by thaws and freezing, and accompanied by a chill humidity that clutches at the throat. In summer, though its temperatures can equal those of Singapore, no one can be sure when an east wind will arise from the Atlantic, bringing cold and fog. This sort of thing makes in time for a very hardy race and also explains why no one in Boston cares unduly for small refinements of dress, why everyone wears rubbers and mittens, and why Boston faces have a coldly austere and at the same time a philosophic cast — why Bostonians appreciate small favors and suspect large ones and are unique in their ability to withstand adversity. It is weather, perhaps, that has also engendered an indifference to certain small graces of living and a tolerance to inefficient civic administrations, and finally an acute awareness of the misfortunes of others. It has always been the frame of Boston character, and one doubts whether this will change much until the Gulf Stream alters its course or there are different spots under the sun.

Climate, time, and, in some degree, the pigeons and their more recent competitors, the starlings, birds that always behave more decorously than their New York counterparts, have placed a patina over Boston that conceals much that has been going on there recently. Anyone who has wandered from boyhood through its streets, until their windings and their agreeable botanical and proper names have become ingrained upon the subconscious mind, is aware of the disappearance of old landmarks, but not acutely or unhappily, because against a backdrop of icicles, or snow banks, or a heat wave, nothing seems to have occurred as yet to upset the grand design. Part of the iron fence, for example, that bordered the Beacon Street side of the Common disappeared during the war and is yet to be replaced. The traditional grocery emporium of S.S. Pierce Company has moved from the corner of Beacon and Tremont. Science has now discovered that parrots are a detriment to public health and thus they are no longer on sale on Bromfield Street. The old New England House, that once catered to the market district after it ceased to be a water-front hotel, has been out of business for thirty years. The *Boston Evening Transcript* has closed its doors. Thompson's Temperance Spa on Washington Street has had its face lifted, and the young ladies who dispense food there, each from an individual pulpit surrounded by favorite customers, no longer seem as beautiful as they used to be. Prohibition has wrought such havoc with the bars and restaurants which once brought comfort to the alleys of the downtown district that anyone who turns to old entrances out of instinctive memory will only encounter a soda fountain or an armchair lunch, if anything at all. The Café de la Bourse has disappeared, and so have such fine period pieces as Young's Hotel and the Adams House, and it is not possible to meet anyone any longer in the library of the Hotel Touraine, and the Copley Plaza itself has changed its name.

This is all a very serious business, if one goes to Boston for Old Home Week, but it is strange that the sum of these misfortunes is far from adding up to calamity. The reason is that so many places still exist that cannot possibly disappear, like Stearns, Raymond's, Jordan Marsh, and Filene's, and Clough & Shackley's Drug Store. They are as certain to continue as Locke-Ober's Restaurant, which will surely exist as long as sailors meet their girl friends by the subway kiosks of the Common. If there are gaps in the ranks, these ranks have not lost their formation. The Boston pigeons are exactly the same as they were fifty years ago, and so are the old ladies and gentlemen who feed them, and so are the newspaper readers on the Common benches and the amorous couples who walk the shady paths.

It is inconceivable that there will ever be a time when lawyers do not inhabit Pemberton Square or when a newer type of idler will appear in the vicinity of City Hall on School Street. The same sort of Bostonians are walking down State Street still (with a few variations in costume but seldom in name) as the ones who conducted business there at the time of the great Boston fire. The lion and the unicorn on the old State House, itself suspended over a subway, like the Boston Common dead, look down upon a modern pageant of motors and pedestrians that streams all day past the pavement marking of the Boston Massacre, but the same elements are still in this shifting crowd that existed when the Redcoats fired on that disorderly Boston mob. Indeed, if a file of British Grenadiers were to march into Scollay Square today, they would do well to be as watchful as they were in General Gage's time, for they would encounter similar anti-British feelings, and an identical dislike of uniformed authority. There was trouble in Scollay Square at the time of the Boston Police strike that sent Governor Coolidge on his road to the White House and made him the author of a volume entitled *Have Faith in Massachusetts*. The faces in Scollay Square are indistinguishable from those of the Coolidge era, and it is pleasant to observe that the atmosphere of Scollay Square is finally attracting the attention of regionalist writers. It is still the gateway to Bostonian pornography, pugilistic gymnasiums and small sporting games of chance. It continues, too, to afford an arena where Harvard freshmen can face various forms of reality of a Saturday night by rubbing shoulders with their less scholarly contemporaries. Adventurous youths can still enter the local tattoo parlors and emerge, for a nominal sum, with unmodernistic designs inscribed upon them, as surely as those of a more serious bent can still buy odd old volumes in the bookstalls on Cornhill. It is inconceivable, though I have not been there for some time to check, that the Old Howard Athenaeum — not to be confused with the Boston Athenaeum — is not dispensing its old, robust form of vaudeville. When I was a college youth, Cora Livingston, then the lady wrestling champion of the world, was willing to encounter on the Athenaeum stage any ambitious lady wrestler in the audience — not that this information is particularly pertinent at present. The Old Howard, however, as it affectionately calls itself, is still one of the best examples of the early American theater extant, and it once entertained, in its archaic interior, the gay young Edward when he was heir to the British throne and long before he founded the conventions of the Edwardian era. It is worth a visit still, for various conflicting reasons. There is comfort in these reflections, to which many more might be added, but perhaps they indicate as they stand that every section of Boston maintains its permanence.

This sense of continuity and well-being which one gains from revisiting these scenes is enhanced by the city's fine provincial language. Boston is the only large city in the world, except possibly London, where one can use in speech Senator Saltonstall's broad flat "a" without causing the raising of an eyebrow. It is the one place in the world where Harvard is properly pronounced, where Amory is called Emery and where Tremont Street and Waltham are given a truly correct inflection, and mingling with these puritanical niceties the Irish "a" which turns "coffee" into "cahfee" is not in the least out of place. In fact Boston is the one city in America where English is properly spoken and suitably refined, but then Boston is unique in many other ways.

There is no other American city where one can see so much that is so varied in such a short space of time. In a comparatively brief walk one can see small sailboats racing on the Charles, a ball game and perhaps an illicit crap game on the Common, a water fight in the Frog Pond, a glimpse of the swan boats in the Public Garden, and then the statue of the gentleman who invented ether. Any Bostonian can not only see all this in a few minutes, but he can end up in his trustee's office for a chat about his will, with an opportunity to observe from his trustee's window the mossy but well-preserved stones of the old Granary Burying Ground. There is food for thought anywhere in Boston. Beginning with Fighting Joe Hooker at the State House and continuing through the Public Garden and thence to Commonwealth Avenue, its statuary makes a pleasant guessing game of mingled local and national celebrities. Boston is the only city that I know of that keeps palm trees through the winter and places them in its garden in the spring, the only city that owns the portrait of King Kamehameha of the Sandwich Islands. It probably has the best gold and ivory snake goddess that ever came from Crete, and it owns half of the Greek archaic Ludovici throne. Wherever one goes one encounters something that is quite unique, like the iron handrail on the steep part of Mount Vernon Street or the ancient iron scrapers for muddy feet on the doorsteps of Beacon Hill.

So much has been written about Beacon Hill that it is hardly possible to add much more to its collective word-picture. It has always been the center of whatever Boston means, although its meaning has been defined in many conflicting ways. Every visitor to Boston has climbed the slopes and has observed the architectural unity of Chestnut, Mount Vernon, and Pinckney Streets and has admired the Georgian Federalist influence on its rows of brick dwellings. The creative power of Boston's great architect, Bulfinch, has marked them as much as Wren has marked London. There is hardly a novelist who, coping with the Boston scene, has not turned to Beacon Hill for some of his settings, and with very few exceptions these authors have ended with Louisburg Square and the small communal park in the center of it. There are finer houses in the Beacon Hill neighborhood, like the Sears houses on Mount Vernon Street with their private driveway, or the other Sears mansion and the Gray mansion that face the Common, but nothing is so complete or so orderly as Louisburg Square and nothing so removed from contemporary troubles. It is the center of Beacon Hill and gives it its austere atmosphere of peace. Beacon Hill may be an anachronism, an echo of the past, but it would be necessary to go to England to find anything resembling it, and its English prototype would always be British and not American. At any rate no city in this country has anything like it.

Among the most perceptive visitors to Boston are the people in the show business, mostly New Yorkers, who stop at the Ritz Carlton

Hotel on the corner of Arlington and Newbury Streets while they try out their comedies and musicals on the local audience before the final test of Broadway. These individuals, all students of the human equation and cosmopolitan in their viewpoint, often find it hard to render a verdict on the Boston they have observed from the windows of the Ritz and in the more garish theater district near the old Touraine. They admit that Boston is an intelligent city and that the Bostonians these outlanders meet are as well traveled as *they* are, with an educated taste in food and wine. They also know all about the Symphony Orchestra and about Boston's large student population. They rate it as a discriminating town, although they are sometimes puzzled by its lack of theatrical sophistication and by its restrained enthusiasms. Yet when they discuss its general aesthetic qualities, their verdicts are seldom in agreement. Some speak of it as a quaint old town with an excellent hotel, and they add that the bow fronts and the balconies of Louisburg Square remind them very much of Georgian London. Others who have explored the city more thoroughly have been known to say that Boston is a very tough and ugly town. Very few of these visitors ever call it beautiful, and they may be right in withholding this compliment.

It may be that Boston has only beautiful elements and that the gold-domed State House, crippled by its more modern marble wings, the Old State House, Park Street Church, King's Chapel, Trinity, the Public Library, the Fenway, and Mrs. Jack Gardner's Palace, are beads on a string that have no relationship or unity. Nevertheless I doubt this, because most of these critics have not lived there long enough to have the loyalty that makes all of Boston beautiful. They may have seen it after a fresh snowfall. They may have seen it at the end of a hard winter, in early spring, or in the dry heat of summer, but they have seldom lived through the full palette of its changing seasons. They have not seen an early spring sunrise there, or the glow of its bricks in summer or winter sunsets. It would be fantastic to compare the naively Victorian planting of the Public Garden with the beauties of Kensington or the Tuileries, but still there is nothing anywhere else that is just like the Public Garden, any more than there is anything else like the Common. It would be equally fantastic to compare the islands and the chill murky water and mud flats of Boston Harbor with the Bay of Naples, but then as one sails into that harbor and sees from a ship's deck what is left of the old water front and watches the buildings of the old town rise upward to its hills, there can be no doubt it is unique. It is a harbor that can speak in terms of both the future and the past. There is nowhere else where one can both think of the atomic age and still hear the echo of the gunfire of the *Chesapeake* and *Shannon* in the War of 1812. That was when Lawrence, the captain of the *Chesapeake*, who, some naval students feel, did not use good judgment in that battle, said as he was dying in the surgeon's cockpit, "Don't give up the ship."

It is difficult to see why this simple admonition should have become a schoolbook slogan any more than Admiral Dewey's remark at Manila Bay, "You may fire when you are ready, Gridley." Still the Lawrence quotation is peculiarly applicable today to the Boston from which he once sailed aboard the *Chesapeake* with a half-trained crew. Boston has never faltered in the three hundred years of its growing, and it is as alive and vital now as at any time in its history. To a Bostonian its beauty lies in an accumulation of memories which nothing can ever wholly displace. Its charm lies in the varied memories of the great men and women who have lived there and have left their indelible imprint. Dr. Holmes's Autocrat of the Breakfast Table might have a hard time finding his way about right now but he would still understand the town. He would understand it as anyone who has lived in Boston does the moment he returns, because its spirit is in the air he breathes and in every stick and stone.

Federalist Newburyport

or

Can Historical Fiction Remove a Fly from Amber?

(1952)

ONCE, like many of my contemporaries, I tried very hard to write what is academically termed "historical fiction." Why I ever thought that I might be a Dumas Père or a Scott or a Kenneth Roberts, or my boyhood hero, Stevenson, I have now entirely forgotten. Yet I can remember my acute shock in 1923 — a year which has become a period piece itself — when I heard a revered acquaintance of mine, Mr. John Taintor Foote, speak disrespectfully of Robert Louis Stevenson while lunching with a British novelist named Roland W. Pertwee. In those days I was a very young writer and it meant a great deal to me to be at luncheon drinking bootleg gin with two successful craftsmen.

"After all," Roland Pertwee said, "we do have to take off our hats to good old R.L.S., don't we?"

"Stevenson?" John Taintor Foote said, and then he concluded his remark with an Anglo-Saxon monosyllable.

"Oh, I say now," Roland W. Pertwee said. "Hardly that."

"And why not that?" Mr. Foote said. "All he ever did was horse around and write about unreal people in short pants."

Without realizing that I would do so, I find that I have once more written a passage of historical fiction. The opaque veil of time has dropped between me and that scene. I have been using direct discourse, though of course I cannot recall accurately the exact words of Messrs.

Foote and Pertwee any more than I can know exactly what General
Washington said to General Lee at the Battle of Monmouth. I cannot
even reconstruct a clear picture of myself at that time. I can recollect
that everything was natural and modern. I can still remember my surprise at John Taintor Foote's remark about Robert Louis Stevenson,
but I cannot tell you exactly why I was surprised, because I have forgotten the details of my drives and of my past behavior and I doubt
whether even a psychoanalyst could bring them back to me. I only
know that in the light of the present I agree with Mr. Foote partially. I
don't hand as much as I did once to good old R.L.S.

Many of the reasons why I have ceased trying to resurrect scenes
of the past in fiction are inherent in this ephemeral introduction. An
endeavor to set the clock backwards, I grant, is a fascinating pursuit
and one of the best forms of escapism I know, both for a writer and
a reader. There is only one great objection to the process. The past
must forever be described in the patronizing terms of a fashionable
present, and the present can never comprehend the past. The dead past
has succeeded in interring its dead so thoroughly that no archaeologist,
no imaginative writer however great his piety and wit, can resurrect
them in their living form.

Sometimes, of course, you can see the fly in amber, preserved exactly
as he was in life, and you know that once many thousands of years
ago this unhappy little insect alighted on the soft gum exuding from
some conifer in an ancient forest and found himself unable to escape.
He is still stuck where he landed, preserved for the contemporary eye
to see, but no one can tell the extent of the forest in which he flew. No
one can hear the wind sigh through the vanished branches of its trees.
Human beings also have been preserved by a subtler but not dissimilar
process. For example, young Mr. Boswell, nearly two hundred years
ago, succeeded in getting himself enmeshed in the web of his own
words and now has been presented to us, heart, liver and glands intact,
in the pages of his *London Journal*, exhaustively annotated by Professor
Pottle. We can examine at our leisure his enormous egotism and the
almost indecent exposure of his pedantry, conceit and snobbishness, as
well as the assiduous beginnings of his literary skills. We can see all of
him, but even Professor Pottle can evaluate him only in the delight of
his own experience, which has been chiefly confined to the Yale library.

Neither he nor any other modern writer can ever really know the Boswell who walked and misbehaved in the streets of an older London. In the end we are moderns only, living a life as different from Boswell's as the life, if any, on another planet. We are confronted with a phenomenon beyond our comprehension — the eighteenth-century mind. We can never thoroughly understand its convolutions, because the dead past has buried its dead.

At least I have found this true from my own experience, when once I collected some notes on manners and customs in the town of Newburyport, Massachusetts, as they existed in the Federalist era. If one wants to write of a period, I know of few more susceptible to adaptation. It was a short period in terms of years, starting with the growing pains of a young republic and ending, roughly, with the embargo that preceded the War of 1812. It was a time of great change but also one of strong conventions. Furthermore, it is close enough to persons still living so that the hearsay and word-of-mouth evidence that emanated from it is still an actual echo.

From a writer's point of view, Newburyport is a sort of Federalist Pompeii. Not the ashes of a volcanic eruption, but the Jeffersonian embargo, followed in the Year 1811 by a disastrous water-front fire, conspired to give it a shock of commercial paralysis from which it never wholly recovered. After that fatal year, the inhabitants of Newburyport began to adopt the unprogressive habit of looking backwards to the good old days, in much the same manner as Southerners now view the days before the War Between the States. In fact only the other day I heard a Newburyport citizen state with deadly seriousness that nothing good had happened in Newburyport since the Year 1811, and actually one can sustain his point. The mouth of the Merrimack River, on which the town is situated, was never an ideal seaport. Even in the harbor's best days, only vessels of a few hundred tons burthen could conveniently unload at the Newburyport wharves, though heavier shipping might be launched. But during the last century channel conditions have grown steadily worse, until the bar which was always at the river's mouth has now built up to an extent that small craft drawing as little as five feet find it difficult to enter from the sea. In New England's industrial period a few factories were established here, but Newburyport was off the road of progress. There has been no serious building boom in Newburyport or any very large-scale civic improvement since the Year 1805. In a very real sense its clocks and its initiatives stopped at the turn of the century.

Thus physically Newburyport still looks very much as it must have in the Federalist era. Seen from the bridge that now spans the Merrimack, the water front still closely resembles an engraving published in 1835. Along lower State Street in Newburyport — always the business center of the town — the buildings are of an 1810 vintage. The residences on High Street are predominantly Federalist — or even earlier — survivals, and most of the old churches are still standing, and so is the old courthouse. Any stranger arriving there immediately becomes aware of this Federalist façade and cannot help but wonder what the old impulse was that made these ancients construct so many pretentious and beautifully designed dwellings. They obviously reflect a bland faith in a stable future which was never realized, and are monuments of manners and beliefs that no longer exist, reflecting a vitality and ambition and a way of life curiously unconnected with modern thinking.

In addition to these landmarks, Newburyport is also a well-documented community, especially as far as the Federalist era is concerned, because the town has been fortunate in the number and skill of its literary observers. Some of the best local history ever to be written has been done by John J. Currier in his volumes on Newburyport. There is also Coffin's history and a florid history by Mrs. E. Vail Smith, and on the less accurate side a remarkable book by a Mrs. Emery entitled *The Reminiscences of a Nonagenarian*. There are many detailed passages, occasionally almost poetical, that touch on this Federalist golden era.

Let us turn, for instance, to Mrs. Emery's description of the town before the great fire, on a Friday evening, May 31, 1811.

"The sun," she writes, "set in unclouded splendor, gilding the church spires, and gleaming upon tree tops, window panes, and the masts of the little fleet anchored at the wharves up and down the river. For the last time its rays illumined the ancient town; when it sank behind the western heights it bade a final adieu to many an antique landmark and to many a goodly heritage. The last lingering gleam died away from the old 'port,' which henceforth would only be known in tradition and song. For the last time busy feet trod those long lines of lofty warehouses; carts and drays rattled up and down the wharves; the evening stage coaches dashed up to the Old Wolfe tavern; merchant and artisan turned the key and wended their way homeward; the tea urn steamed on the luxurious board in stately mansions, and the more frugal supper was served in the dwellings of the mechanic and laborer. Little did they reck that ere another day should dawn, each would be reduced to a perfect equality, alike homeless and penniless."

This passage, which is quite typical Emery, sounds like a cloak-and-sword story itself. To her, old Newburyport was always a great metropolis and a gilded center of wit and beauty, but then, aside from a glimpse or two at Boston and Salem, it was the only metropolis she knew, and Mrs. Emery was a country girl who lived on a farm on Crane Neck Hill, a good seven miles from the seaport, or four hours' travel time distant. In spite of a snobbish predilection for family and breeding, she had no way of knowing that Newburyport houses, in spite of their appointments, could not entirely escape the stigma of small town.

Fortunately, perhaps, it is not necessary to take Mrs. Emery's word alone on the subject of Federalist Newburyport. In his early manhood John Quincy Adams spent some time there reading law in the office of the town's great jurist, Theophilus Parsons, and he viewed the place with a more jaundiced eye, speaking of a pretentiousness and priggishness observable in the higher social cliques. Samuel Knapp, an established writer a little before the literary flowering of New England, was a Newburyport boy himself, and in his life of Lord Timothy Dexter he has left his own more aloof but kindly impressions of Federalist Newburyport in a description that gives an excellent base for further speculation.

"The town of Newburyport," he writes, "is situated on the right bank of the Merrimack. The whole territory belonging to the corporation is but little more than six hundred acres, and nearly one half of this is low pasture lands, but the thickly settled part is a lovely spot of ground. The southerly line is on an elevation about sixty or seventy feet from the surface of the river. The main street, called High Street, running about a mile and a quarter from east to west on the town boundary, extends either way much further, making a delightful riding course of more than three miles distance. The streets running at right angles with High Street to the water are intersected by others, throwing a great portion of the whole site into squares convenient for building lots. The soil is light, gravelly and warm, well suited for gardens, for which the town is famous. Many of the buildings are still of wood: forty years ago they were chiefly so. The water here is good and the streets are wide and kept clean, and every thing about the 'sweet village,' bore marks of industry, thrift and comfort. Numerous churches and school-houses were placed at convenient distances. The shipping was extensive, for the size of the place. The town was thrifty for many years before the Revolution, and when the war broke out several merchants left Boston to carry on their commerce in Newburyport. Their business flourished from the peace of 1783, until the embargo of 1807, when it received a grievous wound, but, thank heaven, not a vital stab as many thought it would have proved. . . . The education of this people was plain and wholesome. Reading, writing and arithmetic were taught to all, and their moral precepts were all drawn from one book. The Bible was read from lisping infancy to purblind decrepitude. . . . There never was any canaille here: some few there are, as everywhere, the unfortunate and poor; but the mass of people were well to do; intelligent and active, they of course were happy. The wealthy and intellectual portion of the community formed a circle that had sufficient of the comforts and refinements of life to give society a charm which is seldom found in overgrown cities. The population was not so large as to hide any individual, however humble. Each stood out as it were from the canvass, and could be examined by every one who wished to observe."

The most conspicuous aspects of this ancient town must have been its amazing self-sufficiency and the extraordinary self-reliance of its inhabitants, but then these attributes were an absolute necessity in that period. Federalist Newburyport was compelled to achieve a large measure of economic independence, because it was a remote town on the seaboard of a half-explored continent, largely dependent on itself for its food, its clothing, as well as for its luxuries and entertainment. Its traditions and manner of living were derived more from Europe than from the land around it, but remoteness obliged Newburyport to create its own culture, since most of the time it was left completely alone to develop itself as best it could with the tools and graces allowed it by a very distant world. This isolation was cheerfully accepted as nothing out of the ordinary. This was all part of that distant present, but it forms a social problem impossible for a modern mind to grasp. It was about a day's journey by land from the other place that mattered. Thoughts turned automatically eastward because there was not any west excepting backwoods settlements. Because of road conditions, all heavy goods had to be brought by sea and distributed from the town's warehouses to the shops, and the bluff-bowed cranky vessels of the period were utterly dependent on tide and weather.

The basic necessities of life were drawn from the hinterland farms and supplemented by foreign importations. The meat which Newburyport consumed came thither on the hoof to be processed by butchers and sold fresh in their open stalls at the foot of State Street. The clothing worn by its simpler people was local homespun. Silver, which appeared on well-to-do tables, was made by local silversmiths, and earthenware crockery was made in a pottery not far from Bartlett's Mall. Essential hardware was made by the blacksmiths, and the ships' rigging came from the old ropewalk.

The local economy and culture of Newburyport has no counterpart in the contemporary world, unless one can find a vague parallel in some walled town of central China. The truth is that a dweller in a city-state of ancient Greece, if he could have been transported through the centuries and set down at the mouth of the Merrimack River in 1800, would understand the meanings and values of Federalist Newburyport far more clearly than any modern today, because Newburyport was not far from being an Aegean city-state. It never became an Athens, but it had its own artists and artisans who developed art forms of their own and who were something more than imitators of European culture.

Newburyport's population was less than half of what it is at present, but its aggregate of skills, initiative, and similar cultivation too, can only be found now in a vastly larger community. There was something stupendous in the sum of its individual achievement. The town had two newspapers, the files of which exhibit a sophisticated taste in printing and writing. Newburyport had several silversmiths, some excellent clockmakers, fine cabinetmakers, and its own engraver. Newburyport printed and bound its own books, and not merely the sermons and funeral orations of its ministry. Bowditch's *Navigation* was published here, and so was Blount's *American Coast Pilot* and volumes of the classics and the pirated works of contemporary British authors. In fact a list of books with the Newburyport imprint is startling in its variety. The truth was that Newburyport was capable of turning its hand to almost anything.

The silver, the clocks, the chairs and tables, the books, and the grace of the architecture that survive from this era indicate a leisure and prosperity and taste that could only have rested on a foundation of planned prosperity. There was a heavy concentration of intelligence, because there were few places for that intelligence to spread, and thus the genius of America was not dilute but in a saturate solution. The first large sums of money to reach Newburyport were derived from licensed privateering in the opening days of the American Revolution, but by the turn of the century business risk was organized and calculated. Merchandise from Europe, sugar from the Indies, iron from the Baltic, were arriving in Newburyport in quantity in exchange for lumber, fish, and rum, and Newburyport counting houses offered all sorts of business ventures to intelligent speculators. There was an inventor in Newburyport, Mr. Jacob Perkins, who perfected, among other things, a method of gold-plating beads, a machine for making nails, a new model of stove, and hot-air furnaces. America's first woolen mill was built in Byfield, a suburb of Newburyport. Local promoters were responsible for the construction of the Newburyport Turnpike, to afford a means of rapid travel between Newburyport and Boston. They also financed the Essex-Merrimack Bridge across the Merrimack to replace the old Carr's Island Ferry — a bridge suspended by chains, the first suspension bridge in America. But Newburyport's greatest contribution was to the modernization of shipbuilding. It was a Newburyporter who evolved a scheme for making a half-model to exact scale of the proposed hull of a sailing vessel. Because of this invention large timbers for ship construction could be fashioned where the trees were felled. It was an idea which did more to change shipbuilding methods than any improvement since the times of Homer. Donald McKay, the father of the nineteenth-century clipper ship, first started building in the yards of Newburyport, naturally enough because of the town's reputation, and local shipwrights in the Federalist era were among the most skilled in the world. Their ships are gone, but proof of their impeccable sense of form and line remains in the finish they made in the houses of Newburyport shipowners. Federalist Newburyport, in spite of its remoteness, offered more refinements of its time than it ever will again. By scanning the back files of the old *Imperial Herald*, it is possible to walk in imagination down Federalist State Street. There were no mass-produced goods, but it was possible to purchase silver service made to order, or to select from "an elegant assortment of Lockets, gilt, pearl and glass earrings, Broach Pins, Bracelets, Gold and Silver Cord, Spangles, Key Rings, India Rubber, Tooth Brushes and Powder." Further along the street was a mercer's advertising "Broadcloths, Casimeres of various colors. Striped Elastics, Superior fine color Shalloons, and Ratinettes, Baize of all colors, Yellow, Black and White Flannel, Wilton and Brussels carpets, Callimancoes, Black Ruffles, Prunella, Florentine Satin, Men's Plain Ribbed and Twilled Hose, Black, White, Blue and Pine Satin." The town supported a portrait and miniature painter, who also could work on "Real Hair Devices." There were a saddle and chaisemaker, and a wigmaker ready in their shops, and a wine merchant with imported Malaga, Lisbon, Madeira, and Sherry. Perfumery was on sale, and French pot and roll Pomatum, and there was a Druggist at the "Golden Mortar," ready to dispense Duffy's Elixir Salitis, Stoughton's Stomach Elixir, and Turlington's Balm of Life.

There was also a heavy foreign importation of ideas and tastes and entertainment brought thither by traveling showmen and teachers, including emigrees from revolutionary France. An educated pig passed through Federalist Newburyport, capable of entertaining ladies and gentlemen with feats of reading and addition, whose precocity was so unnatural that he was later burned alive and his master imprisoned by the Inquisition in Havana. A bison and an African lion also visited Newburyport. So did a slack-wire artist; and a Monsieur Perret, a machinist of Paris, appeared with a self-moving carriage drawn rapidly by an eagle automaton. Messieurs Renard and Dupatty opened an academy of the dance, and Monsieur LeBarr, professor and composer of music, who had once instructed the Duchess of Orléans, arrived also, to teach ladies and gentlemen the "Piano Fort, Spinet, Spanish and English Guitar, Flute and Violin." There were academies of dance and song, schools for genteel young ladies and gentlemen, schools for drawing and painting and swordsmanship, and also a school of psalmody. There were many evidences of intellectual ferment and clashes between old virtues and new luxuries. When Mr. Perkins, the inventor, offered to install in a Newburyport church a furnace of his own contriving, the congregation turned him down on the grounds of degeneracy. When a choirmaster of another church attempted to set a psalm tune by blowing a pitch pipe, the minister was constrained to shout to him from the pulpit to "put down that papish pipe." On the other hand, one reads of weekly balls and routs, of cellars filled with hundreds of gallons of wines and spirits, and of coaches with liveried footmen.

There was an abundance in Newburyport quite different from the abundance preached by Mr. Henry A. Wallace; but nevertheless it reached far down the social scale, if only because Newburyport rested on the edge of an unplundered continent. The waters of the Merrimack River were undefiled by the pollution of mill cities that have now made it an open sewer. Salmon and herring in vast quantities ran upstream in 1800, and the mud flats near Plum Island teemed with shellfish, so that anyone who was hungry could obtain a meal from clams. There were fine beds of oysters in Parker River. Dense flocks of shore birds and waterfowl covered the tidal creeks and marshes, and the woods were filled with passenger pigeons and partridge and woodcock. Venison in season was often commoner than beef.

There was no need for anyone to go hungry in Federalist Newburyport, but there was an exacting social scale at the top of which stood lawyers, doctors, and divines, followed by shipowners and smaller merchants, who in turn were followed by artisans and clerks, and then by laborers, and finally the ne'er-do-wells. There must have been a good number of the last, because, as Mr. Knapp has told us, the poor are with us always. We read of barefooted women drying cod on the river bank while their children, dirty little urchins, splashed in the shallows and sailed boats made of chips and shingles. We hear of tramps and vagrants wandering on all main roads and of witchlike women in rags riding to town on scrawny horses from a place called Dogtown, a social sore

spot that was settled by unruly runaway bond servants and even a
few stray Indians. There was also a settlement not far from Bartlett's
Mall called Little Guinea, where the town's small colored population
gathered, one of whom, a tall majestic woman of high intelligence, was
the daughter of an African king. There were several witches and sooth-
sayers in town, the best known of whom was Madam Hooper, who
could find lost objects and dispense love philtres. We are told that she
had a double set of teeth all the way around and was expert with the
broadsword.

We find that two famous eccentrics were created by this mingling of
thoughts and manners, whose behavior must have been a good parody
and caricature of local custom. Lord Timothy Dexter, a tanner who
had made a comfortable fortune by speculating in Continental currency, constructed a bizarre palace for himself on High Street, and had
himself driven in his own coach to the Ipswich jail, where he was confined briefly for shooting a pistol at an inquisitive visitor. He employed
at various times an astrologer and poet laureate named Jonathan Plummer, who was also an itinerant fish dealer, selling haddock and scrolls
of his own works from door to door. These Plummer broadsides —
now great rarities — exhibit a humor and ability greater than that of
his employer.

One might go on at great length about this remarkable town, so
different from anything we know from present experience, partly humdrum, partly rich and strange, heated only by open fireplaces, lighted
only by candles and perhaps a few whale-oil lamps. Its component parts
still lie profusely on the record. They are like pieces of ill-assorted material, slips and tatters that the local housewives once collected for
sewing into a patchwork quilt, some of which are gaudy and more of
them pedestrian. Anyone can put them together, but no one — not even
the best-trained and most assiduous historian — can rearrange them in
their true relationship. With the evidence on hand, anyone can achieve
some sort of picture of the vanished town. It can be a romantic picture
or a coldly realistic effort, but neither one nor the other can be a factual reconstruction. Samuel Knapp once attempted to set this era on
paper as early as 1848. Having lived through these years himself and
seen the place with his own young eyes, he was better equipped for
the task than either you or I. Yet he admitted failure. "The past," he

finally wrote, "seems a dream to those who lived in it and almost a legend to those who take it from history. From history, did I say? History was afraid to record a tythe of the truth." One may achieve an illusion of reality, but that illusion will only contain a tythe of the truth.

Joseph Hergesheimer, you will remember, wrote a novel called *Java Head*, the scenes of which were laid in Salem only a few years later than the time we are discussing. Few writers have possessed Mr. Hergesheimer's sensitiveness for a period's characteristic atmosphere. You will find his Salem rooms so academically perfect, down to the last detail, that one is almost conscious of a very correct smell of tea and spice, but it is easier to describe authentic furniture than human beings. There are plenty of period pieces but no period people in the American wing of an art museum. Mr. Hergesheimer's characters, too, have life and dimension, but only one of them seems to me to fit convincingly into his artfully prepared backgrounds. This, curiously enough, is a Manchu lady whom his Yankee hero had brought home to Salem as his wife. It was easier for Mr. Hergesheimer to be more successful with his Manchu princess than with her Derby Wharf sailorman. The Manchus, it happens, are period pieces in themselves, who, when I was in China a few years back, still maintained their original customs in a changing world, even down to making crossbows.

Perhaps, if I wished, I might not come so very far from doing for Federalist Newburyport what Mr. Hergesheimer did for Salem. My performance would lack the depth of his imagination, as my style would the Hergesheimer graces, but the result might have its creditable moments. I know exactly what a Federalist room in Newburyport would be like, from its books and bric-a-brac to the Turkey carpet on the floor. I would know exactly how to place objects in a relationship that would enable a contemporary reader to follow my picture. Yet something essential to life would be lacking. My room would be a museum piece. In spite of all I could do it would seem to have steam heat and electric light. Its open fire would only burn artificially. Its candles would somehow be superfluous. Still I could also bring people into this room. I have seen enough old portraits to describe the typical Federalist face, disciplined by an older mode of life.

I could put correct clothing on my characters. Their wardrobes are still in plenty of historical societies. I could even put proper words in their mouths. Some very realistic fragments of their speech are still extant. But in the end, in spite of all my piety or wit, my result would only be a thin conceit resembling a charming marionette show of dancing men and dolls, or at its very best a masquerade of modern men and women in antique dress. I hope that it might be a good costume party with plenty of Madeira and rum and lemon, some good Virginia tobacco and a few good songs, but in the end it would only be a fancy-dress gathering, not an evocation of the past.

I should only be struggling, like Professor Pottle back at Yale, with his Boswell's *London Journal*. Boswell will always be a denizen of another world to me. I may know what he is saying, but Mr. Pottle can never make me understand just what made him say it — and the same is true with my ancestors who once walked the streets of Newburyport. I may have inherited some of their genes, but I know nothing of their genius, because I and my time were both unborn. I shall never know the silence that must have hung over their lives. I cannot feel, as they must have felt, the slower passage of time. I cannot share their excitement in debates on infant damnation, or the virulence of their dislike for Thomas Jefferson, or their liking for feather beds, or their tolerance for insects. I cannot think, as they did, that the housefly is a cheery little creature. I would not be pleased, as they were, to have him sip a bit of tea from my Lowestoft teacup. I cannot understand their aversion to open windows, or their belief in the curative powers of a dose of calomel. I am impatient with the intricacies of their courtships and with their interminable diary- and letter-writing. I cannot share their belief that too-frequent bathing was dangerous for the body. I should not have enjoyed their hours for meals, nor, I am afraid, their dinner-table conversation. Even if I could go backwards in time, I would not be able to understand my ancestors, because the iron curtain has fallen and still falls, quite fortunately I think, between each generation. These few details I have mentioned may be small, but added together they are a part of that iron curtain. One may glance through the chinks, but I would much rather leave to Robert L. Stevenson or Kenneth L. Roberts the task of trying to tear it down.

The Social Future of the Harvard Man in the Free World of Tomorrow

(1948)

Some years ago I became acquainted with a very versatile young man, during my course of studies at Harvard University. In those rather distant days, it was possible to contract athlete's foot upon the venerable floors of the Hemingway Gymnasium. Gore Hall had not been demolished to make place for the Widener Library, and a relative of mine was still alive who could recall distinctly a pump and a row of privies in the neighborhood of University Hall. Yet I do not believe that the general atmosphere of Cambridge has greatly changed. Harvard still seems to be in a state of flux and still needs more plumbing and more libraries.

This versatile young man I have mentioned wished to enter the diplomatic service, and he was also a composer of songs, some of which he paid to have published. I remember the beginning of one of these songs with amazing distinctness. It was entitled "Harvard Man" and its words ran as follows:

> Harvard Man, Harvard man, you are so fascinating.
> I love you, honey, 'deed I do.
> You can hug me, cuddle and squeeze me.
> Promise me you'll never leave me.
> I'll be true.

This song, I remember, he wrote especially for Elsie Janis, who was appearing with Montgomery and Stone in the Colonial Theatre in Boston. It was his thought that Miss Janis might sing the song and that he, as its composer, might personally conduct the orchestra on the night of the Harvard–Yale game. I also recall that he was bitterly hurt, not only by Miss Janis but by Messrs. Montgomery and Stone, when none of them warmed to this suggestion. I do not say they were not right. I can see that the thought-content was not profound and that the rhyming, especially of "squeeze me" with "leave me," was unconventional. I can also see that the indirect amorous proclivities of the absent male character in the song did not give a fully rounded picture of a Harvard student. This struck me forcibly the first time I heard it, but I remember the verse for another reason. I remember it because at this moment I was first confronted with the thought that a Harvard man might be a being distinct from other American males, not fascinating, perhaps, but a social phenomenon.

I have faced this same idea since in many different forms. I have usually faced it uncomfortably, and possibly all of us from Harvard have been exposed to the same thought — since we would not be here tonight if we were not all tarred with the same brush, all Harvard men together.

I still do not know what this phrase Harvard man means, but I have observed from my own experience that it must convey some very definite mental image to a great many people who are not Harvard graduates, especially beyond the boundaries of the state of Massachusetts.

Only a year ago, for example, I was seated at a table eating a bird's nest soup and thirty-year-old eggs at a small Chinese dinner in Peking. The dinner was given in honor of an American admiral by the mayor of Peking, and present, besides a handful of American officers, was General Li, commander of the North China army and known affectionately to his countrymen as the Tiger General. He is the same Li, I believe, who is now vice-president of China. With him were some other Chinese officials, in black-silk gowns, but besides myself there was only one other guest in European civilian clothes, an English-speaking Chinese in a dinner coat who interpreted for the Chinese general and the mayor. The evening might have been stiff and difficult had it not been for large quantities of warm rice wine, consumed in a great number of personal and graceful toasts. It was hard to strike a general subject of conversation, sitting between a colonel of marines and this impeccable Chinese interpreter, and consequently I was delighted to hear the interpreter say that he was a Harvard man. When I told him that I too was a Harvard man, both he and the Tiger General, when the fact was conveyed to him in Mandarin, were delighted that I was a Harvard man, and we paused to drink several cups of warm wine to Harvard University. At this point it turned out that the Chinese Harvard man was a graduate in the class of 1920, and when I said that I was older, a graduate of 1915, General Li and even the mayor of Peking expressed deep pleasure and conversed volubly in the Chinese tongue.

"The mayor of Peking says," the interpreter told me, when the Chinese conversation was over, "that in China all who attend the same institution of learning are brothers. You went to Harvard first and so you are my elder brother, and General Li suggests you and me should take one drink for being brothers and another drink for being Harvard men."

At this point the colonel of marines who sat beside me spoke softly in my ear.

"For Christ's sake, Mac," he said, "if you can manage it, and it's all the same to you, let's get off this Harvard-man angle. I'm just a poor boy from Iowa and I personally cannot stand much more of it."

I could see that he was suffering and I asked him a simple question.

"Why does it hurt you?" I asked him. "Are you sorry you're not a Harvard man?"

His reaction, though perhaps more violent, was identical to other reactions I have observed in other parts of the country.

"For Christ's sake," the colonel said, "why should I be sorry that I'm not a Harvard man?"

It was obviously not the time and place to tell him why, though I like to think I detected a note of wistful inferiority in his manner. Besides, not being an educator, I was not the suitable person to tell him or to explain why a Harvard degree might help in the Marine Corps.

I have retailed this anecdote because it shows that an idea of Harvard and its reputation has gone as far as central Asia, and that for some reason a graduate of Harvard excites more interest through this educational accident than any graduate of Oxford or Cambridge or the University of Moscow. I cannot say that this is always a flattering interest, but obviously there does exist a universal, preconceived idea that every Harvard graduate will exhibit certain definite traits of behavior. Yet I still do not know what is meant by a Harvard man.

In Paris once, in World War I, there was another marine officer, a captain, with whom I became quite friendly, and I think he really liked me, because he said to me once: "You really wouldn't be a son of a bitch at all if you weren't a Harvard man." It did not appear to occur to him for a moment that I might still have been what I was if I had gone to Dartmouth or Cornell. I like to think he meant that I speak with a broad *A*, and obviously many people feel that all Harvard graduates should. But a few experiences such as these — and perhaps all of us here have shared in them — have taught me one great truth. If you have ever been to Harvard, you will never be allowed to forget it. Actually I have found that I can get on very well with most people until they discover this error in my past. Then there is a slight pause in the conversation, a lifting of the eyebrows, an exchange of meaning glances, and someone always says, "You never told us you were a Harvard man." It is time then to select some new and learned subject of conversation, and ever after things are never quite the same. Something more is expected. A mental picture has arisen and an iron curtain has descended. Yes, for some reason, in the hard outer world through which we have all struggled, there is a fixed belief that a Harvard man is more studious, more conservative, more easily shocked than other men. He loves to quote Ralph Waldo Emerson. He is different from other American boys. Now what have we all done — or have any of us done anything? — to have earned this reputation?

Harvard graduates, as I have known them, do not discuss the classics in their leisure hours, or consistently vote Republican. Instead they come from divergent backgrounds and react in startlingly different manners, both socially and politically. A Harvard man now lies buried in the precincts of the Kremlin. Another was the founder of the New Deal, and several are still economic royalists, in spite of everything. There are devout Catholics, pagans and atheists in the ranks of Harvard men. There are Harvard Frenchmen, Germans, Chinese and Siamese. There are some very intellectually brilliant Harvard men and a great many more very dumb ones, and yet the belief still persists that we have all been poured into a mold, and, collectively, we are a part of American folklore.

If you do not believe it, turn to H. L. Mencken's *New Dictionary of Quotations*. Harvard and Yale, I think, are the only two institutions of learning specifically mentioned in this dictionary, and Yale University is merely dismissed as follows: "See Education." For Harvard, however, there are four quotations which together tell such a great deal about Harvard that I shall take the liberty to quote them all.

Harvard University
They have a college at Cambridge, about four miles from Boston, where divinity, mathematics, philosophy and the oriental languages are taught. — Patrick McRoberts, *Tour Through Part of the North Provinces of America*, 1775.

The second quotation:

"If this boy passes the examinations he will be admitted; and if the white students choose to withdraw all the income of the college will be devoted to his education." — Edward Everett, President of Harvard, 1848.

The third:

"This celebrated institution of learning is pleasantly situated in the barroom of Parker's in School Street and has pupils from all over the country." — Artemus Ward, *His Book*, 1862.

And the last quotation of Mr. Mencken's brings us back to where we started. It is ascribed to James Barnes:

"You can always tell a Harvard man but you can't tell him much."

I don't believe it. Everyone outside of Harvard feels it is a personal duty to tell a Harvard man a great deal, and I believe that it is a fallacy that you can tell a Harvard man from a Princeton or a Rutgers man, and so do you. Every one of us here has been confronted with this attitude and we have all tried to do the best we can within its limits. There is a strange sort of magic in the name of Harvard, whether it is spoken in Phoenix, Arizona, or Cairo. The name has become a myth, even in this uncertain world, and more is expected of us and we are obliged by public opinion to conform to that myth simply because we have stopped for a few years in Cambridge. Actually we are all placed under a definite social handicap which seldom has helped us in a business or a professional way, but at least this is not your fault or mine. Let us put the whole blame where it belongs, on Harvard University.

Harvard is a large-enough institution to bear the blame for what it has done for us and for the inferiority complex it has created. Even its faults may be great faults in the eyes of outsiders, but with them and in spite of them most people obviously believe that Harvard is the greatest and freest institution in the world. In spite of themselves they have become convinced that even a casual exposure to it must in some way change personality, and this is all I have tried to say.

I am not intellectually equipped to discuss what Harvard means. I only know that I have been there and have obviously brought something of it away with me, and perhaps no one else here knows either what this experience has meant to us all as individuals. I do know, however, that I feel a little more at my ease tonight, a little more at home with everyone here, because we have been through quite a lot together. Let us not say it elsewhere, but perhaps we are all more fascinating and a little better than other people for being Harvard men.

Golden Lads

(1931)

Encountering this story after a lapse of more than twenty years has many of the embarrassing elements that are involved in the meeting of an old acquaintance whom one has not seen for a similar period. Features are not as you remember them, and it is often difficult to recall what you once had in common with this half stranger.

As I find myself wondering what on earth ever induced me to write such a sentimentalized and over dramatic tale as "Golden Lads," I can recall that I was actuated by several honest motives. The conventional magazine short story was already making me restless. I was violently anxious to prove that this form of writing could be popular and at the same time exhibit more serious elements. Also I was beginning to realize the frustration connected with all short story characters, which are developed for a few thousand words only to be abandoned as soon as they become interesting individuals. Thus "Golden Lads" was a part of a so-called series — each story an independent entity but each the better when connected with its predecessors — a dubious form of fictional compromise. Finally I was involved with methods of connecting past and present in order to give reality to romance.

The result, I can see today, is not an unqualified success but parts of the story may be interesting to a reader and its moral, for a writer, is never to try to ride several horses simultaneously in different directions. The most obvious fault of "Golden Lads" is its heavy atmosphere of artificial unreality. The characters, both modern and ancient, would be at home only in a never-never land. There was never a family mansion in Massachusetts or anywhere else remotely resembling Indian Creek; and never such preposterous goings on among ancestors in any family whatsoever. The historical background of slaves and the duello is utterly devoid of any factual validity. Furthermore, the whole story is brutally crowded into its frame. In fact there are two stories here, and possibly a third, all compressed into a disunified capsule. It is amazing to me with all these obvious defects that the show can go on as well as it does. One of the few things that makes this possible is an enthusiasm in the writing which I certainly could not approximate today, and which I cannot even wholly comprehend. Somehow after periods of stumbling "Golden Lads" occasionally gets on its legs in a manner which causes me surprise, and permits me, and I trust other readers, to forget its unreality in temporary illusion.

> Golden lads and girls
> all must,
> As chimney sweepers,
> come to dust.

It was like my cousin Bill to leave his sister Sue waiting in the street. The family has always been vague about time and waiting. I had not heard that Sue was in town until I met Bill at the club in Cambridge after the game. There was not a speck on his shoes, not a fold wrong in his tailored suit, nor a lock of his red hair out of place; and his eyes puckered up at the corners when he saw me, so that you could not tell whether he was smiling or nearsighted. Bill was talking to a fair-faced, heavy man, whose look reminded me that we all were getting older. Bill was talking to him in the utterly disarming way he had when he wanted something.

"Hi, Bill!" I called to him. "How's everything?"

"Rotten," said Bill, and he turned to the man beside him. "Sam," he said. "Oh, Sam." And the other one gazed at me. He had a pink complexion, and he was heavy enough to be a football man whose intellectual blooming might have taken place in the stadium ten years back. "Do you know my cousin, Lee Dansel?" said Bill. "If you don't, you ought to. This one is Sam Crosby."

I suspected then that he was one of the Crosby Motor family from the trouble Bill was taking, and I tried to pull myself together, but Bill never let matters go at that.

"Crosby Motors," said Bill.

"Look out," I answered. "Bill's trying to get your account. Don't you let him, Crosby."

"Don't mind him," said Bill. "You'll like Lee. . . . Where's your glass?"

"I've had enough," I said, "and he wants your account. Don't you let him, Crosby."

"Oh, no," said Crosby, "we're not talking business, old man." And then he raised his voice. He had to, because someone had tipped over a chair. "Are you the Dansel who rides — that Dansel?"

"Yes," I answered, "I ride, off and on, but don't you believe what Bill says. He wants to get your account."

"Yeh," said Bill. "He's off more than he's on. Lee, I was telling Crosby about Indian Creek, and how everything goes cuckoo once you cross the bridge. It's amazing. Everything goes cuckoo once you cross the bridge."

Indian Creek seemed utterly remote from everything about us then.

"It's one of those family places owned in common," I explained. "An aunt of ours is living there, and we go down there sometimes. You see them around here off in the country, the sort of place that everyone has left."

"That's it," said Bill. "Everything goes cuckoo once you cross that bridge. Lee, are you going down?"

"Yes," I said, "I'm driving down."

"Great!" said Bill. "We're coming too."

"Who?" I asked. "Who's coming?"

"Crosby's coming," said Bill. "Sue's waiting in his car outside. We just came here for a minute, and then Phippen and Joan are coming."

"You mean to say," I said, "you're bringing Crosby — there?"

Even then I knew there was something wrong about bringing Crosby down. I received a violent kick in the leg. It was Bill.

"Of course he's coming down," he said. "Sue asked him."

I looked at Crosby uncertainly, and perceived that Bill was making mysterious gestures behind his back.

"Now look here," I said. "Crosby won't like it. Now listen, Crosby! All the furniture is broken, and the food is terrible. There's only a farmer and his wife. There isn't anything to do — "

I stopped, because I was suddenly aware that Bill's face looked sharp.

"Since when," said Bill, "did you think you're running this show?"

I am glad I kept my temper. I have always hated a family scene.

"I simply don't want anyone to misunderstand the place, and you know that," I said. I knew that Crosby would not understand it.

Bill began to laugh, and I could never stay angry at Bill once he started laughing.

"I like it as much as you do," he said. "You know that. Don't you know that? And Sam's going to like it too. I've telephoned Aunt Het and we're all set. I only say that everything goes cuckoo once you cross the bridge."

I had to say something to Crosby then and I found myself telling him what was really the trouble with Indian Creek.

"It's the family," I said. "There's too much family. We've been there too long. They manage it in England, but it doesn't work out here. I simply mean you get there, and there isn't anything to do — except we might go after ducks on Monday morning."

"Of course," said Crosby, "that's all right, old man."

"Sue can show you the way," said Bill. "I'll drive down with Lee."

Everyone was going and the room was thick with the heavy air as Bill and I put on our coats. Bill slid into his with a quick shrug of his shoulders, but every fold of it was right. Bill jammed his hat down with a jerk over his short red hair, but it fitted as though a salesman had placed it on his head. Then he took my arm and began pushing me toward the stairs.

"We've got to move," he said. "I want to get there first, you see!"

I looked at him, and he was grinning, so that his whole face went into wrinkles.

"You ass!" he repeated. "Didn't you know?"

"Know what?"

"He's in love with Sue, you ass. He wants to marry Sue."

Suddenly I felt as empty as an inverted jug, and I felt my knees give as if he had struck me. I must keep my face perfectly unmoved, and I must walk down the steps steadily — one, two.

"Does Sue want to?" I was saying.

Bill's fingers were tight on my arm. "She'd better, if she doesn't."

"And you're asking him down there." I had not meant it, but my voice was sharp.

"And you've got to help us," said Bill. "This has got to go, boy. It's the family — do you see? The family."

"Yes," I said, "of course — the family."

The sun was already setting, I remember, and the street lights were on, and the air already had that penetrating chill of a New England autumn that precedes the pitiless grip of a North Atlantic winter. The harshness and the meagerness and the grimness of our soil were in the air, and you could tell why faces and minds and consciences grew fanatical and narrow, and why spirits would always rise in weird perpetual revolt. Bill and I were walking arm in arm, but something stronger than linked arms was holding us. We were the end of a nebulous progression of other people's thoughts and acts. We were the end of a formless, chaotic accident, filled with the evil and the good of the Mendelian Law, walking in an unasked intimacy which came of common blood.

"Yes," I said, "of course — the family."

Bill edged nearer to me, and I saw he was grinning.

"It so happened there was a bridge game on the train, and I've gone bust. Slip me fifty dollars."

I slipped him fifty dollars, which left me with a five, and Bill's eyes wrinkled into narrow violet slits.

"Dependable as prewar proof," he said. "You always come across. Lee, you're the golden boy."

But it was not so. I did not have that intangible radiant inheritance which makes for carelessness and joy, or that heaven-sent serenity and regardlessness of others' rights which was so beautiful yet cruel. It touched me, but I did not have it. Bill was the golden boy, and Sue the golden girl.

By the shore way, Haven's End is some forty miles north, and Indian Creek is another eight miles off upriver, a narrow, sluggish tributary of that greater stream, crossed by a rickety plank bridge close by the mud flats. The country there has not changed much in the past hundred years, and that was what you always felt — a sense of changelessness, once the main road was behind.

When we arrived I remember that it was almost dark. The mist, that was rising now the air was cold, was like a hand across the face. The tide was out, and the smell from the mud about the reeds and the damp, sweet scent of new-fallen leaves and the wood smoke came together like a voice.

"You're back," it seemed to say. "You're bound to come."

It was as though you'd dreamed it when you came there in the early evening, when the trees and the stone wall and the corners of the dwelling and the barn were half-formed masses. The flicker from the backlog of the West Room fireplace glowed through the windows on the blackness of the lawn in a crazy, dancing light. And the rattling of the planking on that bridge intensified the stillness which always came with autumn. You always thought of the next sound that would follow. It would be the dripping from the elm limbs on the dead leaves of the lawn.

"Judas Iscariot!" Bill said. "The bar's up on the front door. It's what I tell you. Everything goes cuckoo once you cross that bridge."

He began fiddling with the latch, though he knew it would not open, and I slammed down the knocker. That door was like a drum, once you brought the knocker down. All sorts of voices were calling through the echoes, and a dog began to bark, and from everywhere you seemed to feel that other dogs were barking. Aunt Het opened the door and shaded from the draft a candle she was holding.

"Bill, Lee!" she said. "Don't do so. You mustn't pound like that. Gip — Mike — what is your name? Swipe, will you please be quiet?"

Swipe looked like a walking cider keg. His tail moved like an electric fan, and he had been rolling in dead fish.

"He's been rolling in something," I said.

"Yes," said Aunt Het. "Lee, did you have the black frost in New York last week?"

"Hi, Aunt Het," said Bill. "What have you locked us out for? You knew we were coming tonight."

"Yes," said Aunt Het. "Lee, the radio's working."

I told Bill to find Mrs. Royle, and to get lamps lighted in the parlor and in the hall. Then Aunt Het and I went into the West Room. The fire was smoking, and the portrait of my great-great-grandfather, Samuel Dansel, above the fireplace was faintly white with wood ash. Except for that, the rest of the room was a brown color — brown woodwork, brown mahogany and brown-calf bindings of old books. The windows which overlooked the river were squares of inky black.

The lamp burned dimly on a littered center table. It all gave the curious illusion that someone had left the room just as we had entered.

First I opened a window. Then I took the tongs to jab the backlog into place.

"Has Swipe been here all afternoon?" I asked. "The room smells as if he had."

"Yes, of course," Aunt Het replied, and sat down in her upholstered armchair. "He's been sleeping on the sofa. . . . Lee, you were asking why the limb on the old elm was bent. I remember now — because a pig was hung there for the winter once."

I snatched Swipe by the collar and shoved him out the door.

"Lee," said Aunt Het, "Bill has grown very distinguished, don't you think?"

"Yes," I answered, "Bill's all right."

"And he appreciates the beauty of everything so. . . . Oh, Lee, did you have the black frost last week in New York?"

"Black frost?" I said. "Yes — I don't know."

Aunt Het weaved her handkerchief in little knots between her fingers. We had disturbed her kingdom. She was always nervous when many of us came.

"Lee," she said, "who is the young man Sue's bringing down?"

"Crosby," I said — "Sam Crosby." And I shut the window.

"Yes," she said. "Lee, have you read the *Magnalia?*"

"The what?" I said.

"The *Magnalia Christi Americana*. It's among the Phippen books. Personally I always find Cotton Mather so delightful. He speaks of a black frost."

"Listen, Aunt Het," I said, "this Crosby's rich, and Sue'll marry him if she has any sense."

"Yes," said Aunt Het. . . . "Lee, we have five small gray kittens down cellar. I knew you'd like to know about them."

The firelight was flickering against the carving of a Jacobean armchair and against a broken-backed Chippendale beside it. A spurt of flame had lighted up a corner of the room, showing a cupboard where the family china stood. There was a great Lowestoft punch bowl on the lower shelf, like everything else a part of an old story, for everything had its history down at Indian Creek. It was the bowl that

Samuel Dansel used for punch when he came there for the shooting. It was not hard to picture his black boy bringing it in from the kitchen; and there above the mantel Samuel Dansel still remained, staring at desiccated memories. In spite of the dust, his eyes, steady and half insolent, made all the sadness and confusion leave that room.

"Very like Bill, don't you think?" Aunt Het was saying. "Bill has the eyes and hair."

"Aunt Het," I said, "why did you bar the door?"

"You should know," she said; "because I was afraid."

She did not say why, but I could understand. It was the thing that made one feel that someone had left that room just as one came in. The backlog spurted into flame again, until everything became indistinct with lights and shadows, and then Bill was calling from the entry.

"Here comes Crosby," he was calling. "Here come Joan and Phippen."

Nothing could thrust away that sense of all those others who had stood in that front entry, laughing and stamping from the cold. In the chill there was a cold, musty smell, and that was what you remembered best — cold, and a little lamp smoke, and the mustiness of aged walls and timbers like the dry wood in a shed.

Sam Crosby had his hat off. Bill was pulling at his coat, and the others had gathered behind him, until he seemed like a prisoner being pushed indoors.

"Hi, Crosby!"

"Phippen, go out and get his bag."

"Take care it doesn't break."

"Sam, do you know Aunt Het? — Miss Dansel, Mr. Crosby."

Sue looked over toward me, wide-eyed and very merry.

"Hello," called Sue, and once again I had that empty feeling when I tried to smile.

Her hair beneath her beret was what you always noticed first. It was like the color of a light-gold cigarette case, almost greenish gold. The wind, or something else, had made it into a tawny snarl, and her lips were a carmine gash, too red for her cheeks. Her black coat had a stack of orchids on it that must have cost an even forty dollars.

"Aren't you going to kiss me, Lee?" she called. "Come into the dining room. Come in and close the door."

She closed the thin old door, still holding to my arm. Mrs. Royle had lighted the candles, and all the silver was out on the sideboard, white and cool. A smell of cracked cocoa made a curious contrast with the teapots and the tankards. She made a face, twisting her little lips and wrinkling up her nose.

"Judas," she said, "I'm cold! The only thing that kept me living was Crosby. I thought we'd run into a tree, and then a cop — "

"What are you thinking of, bringing Crosby here?" I said.

She yanked her beret off and threw it in a corner and gave her head a shake.

"Judas," she said, "where's my powder? Untie your inhibitions and get out of your complexes, darling." She began pirouetting around the table, as though she were dancing away from something. There was a neurotic element in the whole thing which rang like a counterfeit coin. Her teeth were chattering, and she was very cold in spite of all that motion.

"Show a little enthusiasm!" she cried.

"Don't yell so," I told her. "I can hear you."

"Snap out of it," said Sue, "and put your arms around me — not like that — like a human being. Judas, Lee, I'm glad to see you, darling — and I'm dreadfully cold."

"Sue," I said, "aren't you going to marry Crosby?"

I felt her shiver, and then she gripped me tighter. "Lee," she whispered, "darling, let's not talk about that now."

"Look out," I said; "you'll break these orchids."

"Hang the orchids!" she said. "Darling!"

"You want everything," I said, "don't you? Are you going to marry Crosby?"

She stepped away and looked at me. We no longer were quite ourselves as we stood there near the cool whiteness of the silver in the candlelight.

"Why?" she asked me. "Why?"

And I told her why, although she knew already, and as I told her it made me angry that none of them could face the facts, from habit or inclination.

"You have to have money," I told her, "and we can't give you any. I don't say marry him if you don't love him, but won't you try to love him? It's just the way things are, and you know that. You're made to be ornamental, Sue, and we've been brought up to be used to money. You'd never be happy without it, never in this world. Sue, don't you see I'm telling you the truth? There isn't one of us with the commercial sense to earn a decent living. Don't you feel, when you come down here, that everything is slipping? It's the family, — Sue the family. Look at Bill, look at Phippen, look at me. The family's going on the rocks. . . ."

I always felt that way when I came to Indian Creek. Sue was looking at me.

"It's always been on the rocks," she said. "Why do you like the family, darling?"

And Lord knows why I liked it. I couldn't tell her why. Instead, I said: "Confound it, Sue, won't you try to love him?"

Sue began to laugh, and it was high-pitched and neurotic like all the rest.

"What do you think he's down here for?" she asked. "I wouldn't take all this from anyone but you."

"No," I said, "I don't suppose you would. What is he down here for?"

As I stopped I became aware of Aunt Het's voice. She was talking in a high key to Crosby in the entry, and we both moved toward the door.

"Lee," said Sue, and suddenly her voice was soft, "did you ever see the mist so thick over by the bridge? It moved — great wisps of it were moving down to the big river."

It was like her to see the mist just as I had seen it — clouds of mist like ghosts, moving through the trees.

Crosby had what we called "the big room." It was square with a very low sooty ceiling. Someone had lighted the fire, and the fourpost bed in the corner was stately enough to make the whole place fine — fluted columns with a pineapple base and an eagle at the head. A lot of us had died there, but I did not tell Crosby that. There were three good Chippendale chairs and one with a broken back, an Empire bureau, a candle stand and a worn-out Turkish rug.

"I hope everything isn't too much of a mess," I said.

"Oh," said Crosby, "that's all right, old man."

"Is there anything you want?"

"Oh, no," said Crosby. "Thanks."

Our glances met, and we both looked away.

"Would it be all right," said Crosby, "if we had a drink, old man?"

"Never mind about yours," I said. "I've got some."

"Oh, that's all right, old man," said Crosby. "This is prewar stuff."

Sitting irrationally on the mantel was a Lowestoft teacup. I took it and sat on the edge of a chair, and there was an awkward silence.

"Now you're here," I said, "I hope you're staying."

"Thanks," said Crosby. "I'm staying on with Sue."

"Good!" I said. "I think a lot of Sue."

"Yes," said Crosby, "yes, of course." And again our glances met and parted with that vague embarrassment. You always wonder what a girl sees in another man. He was very strong with that blind sort of strength which needs a daily outlet in exercise or hard drinking. Was his face kind? I could not tell; it was too blank and too much without a trace of the wear of life, dull-gray eyes neither sympathetic nor harsh, heavy cheeks and mouth. He would fight and live and love without knowing why — but then, after all, did any of us know?

"You staying down too?" asked Crosby.

"Yes," I said, "I'm going to try some shooting. My ancestors started this place simply for the shooting."

"Yes," said Crosby, "yes, of course. Let's see. I saw you ride in Green Spring Valley once."

"Last year," I said, "for Brewer. We're always using somebody else's things."

"Oh," said Crosby. "Let's see. You're Sue's cousin, aren't you?"

"Yes, second cousin. . . . Sure I can't get you anything?"

"No, thanks. Have another touch, old man?"

The door opened and Bill came in; the corners of his eyes wrinkled and his lips turned up.

"Holding out on me, are you?" said Bill. "Shove it over. We'll need it before supper."

"Have another?" said Crosby. "Just a touch?"

"No, thanks," I said — "thanks just as much."

Sue was in the hall oustide. There was moonlight coming through the window, and she was standing in a patch of it, wrapped in blue silk which was almost like moonlight. The old carpet had deadened the sound of her footsteps, so that there was only the rustling of that thing she wore, and then her voice dropped to the faintest whisper:

"Is he all right?"

"Yes," I answered, "he's got everything. Will you take him out to ride tonight?"

"Yes," she whispered, "darling!"

Then we heard a laugh through the closed guest-room door. It was Bill's laugh, and you always wanted to laugh, too, as soon as Bill was laughing.

"Yes," I said, "I like him." And that was a lie, because I have always hated Crosby's type.

My room was very cold, but the chill was pleasant, for my head had begun to ache. When I closed my eyes little red lights were darting across the black, and I could still see a figure in light blue with the moonlight on her face, and she was not like Sue.

She was in a tarnished oval frame, in a light-blue silk, carelessly opened at the throat, with lips very softly closed, like someone listening to a bar of music. She was a pale, oval face looking from a frame, lonely, appealingly, as pictures sometimes look across a hundred years. It was Mary Phippen, and not Sue, whose portrait hung in the front parlor by the silver Indian basket from Peru. They had never put Sam Dansel beside her, but there they were, only a door apart, as though atoning still for indiscretion.

Looking from the window, everything was mist and moonlight. The square of the house with the ell and the broad front chimney made a shadow which spread across the lawn to the river bank. Behind the old oak and the fringe of locust trees, the creek was like a twisting seam of weltering white smoke, but the big river was inky black where the creek and the reed grass met it, black and broad with a silver sweep of the moon upon it. You could think of water swirling at the narrows, tearing at the channel markers by the Old Island Bridge, and then dancing down in rips and eddies past the steeples and the streets of the town, and then pausing broad and empty as a river in an unknown world before it met the sea.

It must have been the same, for nothing could change that river, when old John Dansel built the place for his son, Samuel. The oak tree would have looked on clearer water, but the shore would not be changed. John Dansel, as the family legend went, used to sail up in a small-draft sloop, and beach her on the gravel by the old boat landing. You could still see the iron ring in a boulder where they made her fast, and the black houseboys, brought from the sugar islands, would come scurrying across the lawn.

There was a letter in the chest downstairs which told of such a night. "They would go to Indian Creek," it said, "and matters would be very merry far into the morning."

First, two men in the Dansel livery would climb ashore with the hampers and the sporting guns, and then the boatmen would follow with the other boxes. Then old John Dansel would step out, a large-boned, rough-grained man in a greatcoat and silver buttons, who always tossed a handful of silver to whoever might be waiting. Then Sam Dansel would follow, stepping carefully through the tall wet grass, and then the other gentlemen, all of them red-faced from the sea, and still a little stunned by sudden wealth. Thomas Phippen would be there with his son, George Phippen, and Roger Gale, who owned the sugar plantation at St. Francis, and then perhaps four more.

And then old John Dansel would be saying in a slightly foreign voice, "You are very welcome, gentlemen. This is Indian Creek, and you are very welcome."

And there he stood, the founder of our family, rich with privateering money from the Revolutionary War, and kindly with easy wealth, but very plain, no doubt, like the founders of most families.

Someone was knocking very softly on my door. The house was full of unrest and creaking boards and voices, and yet that knocking made me start.

"Lee." It was Aunt Het speaking. "Lee, may I come in?"

And she came in holding a thin box of some dark wood beneath her arm. "Here they are," she said.

"What are?" I asked.

"I knew they were about somewhere," she said. "And they were in the cupboard where the cat had the kittens all the time. Don't ask me how they got there. They used to be in the lower cupboard by the stairs."

"What used to be?" I asked. And she looked at me in a puzzled, gentle way.

"The pistols," she said. "I thought they would amuse you."

"Pistols?" I asked. "What pistols?"

It was uncanny when one stopped to consider the things that were only clear to her in the shadow land where past and present mingled.

"The ones they fought with on the Point," she said. "See, you snap the box open, so. You may have them, Lee, so you won't be jealous."

"Jealous?" I said. "Look here, what's the matter now?"

"Lee!" She put her hand up to her head. "Don't shout so. I've just given Bill my money to look after. He asked me and I knew he would appreciate it so."

"What?" I shouted. "Look here. Have you signed anything?"

"Bill — Phippen — Lee!" she said. "Don't shout so! He knows so thoroughly about banking. Now hurry and brush your hair. Mrs. Royle will be so upset if you come down late, and Mrs. Royle is a thoroughly good woman. Did you know she was buying a new fur coat?"

As I looked down at the box she had laid upon the table, it seemed like a symbol representing all the latent eccentricity of our stock. It stood for the egotism and sensitive foolhardiness that made us unfit to cope with a prosaic life. It explained why fortunes went up and down, and it explained the lack of physical fear that was not exactly courage.

On a silver oval in a flowing, engraved script was the name, "S. Dansel." The inside was lined with stained and corrupted plush, but everything was in its place. The pistols were those exquisite, light weapons that represented the acme of the gunsmith's art just before the percussion cap came in; balanced to a hair so they were light as pointing fingers. The silver inlay about the butts had tarnished, but the maker's name was clear — John Pell and Son, 6 Albemarle St., London.

It was not hard to believe that Sam Dansel could shoot the spots off a card at twenty paces with such a set of weapons. There would be dark coats, such as one wore when one went out, and then the morning damp. There would be a clear report and a blow, heavy enough to shake the footing, and a comforting, soft warmth. A shell splinter had lodged in my shoulder once, and since then I could never raise my arm to a perfect horizontal, so that I could tell the feeling.

First, there would be the sense that everything was quite all right, and surprise that there was no pain. That was how Sam Dansel felt, as sure as I was standing, when George Phippen bowled him over with a bullet through the chest.

"Good gracious!" It was Aunt Het's voice. "There's the supper bell. Lee, supper's ready."

"Look here," I said. "Have you signed any papers?"

"Yes," said Aunt Het, "yes, naturally. . . . Lee, supper's ready."

The world might come to an end at Indian Creek, but supper would be ready, with cracked cocoa and mustard pickles on the table. There might be ruin, there might be death, but supper would be ready. I knew that Bill and I would quarrel, and I hated family quarrels. I could picture him already standing in the dining room with too much red in his sharp, thin face.

On such occasions his eyes were dark, and they would be made doubly striking by his smooth, reddish hair. I could see his lips and chin, both too fine and delicate. As sure as fate, we were bound to quarrel when I told Bill exactly what I thought.

After supper they all went up to Crosby's room, but I did not go with them. It must have been an hour later when Bill and I met in the West Room, but as I look back on it, the time is hard to place, as time always was down there. Sue and Crosby must have gone out and Phippen and Joan must have known that they would be better somewhere else, so that Bill and I had the West Room to ourselves.

That room was always peculiar after dark. Its sliding wooden shutters were always drawn at six o'clock, making the place into a box of brown paneling which was worn smooth in spots where hands had touched. The fire and the lamp on the center table made it very hot. This heat was what you remembered best, for it was a hermetic sort of closeness where everything from an outer world was shut away, and I recall I asked Aunt Het about it before she went up to bed.

We were playing dominoes, and she had a singular ability with the numbers. Her hands would suddenly become capable and steady as she moved the rectangles of ivory.

"Fifteen," she said. And then I made a twenty.

"Twenty-five," she said.

"Aunt Het," I asked her, "why do you always draw the shutters?"

And then she gave me one of those startled looks, and then she said: "Because someone might be looking in. You can't tell who's out there. And now I'm going to bed. Light my candle, please."

I remember that the wind was rising, but the sound was very faint.

There is a time of night, I suppose, in any house, when all the objects in a room reflect the personality of all those who have used them. It comes upon one suddenly, in a disturbing way, that unseen details are gathering into a presence. My back was to the fireplace when I had the sense that something was just behind me. I found myself turning very slowly, as though to give whatever it might be a chance to get away, and next I was staring at the portrait of Sam Dansel with my hands clenched and with all my muscles taut. He was staring through his dust film, straight into my eyes. The artist had not glossed the coarseness from his face; his cheekbones were too high and his thin nose was twisted, seemingly broken, at the bridge; and his straight mouth showed a tendency to sudden laughter or hot anger which went perfectly with his reddish-gold, clubbed hair. The desires of the flesh were on him and the vanities were with it. Filigree buttons glittered on his purple-satin coat; there must have been ten guineas' worth of lace about his neck and wrists.

"Damn you!" he seemed to say. "If I weren't dead you wouldn't look at me like that." And I could swear that he had been there, right behind me, that time my back was turned.

That was why Bill found me, when he came in, staring at Sam Dansel as though he were alive.

"Hullo, you skunk," I said.

Bill swayed backward on his heels and yanked his hands from his pockets. For a moment he might have been Sam Dansel conjured into life, for temper had changed the whole texture of his face. And for that moment I hated him as I never had before; and the intimacy of that hatred only made it worse.

"Yes," I said, "you skunk!" And I was not myself and he was not himself. I saw him staring at me, startled, as I had been, by some unexpected revelation. Then I heard my own voice lashed into an eloquence which was not mine — talking. I was telling him of his uselessness; I told him he was crooked, I told him he was a liar, but I said I had thought he would play fair with the family. I asked him if he had no loyalty; I asked him if he had no pride. And then, as I finished, even my anger did not sound convincing. I was like a shadow talking to a shadow. Bill took it standing poised and perfect, without a misplaced wrinkle in his clothes.

Then, as I finished, I became aware of something else. Bill was drunk — not that he showed it in any vulgar way.

"Lee," he said, "I wouldn't take that from anyone but you. Don't get mad at me; I've got to have a friend." Then he threw an arm about my shoulder, and as he did so a stab of pain went through me that made me gasp.

"Shoulder hurting, boy?" he said. "Here, sit down." And he drew me down beside him on the sofa. "Feeling better now?" he said.

"Bill," I said, "can't you pull yourself together?" And I saw that I had hurt him as much as he had hurt me, for suddenly he put his face in his hands.

"Judas, Lee," he said, "you've given me a beating! Why don't you blame the others? Why do you blame me?"

"What others?" I asked him.

"You know," he said — "all the others."

"That's rot," I told him. "Now you tear up those papers you got Aunt Het to sign."

He stood up and straightened his tie; he always thought of appearance as much as any actor. "All right," he said, "I'll tear 'em up. Give me the key to your car."

"Where are you going?"

"Never mind where I'm going. I can drive all right."

"Look here," I said. "Are you going to the Brights'?"

"Yes," he said. "What of it?"

I stood up again, and my shoulder was feeling better.

"Because they don't want to see you. Old Man Bright kicked you out last time."

"To hell with Old Man Bright!" said Bill. "Milly wants to see me. She knows I'm coming. I'll just stand out and whistle on the lawn. Give me the key to your car. There's the golden boy."

"No," I said, "I won't. You better go to bed."

And then his face was like a knife and his eyes were as hard as agates.

"Cut that out!" he said. "You've said your mouthful. Milly wants to see me. You want it melodramatic, do you? Give me the key or, curse you, I won't tear up the papers."

And then he walked away and left me, whistling through his teeth. Yes, Milly would like to see him; Milly would be waiting. A thousand other Millies would be waiting for such a sight as that, since they were all of them rakes at heart and loved rakes best of all. Mr. Pope was right; Milly would be waiting. He might have been Sam Dansel walking out the door, if his hair had been long and clubbed.

And I was in the room alone again, with a fine rain beating on the window, and all the shutters were closed tight for fear that something might be looking in.

I suppose the story of Sam Dansel has been told a dozen times before, in those tomes of genealogy which only the curious read, but we had more than that. There were letters and John Dansel's diary that told of an old man's broken pride at a son's disgrace, and there were letters by George Phippen himself which described the whole affair from the standpoint of a conscientious man.

It had never come to me before that his story was not over, until I saw Bill walking out the door, and then I knew that it was unfinished, moving as we moved, and that it would be unfinished after we were gone.

Sam Dansel married Mary Phippen in the chaos and depression that followed the Revolutionary War. He married her when he came back from the Continent, after drawing on his father's agent at Cadiz for five thousand pounds, and it was not hard to imagine from the letters which were written what old John Dansel said. They met in the West Room, right where I was sitting, and probably the chairs and tables were still in their same places.

Old John Dansel had come up for a two days' rest from his counting-house, where things were very bad. In the last years of the war he had lost a dozen ships, and Continental currency was sinking like the German mark, and there must have been a sadness about Indian Creek already, for there was no money left to run it.

John Dansel looked up and set down his long clay pipe — Aunt Hêt could even show where the ashes spilled and burned the table's edge.

"So you're back!" John Dansel said.

"Yes," said Sam Dansel, "I'm back, and I need money."

"There's no money," John Dansel said.

"There's Indian Creek," said Sam. "Do you forget, sir, that you've given me this place? That's why I'm here. I've come to Indian Creek."

"But you'll not stay," John Dansel said. "You've killed a man. No decent man or woman will speak to you in town."

"Ah," said Sam Dansel, "do they still remember that?"

But John Dansel's own diary could tell the rest; two pages of that scene had been written in his own careful hand. "And then I told him," the page read, "that I would buy back from him his lands and buildings at Indian Creek which I had deeded him as my son, for seven hundred pounds. I told him that God had made me resigned to looses and that he was my heaviest loss. I told him that I'd sent him off in hopes of eformation and that he had killed two men in France and one in Italy.

"And then he said that he would live at Indian Creek, and I told him hat he would not. Then I asked him why he was back, and he told ne he was come for Mary Phippen. And I told him Thomas Phippen vas my friend, who would not have him inside his gates. And then he aid, 'To the devil with Old Man Phippen. Mary wants to see me. Mary's vaiting.' I told him she was betrothed to Roger Gale; he laughed, tating he would call Gale out if Gale stepped in between. And then asked God's pardon for having begotten such a son. And then I called 'or my servant and my carriage, and left him standing in the West Room, calling to his black boy for a bottle."

The bitterness of a century ago was as fresh as though it all were yesterday, and a curious reflection of that gay time was in it. In those two sportive decades which ended the eighteenth century, honor was a deadly affair.

There had been an argument in the upper room of the tavern toward midnight, where some younger men were gaming. Sam Dansel had come back from a privateering cruise which had ended aboard a British prison hulk, leaving him a dangerous man who could not settle down to quiet. There was trouble over the cards at midnight, when a person named Pendel had given him the lie. And Pendel had died the next morning at half past seven in a regular affair with seconds. Sam Dansel had left hurriedly on the next tide.

It is strange what freaks of accidents make letters last, and we had such a letter, which Mary Phippen wrote. It was tied in tape, with clippings and affidavits, beside John Dansel's diary. "Dear Sam," it read, "there is no one to make me laugh, now that you've gone. They talk about you still. Will you not come back so that we may laugh?"

It is too late now to tell whether Sam Dansel really loved her. By that time he was a rolling stone, seized by a thirst for adventure and for violence which was on him like the desire for drink. When he married Mary Phippen he told her that. He had seen half the world by that time and was known in the London clubs, a wholly unfit person for a quiet married life.

They were married secretly in the dead of night by a country parson twenty miles away, after he had waited with two horses by the Phippens' garden gate. They had come to Indian Creek when it was nearly dawn, and Sam Dansel's black boy had the fire lighted and cold meat on the table. There could have been no languor in her face that night but she must have had that look of listening to strange music; she must have had some of his own wildness to make such a match. Coupled with that erratic passion which flares up now and then in the Puritan stock.

Sam Dansel took off his cloak and laid his pistols on the table. "Close the shutters, Scipio," he said. "They'll be looking for us here."

"Sam," she asked him — "oh, Sam, what are you going to do?"

"My dear," Sam Dansel said, "you must not fret. I'll be careful, now that I'm a family man."

Roger Gale and old Thomas Phippen and George Phippen, his son, came in the morning at six o'clock. Roger Gale was tall and silent; he had always labored with a diffident shyness whenever he and Sam Dansel met. Thomas Phippen must have looked very gray and ill, but George would have been cool enough.

"So it's done," he said. "There's no need quarreling for what's done."

And Roger Gale, as the story goes, did the handsome thing. "Sam," he said, "will you shake hands?"

Sam Dansel must have had his decent side, for he bowed to Mr. Phippen.

"I'll be sober, sir," he said. "I swear I will, now that I'm a family man."

Perhaps he meant to be so, but he left her two weeks later, there at Indian Creek; secretly, with only a note and five pounds on the table in the West Room to tell that he was gone.

"My dear," it read, "I'm sailing for the Ivory Coast. We'll be rich when I get home."

If the story sounds fantastic, one must remember that it happened in a fantastic era. The republic was in convulsions; there was talk of a new nobility, and even of a king. The three estates were about to meet in France to end an old regime, and it was a time of homeless, wandering men.

Sam Dansel left her in two weeks, and a year later the news came that he was dead of yellow fever. A merchantman from the Indies brought back the news, and a clipping from a newspaper of the time told of it in stilted rhetoric, stressing the sorrow with which many would hear the report, speaking of his services to the nation upon the sea; and calling him a gentleman, well-known and beloved by all. There is a mystery about the whole thing now which will never be quite clear. Sam Dansel had disappeared into the black of things, with a century and more to hide him. But he came back.

Four years later he dismounted from the diligence at the tavern on the lower square, causing a stir which still has faint echoes in old legends on the river. It could not have been more than half an hour before everyone had heard that Sam Dansel was back home. He had taken the best room at the tavern, it was said, where George Phippen found him watching his black boy brushing off his cloak.

Upon perceiving George Phippen, Samuel Dansel turned from the window embrasure where he was standing and held out his hand. George Phippen himself had said that the gesture did not seem out of place, because they had known each other since they were boys.

"I swear on the Book," he has written, "that I felt no passion. He was thinner and his sunken cheeks wore a sallow, unhealthy tint, like jaundice, but he was dressed with care and elegance. When he smiled he did not seem changed."

"George," he said, "it's kind in you to come. . . . Skip, bring Master George the bottle, and fetch hot water and the limes."

George Phippen must have been slow and staid and heavy, for the Phippens have always had a Puritanical restraint.

"We heard you'd died of yellow jack," George Phippen said. "Sam, you can't stay here. Sam, I've come from the family — "

"So you heard I'd died," said Sam Dansel. "Didn't you know I had enough life in me not to die? I told you I'd be back. Is Mary well? As soon as my coat's cleaned I'll be up to see her."

"You can't," said George Phippen. "Why didn't you write, Sam? . . . I say you can't. She's married to Roger Gale."

Sam Dansel seemed amused. He sat astride across a chair and took a pinch of snuff.

"Hoity-toity!" he replied. "What are we going to do?"

"Don't laugh," said George. "It's no time for laughing, Sam. It's a matter of family honor. I'll not say what I think of you, for is there any use? I'll stay with you here till dark. Then I'll ride out with you before anyone is sure you are back — and you'll go away forever. If you don't choose to think of us or her, think of your own flesh and blood. Sam, you have a son."

Sam Dansel pulled himself up from his chair and straightened his linen.

"Scipio," he called, "fetch me my coat — the purple one with the silver buttons."

"Sam," George Phippen said, "what are you going to do?"

"You fool!" said Sam Dansel. "I'm going to congratulate the lady. It's odd it never should have occurred to me. . . . Thank you, Skip."

Then George stood in front of him, and he must have stood a good head taller.

"I'll kill you first," he said.

"Kill me?" said Sam Dansel. "Have you lost your wits, George Phippen? There's no one in this place can kill me. They've tried in Havana. They've tried in France — "

Then George Phippen struck him so that he staggered back against the wall.

"I'm sorry, Sam," George Phippen said. "It's the only way that's left. It's the family — do you understand?"

"Perfectly," Sam Dansel said, "except you needn't strike so hard. I'll kill you, and then I'll see her, since you wish it. . . . Set out the pistols, Scipio. . . . Shall we try it now?"

"No," George Phippen said, "not now. We'll do this decently and in order. If you name the time and place, I — I'll be there with a friend."

"Indian Creek," Sam Dansel said, "at half past six tomorrow morning. The light will be good then. Bring a surgeon and a friend. Scipio will do for me. We always used to go to Indian Creek for shooting. What's the matter now? Everything is regular. . . . Squeeze out the limes, Scipio, and pass Master George the bottle, and tell me about my son, George. It's all in the family, now that I'm a family man."

At half past six they met in the West Room in the fresh light of early morning, for it was late autumn and the nights were growing long. There was a large fire crackling in the chimney, and both tea and brandy were on the table, and Sam Dansel was warming his hands, looking carefully at his fingers. Scipio was behind him, dressed in an old livery from the attic, and his cheeks had turned a grayish-white.

Captain Ezra Greene, from one of the Phippen ships, had come as George Phippen's friend, and with him was Doctor Tillman, who was very nervous.

"Where's George?" Sam Dansel asked. "Why doesn't George come in?"

"My principal naturally prefers to wait outside," said Captain

Greene. "Dansel, isn't there any other way of settling this? If you leave — if you ride off now, he begs me to say — "

"Yes," said Doctor Tillman, "for God's sake, Sam, ride off now — "

"Positively," Sam Dansel said, "George should come in and get warm. Is he warm enough? He must be careful about his hands."

"He's warm enough," snapped Captain Greene. . . . "Dansel, isn't there any way — "

"I hope you're both discreet," Sam Dansel said. "This is a family matter. Will you take refreshment, gentlemen? I ask your pardon for having a black go on the ground. It would have made more noise if I had sent for someone else."

Indian Creek was already a place of ghosts. Though no furniture had been moved from it, it had that air of a deserted house which starts as soon as doors are closed and fires are out. There was already that sense of others who had been there in fellowship. The trace of old, easy days hung there like fading sunlight in cold weather, and everything felt chill despite the crackling of the fire.

"If you want a nigger for your second," said Captain Greene, "it's your taste. It isn't mine. Let's get on with this."

"Scipio," said Sam Dansel, "for five minutes you will have the inestimable opportunity of being the equal of this pleasant-spoken gentleman. Show him the pistols, Scipio, and let him load and prime."

Then he turned to the fire, holding out his hands, and looked at Doctor Tillman.

"I always found it best," he remarked, "to be careful of my hands. I'm told I have a son. Have you seen him, Doctor? Does he take after me?"

"God forbid he should, Sam," said Doctor Tillman. "I brought him into the world."

"And now you square accounts by helping another out of it? . . . Shall we be going? The ground is by the Point."

It must have been much the same as it is now, though new pine trees have grown up to fill the clearing where they met. There must have been the same sighing hiss of breeze through the fine needles, indescribably lonely, and the smell of pitch and mold and river mud. As the principals faced each other with their weapons, Sam Dansel waved his left hand.

"Good morning, George," he said.

Captain Greene had become fussily officious, pacing distances and estimating the light and wind, but finally they were placed.

"When I count three," he began, holding a somewhat soiled handkerchief . . .

"Get on with it," Sam Dansel said.

Sam Dansel's eyes had wrinkled into small straight slits, like eyes which were trying to see a very long distance off, and then the shots came sharply, each like a flash of light.

Then Sam Dansel lowered his arm, still narrow-eyed and staring. "George!" he called. "How is it with you, George?"

Then his knees began to sag like wilting tallow candles, and he was resting on his elbow, staring at the trees.

"Skip," he said, and he began to cough, "I wish to speak to Master George."

Then George Phippen was leaning over him like a figure seen through water. He was heavy in his black coat, with a pale, drawn face.

"Gad," gasped Sam, "you're black! Don't look as black as that." And his head was sinking slowly backward, and the hot blood was leaving it.

"Sam," began George Phippen, "they'll have to bring you in —"

"Just you mind this," Sam Dansel said: "Don't you go out again. You're slow — oh, Lord, you're slow against a decent shot. I could have dropped you twice before you fired. And don't look as black as that. It was the only thing to do. It was the family. Damn the family. Tell 'em I'm a family man."

I could understand why, when I was a little boy, there was something in the West Room which used to send me running quickly and yet softly up the stairs. Sad or sinister or gay, there was something of him there, but I had never thought that I would have that superstitious sense again until that night. Cold winters had not killed it, nor economy, nor prayer. There was something dancing in the firelight ungoverned by fear or sense. There was something in that close, hot room as heady as strong wine. There was a reckless will which was calling out strange thoughts. It was gathering about me boldly like the sounds of the wind and rain, earthbound, like a soul in purgatory. And then the parlor door had opened, for I heard the hinges creak, and then I heard a voice:

"It's you — thank God, it's you."

I never asked her who else it might have been. She was standing in the firelight, and her face was shining from the rain, and she took a step toward me, as though all the time she were trying to draw back.

"Darling," Sue said, "it's a dreadful night outside. The trees are shaking like old men saying 'no.' "

The freshness of outdoors was on her. Her cheeks would be as cool as the raindrops. Her hair would be like the dead leaves and the rain.

"Where is he?" I was saying, but it did not seem to matter, for we were both like shadows in that room.

"Who?" she asked, and she began to smile. "Crosby? He's gone up to bed. Lee, darling! He's so dreadful, Lee."

Then there seemed to be no time or world, but only the fierce short triumph of taking what was given.

"I had to find you," she whispered — "had to — had to — "

There was nothing in that room except ourselves; we both had the same reckless egotism, and the same futility that seized a moment and let consequences go; and somehow it had a splendor and a strength.

"Just as soon as I saw him in here," she was saying, "he was dreadful. I don't know why I ever liked him, now that I've seen him here."

There was something always just behind us which broke down plans and built up others. There was always at Indian Creek some shadowy and unsubstantial jury, that rendered its decisions of yes and no, approving harebrained actions and disapproving common sense. It was the integration of all which had happened there, and she must have known, as I did, that there would be no common sense that night.

Commencement, June 11, 1953

FIVE years ago was the only time before this present that I have had the honor of addressing a large group of learned men. This was in May, 1948, when President Conant invited me to speak with him at a dinner of the Associated Harvard Clubs in Philadelphia. Since it is often difficult, as President Conant warned me then, to say the right thing happily on such occasions, I asked him if I might read him my speech in advance, and I did so in his office in Massachusetts Hall. After listening to my effort, I recall that he asked a single question.

"You aren't," he asked me, "going to *read* it in Philadelphia, are you?"

This came as a shock, I remember. It seemed incredible to me that he should deem me capable of memorizing a twenty-minute speech, and I realized then what very different mechanical rabbits Dr. Conant and I had been pursuing since we had been Harvard undergraduates. I felt the weight of wasted days upon me then, as I do now. I faced the slowness of my mental processes, and finally I realized how very little I had ever availed myself of what had been taught me at Harvard, and by your leave I venture to enlarge briefly on this subject.

This is the time of year when salmon, due to instinctual urge, leave the Atlantic Ocean and return in large groups to the inland waterways of their youth. So, too, at this same season do graduates of various academic institutions make their own pilgrimages to the halls in which they once encountered learning. The salmon comes back imbued primarily with the purpose of reproducing his kind, whereas an alumnus returns for more sublimated, though often sentimental, reasons. Yet there are certain naturalists who believe that the salmon, too, has his sublimated moments. For instance, once he is in fresh water he will strike at a fly, although he has eaten no such insect for years in the Atlantic, but curiously enough, as an adult he no longer wants to eat this fly. Many inveterate fishermen believe that he leaps for it only because of happy memory, since flies nourished him as a fingerling before he swam down to the sea. In other words, according to these authorities, the salmon, when he is on the hook, has reached this predicament not from love or hunger, but solely from a desire to test again the skills he acquired in his early education.

Most of us, I imagine, follow a somewhat similar pattern when we return to Harvard. At any rate, to make the matter personal, I find myself, although I should know much better, striking clumsily at various intellectual flies which lured me long ago, while I attempt to review and reassess what I learned beside the placid waters of the Charles. Personally, I have found that this retrospective mood is seldom a wholly happy one, because a great many far from reassuring things seem to have happened to me in the world beyond the Harvard gates, including some serious lapses of memory.

Only the other day my daughter, aged thirteen, asked me to solve a simple problem of algebraic fractions. I was amazed to discover that the symbols written by her meant nothing to me whatsoever — and it did me no good to remember that I had once studied calculus at Harvard. The truth is that for some thirty-five years there has never been an occasion in my life in which I have been obliged to resort to algebra. On the contrary, plain arithmetic is all that I have ever needed in my struggles for survival — including a little short division, occasionally addition, but principally subtraction. And even with this equipment I seem unable to compute a modern income-tax return. I like to think, and I often remind myself, that I never did have a head for mathematics. Yet things have not stopped there.

When I was a Harvard student, I specialized in the science of chemistry and spent many hours in several gloomy laboratories coping with various problems of analysis. Yet only the other Christmas, when one of my sons, who had been given a fun-with-chemistry set, asked me how to manufacture chlorine gas, I found myself obliged to turn for assistance to the *Encyclopædia Britannica*. Curiously enough, someone else has always made my chlorine for me, and frankly I have never objected to the arrangement. In fact I can recall only one small facet of laboratory technique which has been of practical use to me. This is a trick of holding a glass stopper from a bottle in the same hand that pours the bottle's contents — a feat that still commands mild respect when I have occasion to handle a decanter. But what has happened to those other scientific skills that I acquired at considerable personal sacrifice? Where are they gone? As far as I can see, they have vanished as completely as the girls in François Villon's ballad. In fact there is only one difference between Villon's old loves and my chemistry courses. He could remember his girl friends' names.

Let us turn to languages next. I emerged from Harvard with what might be called a working knowledge of German, Spanish, and French. Somehow I seldom seem to have been obliged to exchange ideas with foreigners in their mother tongues. Could I do so now? Can I read Schiller or Cervantes or Molière in the original? Do I ever attempt to do so in order to open new windows to the soul? Frankly, I refuse to answer under the Fifth Amendment. Frankly, I'm very glad to find that English is a fairly universal language in most parts of Europe. It has also pleased me to observe that good linguists are often dumb in many other ways, but unfortunately I must go further.

I enjoyed the study of philosophy at Harvard once. I could even discuss a few of its concepts with intelligence, but could I explain to you today the Leibnitz theory of monads? Could I understand it if you were to explain it to me? I prefer not to answer. Once I could set up the Wheatstone Bridge with considerable speed and accuracy, but can I now repair the electric bell beneath the dining-room carpet? I prefer not to answer. Once upon a time I could walk into the basement of the Agassiz Museum, be confronted by a box of mineral specimens and give the right names to the lot. Could I do this now? Once in search of new adornments of the mind I studied Fine Arts at Harvard. Could I tell you now the difference between a frieze and a pediment? I must refuse to answer under the Bill of Rights. Exactly what was the Dred Scott Decision? What was the Era of Good Feeling? Did Père Goriot have any children? Perhaps it is just as well that I don't have to tell you.

I cannot understand, now that I have made this confession, exactly why I am sometimes under the illusion that I am a reasonably well-educated individual, because cold truth belies it. The robes of learning that covered me when I left Harvard College are in shreds and tatters now, and I return here in a state that borders on intellectual bankruptcy. I cannot help but feel self-pity, when I contemplate the end result, and a warm compassion for my teachers, who gave up so much of their time toward this achievement.

I would like very much to think that I am a single exception and that my contemporaries, who have passed with me through these halls, have kept their knowledge with them. I say I would like to think so, but I cannot report this as being true. President Conant, I admit, seems never to have forgotten anything he has learned. A few others of my contemporaries are in the same fortunate situation, but most of them are teachers, too, or scientists or preachers, who have always been cloistered with the books. The great majority, I am afraid, fall into my own category. Why don't we face it in the spirit of good sportsmanship? Let us admit that we are sheep who have strayed far from the academic fold and have been comforted too seldom by the rod and staff of the academic mind.

Indeed it is small wonder, when faced with such results, that certain highly intelligent and conscientious educators are inclined to look with puzzled patronage at alumni in large groups, even when they must appeal for funds to keep the old school going. Further, I can hardly blame some pedagogues if they experience a sense of frustration when they lecture to undergraduates of Harvard. Small wonder if it occasionally occurs to them that their efforts are of little value when nineteen out of every twenty students are bound to forget nearly everything that they absorb. Small wonder they turn with relief to the graduate schools which surround this institution and offer better-screened and more-rewarding minds. Although personally I have come to believe strongly in tolerance, up to certain limits, I honestly cannot blame anyone whose mind has flowered — or even calcified — in this well-regulated academic atmosphere for revealing disillusionment when he looks upon some of the intellectual wreckage that drifts back to the Cambridge beach.

And yet — and yet — although perhaps I should, I cannot quite bring myself to concur with this dim view. Instead I can believe, in fact, that most of us here today have gained a few imponderable gifts from this very negative process of learning and forgetting, and I venture to give this thought validity by calling your attention to the motto of Winchester College, the oldest public school in England, founded by William of Wykham some three hundred years before John Harvard's time. *Abeunt,* the motto reads, *Studia in Mores.* Unfortunately the finer points of my Latin elude me at the moment, and thus my translation, if you need it, will be debatable. Roughly I should say it means that our studies vanish into our attitudes.

However, I can give you a more recent authority to back up this same thought. This is Mr. Justice Holmes, who delivered a speech here on another commencement. Though he spoke sixty-nine years ago, his words, instead of suffering from age, seem to me the brighter for it. "It has been," he said, "one merit of Harvard College that it has never quite sunk to believing that its only function was to carry a body of specialists through the first stage of their preparation. About these halls there has always been an aroma of high feeling not to be found or lost in science or Greek — not to be fixed yet all-pervading."

Let those of us who need it take refuge behind those words. I cannot explain their whole significance any more than that great jurist could, for the *high feeling* of which he speaks is composed of many intangibles not susceptible of accurate definition. I only know, and I think most of you here will agree, that the contagion of this feeling was sensed in some measure by each of us when we were students here at Harvard, and, surely, it is with us still. I doubt if there is one in this company who has not been aware today of its pervasive presence. It has always been, and always will be, Harvard's greatest gift to her erring and unerring sons alike, and curiously our estimation of its value increases progressively with time, and with it our sense of obligation to this university that was so gracious as to give us shelter once. It is a spirit which ennobles all effort, no matter how prodigally it may be wasted, because even at the very worst it has left us with a species of a residue of knowledge — not specific but something which we could have gained nowhere else. No mind it has reached can be closed or complacent.

And indeed it may not be knowledge as much as understanding — the sort of understanding attainable only by having walked for a while in the shadow of great things, by having had a glimpse of great vistas, by having been momentarily a part of a great and ageless tradition. No matter how heedlessly we may have treated what was taught us here, we cannot forget the true dignity of learning. It is this spirit, I think, as well as the memory of it, that brings us back from banks and factories and laboratories, from wars and from the distant places on this earth to pay our humble and grateful tribute to this, and every other, faculty of Harvard University.

The Wars: Men and Places

Ascension Island

(1944)

In the last few years I have seen some very lonely places on the earth's surface. I have seen Iceland for instance, and the jungles in Assam and several very dull coral atolls. But when I think of something that epitomizes complete solitude my mind still goes back to Ascension Island, a pinpoint of land in the middle of the South Atlantic where our planes stopped on the way from Miami to Karachi or back. Ascension as I think of it was not lonely because it was sparsely inhabited. On the contrary we had a lot of troops there, and a flying field whose mess halls and machine shops were running day and night. It was lonely simply because it was a geographical accident so many thousand miles away from anywhere. And perhaps also it was lonely because of the state of mind of most people when they reached it. I imagine that most people, even the navigators on the transport planes, have a feeling of surprise when they first see Ascension Island. You may know it is coming, but when you first see the clouds and its single volcanic peak, the whole thing seems more like an abstraction than a reality. It appears so quickly, and, when a plane leaves it, disappears so fast that it is very easy to believe that there was nothing there at all. Now that the war is over it is quite easy to think that Ascension no longer exists except in the memories of the crews and passengers who saw it.

You cannot separate Ascension Island from a state of mind and from all the sights you experience on the way to Ascension, and this is why I am going to try to describe some of these sights first, not that they are in any way unusual. They are simply what everyone holds in common who has traveled in this war. Almost two years ago I was traveling with a general, and it was the best possible way to travel, because generals rate a good deal of attention when they get away from Washington. There had been a time when my general had wanted to fly over the Hump to Chungking and we had tried it twice, and had been stopped twice by bad wind storms in the valley of Assam. At about this juncture the general was very worried because he wanted to be back in New York on October fifteenth. The second time we turned back after trying to reach the Himalayas the general said he wanted to make it quite plain that he did not want to be in New York, personally, but he did feel that he owed it to the service to be there. I may say, frankly, that I began to understand what the general meant. We had flown about thirty thousand miles by this time, and though I did not want to be back in New York either, the idea of New York began to be impressive, particularly after some weeks in Calcutta. When we got back to Calcutta one night after a second very rough trip up the Assam valley, the general spoke again about New York. After all, he told me, there was no reason whatsoever why either he or I should fly the Hump except for personal gratification. We had finished doing what we were going to do, and we did not have to see Chungking.

"I'll tell you what we'll do," the general said. "We'll go to that field once more at four o'clock tomorrow morning, and if the weather is still bad over Assam, we'll go back to Karachi and cut across Central Africa. I can't stand waiting here any longer with all these people dying in the streets."

The general was referring to the Hindus in Calcutta, who, as you may remember, were suffering from a severe famine, and were crowding into Calcutta to die upon the sidewalk or to worship their gods beside the river just before they died. The general was not impressed by the Hindus, or by the eccentricities of their religion. It was his feeling that the Hindus did not need to die if they did not want to. Someone had told him that there were a hundred thousand sacred cows in Calcutta, and the general had encountered many of them himself, including one that stood for some hours in front of the teller's window of the Calcutta National Bank. It was the general's idea that the starving Hindus if they wanted to live might eat some of those cows. The truth was they didn't want to live. They kept dying in the streets. Vultures sat in the trees waiting for them to die. The river was full of corpses and there wasn't enough firewood at the burning ghats to burn up the corpses, even when the families of the deceased had money enough to pay for firewood. It was a situation which the general did not want to face. He said that the Indians could have India, though he could not see why they wanted it. Personally, he did not want it.

"Doesn't it impress you," the general said, "that all these people are very queer?"

As a matter of fact, I felt that the general was right. The Brahmins were queer and so were the Untouchables, and only the other day we had seen some people who were even queerer. They had been living in a jungle and worshipping dogs.

At two o'clock in the morning the general woke me up at the hotel.

"Pull on your shoes," he said, "and let's get out of this. The car will be outside in fifteen minutes."

There was still a Rudyard Kipling atmosphere about the Great Eastern Hotel. There was a barefooted Mohammedan servant attached to my room who was known as my bearer. I have never known what a bearer meant in India, but I assume in the old days that he must have borne the sahib's rifle for him when he went shooting tigers. Now, however, he seemed to be a general errand boy. My bearer's name was Ali, and he had a number of letters of recommendation written by witty American officers, which he kept pulling out of his waistband to show me. The letters all said about the same thing. They said, "You will just love Ali. He is courteous, brave and honorable and has the fidelity of a lion." The letters were signed by Ulysses Grant, General Robert E. Lee, General MacArthur, and Admiral Nimitz. One of them, if I remember correctly, was signed by Peary. Ali gave me a cup of lukewarm tea and strapped the last of my bags. Then he asked me to write him a letter of recommendation. I wrote that I would never forget all that Ali had done for me, and signed it "Franklin Delano Roosevelt." Then I made him a little present. Ali touched his forehead with the little present and bowed. Even at two-thirty in the morning it was very warm in the blacked-out streets of Calcutta. The air was dusty and full of smoke from the burning ghats and from little cow-dung fires which the natives built here and there at the street corners. It was a long, slow ride out to the airfield in the suburb of Dumdum. This, I believe, was where the Dumdum bullets were first made. Our car crawled behind donkey carts and passed shadows of emaciated natives leaning against the mud walls of houses.

"If the weather's still bad," the general said, "by God we're going to get out of this."

I asked the general whether he'd brought any food with him. He said of course he hadn't; there would be something on the plane. I told him I had a K-ration with me, and the general said all I thought of was food. I was always loading myself up with food. There would be something on the plane, and if there wasn't, he could take it. There was no use worrying about food.

The sky was faintly gray when we reached the airfield of Dumdum, and the weather over Assam was still bad.

"All right," the general said, "that tears it. We'll get the hell out of here. We'll take the Karachi plane."

As I think of it, this sort of travel was something I shall never experience again. The general and I talked of planes and distances as simply as we used to talk of streetcars. We both had a number one priority. All we had to do was to hand it to the airport officer, and we could go anywhere at all at ten minutes' notice. If the plane was crowded, we could bump someone off. We had a number-one priority. The Karachi plane was a C-47 carrying mail and a few officers up to the place where we were training Chinese troops. We sat on aluminum bucket seats, except for a sergeant and myself, who went to sleep on the mail sacks. When the plane started, everyone looked nervous. The day before the Karachi plane had cracked up at the end of the runway and had burst into flames. No one had survived. It was cold in the plane and there was no food. Some time around noon we had a view of Agra and the Taj. I asked the general if he did not want to look at it, but he said I'd rubbed his nose in the Taj already. He did not want to see any more of those buildings even from the air. He wanted to get the hell out of here. We crossed the subcontinent quickly as time goes, but even so time was like a leaden weight. It was eight-thirty in the evening when we landed at Karachi, and the general and I were both very tired.

There was one thing though about traveling with the general. There was a captain and a car to meet us at Karachi. And that was not all. The captain brought us word that there was a C-54 with reclining seats leaving for Khartoum at three-thirty in the morning, and we had rooms at the Old Civilian Airways hotel, and furthermore we could get some dinner. When we got in the car I nudged the general with my elbow.

"What the hell is it now?" the general said.

I looked at the captain in the front seat and made an expressive gesture, and the general understood me.

"And if he does it," I said to the general, "you'd better make him a major."

The general nodded and cleared his throat.

"Captain," he said, "we've had a pretty hard day. Do you know where we can get a pint of whisky?"

"Why, yes, sir," the captain said. "I can get you one."

Suddenly we all felt very happy, very gay. It seemed that the captain was in charge of the hotel and in charge of the mess. He could not only get us a pint of Four Roses rye, but he might even be able to get us a little more to take with us. We had a very jolly meal of baked beans, Spam, pineapple juice and rye, and we talked about India, of the peculiarities of the natives. The captain admitted that he could not understand the Indians. He had been there for two years and he could not understand the British either. "As far as I'm concerned," the captain said, "they can take the whole damned place and keep it."

The general pointed at me across the table.

"Isn't that exactly what I've been saying?" he told me. "Do you remember I told you that?"

I remembered he had told me that and we walked to the rotunda of the hotel. It was one of those places with which one grows familiar in air travel, a circular, modernistic room with soldiers and officers asleep on modernistic chairs. The general wanted to buy souvenirs as he often did when things were going well, and it happened there was a little store right in the lobby, run by a pie-faced native who was selling embroideries and ebony and ivory elephants. I bought an elephant and the general bought two very ugly tablecloths.

"And none of your cheating, Joe," the captain said to the native. "You give the general that shawl for nothing, and give this gentleman another elephant."

The native was very gracious about it. After all, he had to be.

It seemed no time at all before an orderly woke me up and we were boarding the C-54. She was going right straight for Miami just as fast as she could go, and we had seen no plane like her since we had crossed the Atlantic — fine reclining seats, little ventilators, and a thermos of hot coffee. There were three fliers going home, dressed in leather jackets with a Chinese flag sewn on the back. There were also two army nurses, and two bunks, one for a first lieutenant recovering from an operation, and the other for a consumptive Negro. They all were going home. We were over the water at sunrise, and an hour later we were flying over Arabia, looking down at places that no white man had ever seen from the ground. It was hilly desert except for the seacoast, where there were wooded mountain valleys, but no one paid much attention to the scenery. The nurses and the fliers were showing each other the souvenirs which they were bringing home, things which they could have bought as easily at an Oriental store in the States — embroideries, daggers and brassware. One of the fliers was telling about a fight with the Japs the last time he had flown the Hump. Another flier knew a friend of mine who had been out with General George a month before. The desert and the mountain gorges rolled beneath us, and then the plane was letting down at Aden. The Aden airport was like all the others, the same greenish-yellow buildings, the same officers' mess. The ocean had a hot, salty smell, and we had bacon to eat, and powdered eggs and coffee. And then we were off again over Somaliland and Ethiopia, with a fine view of sunken ships in the old Italian harbor. Near sundown we set down at Khartoum, where the commanding officer of the airport met the general and took us to a stucco house that overlooked the Nile. The heat was so great that it clutched at our windpipes, and even when the sun went down there was still that desert heat. The general went to sleep beneath an electric fan, and the commanding officer and I drank beer on the terrace, looking at the date palms and the Nile. The CO was not interested in them. It seems that he owned a place at Carmel, California, and when he learned that I had once been at Carmel he called for a bottle of gin, and we talked about Hollywood until ten o'clock. He wished that we could stay another day because we could take a plane and look at the lions and giraffes in Central Africa. But the general, who had waked up by then, wanted to get the hell out of there. The only lions he wanted to see were the lions in the zoo. We were off, as usual, at three o'clock, but this time the plane was crowded with ambulatory wounded from Sicily. A captain in a plaster cast sat beside me. He had been hit in the shoulder just as he had landed on the Sicilian beach. He said it was annoying after he'd spent a year learning what to do on a beach to get smashed up while his feet were still wet. He said it was an economic waste. What he wanted to do was to get to the hospital in Denver near the family. And one of the fliers knew a place where we could get a fish dinner in Miami. In the meanwhile the plains of Africa rolled beneath us. There were trails and beehive huts of native villages. Then there were rivers and jungles and Lake Chad. We were down on the field at Kano in time for lunch. Some natives dressed in gingham had some lion skins for sale, and there were green slippers and boa constrictor skins on sale at the post exchange. Luncheon consisted of pineapple juice, powdered eggs, Spam, canned pineapple and coffee. As we stepped from the officers' mess, the general gave a startled exclamation.

"Do you see the same kind of bird I see?" he asked.

It was a bird, larger than a heron, but not as large as an ostrich. It had blue wings and a gold topknot, and it lifted its feet gracefully. We asked the bird's name and we were told, but I've forgotten it by now. It was time to take the plane. Again at sundown the plane was letting down, this time over the swamps and jungles that surrounded the great field of Accra on the west coast. This time the air was cool and humid, and a general met the general. It seemed that the weather on the Atlantic was bad. We would spend a day in Accra, and the general could have a car in which to amuse himself. The next morning the general and I motored from the airport to the town. The natives were dressed in calico togas, and once again the general was interested in souvenirs. We found ourselves in a native shop where an old black gentleman was carving figures from mahogany. One of the objects in the shop was a coffee table in the shape of a mahogany elephant. It weighed about one hundred and fifty pounds.

"Now there's just what I want," the general said, "to bring home to the family."

"It weighs one hundred and fifty pounds," I told him. "You can't get it in the plane."

"We can wrap it up," the general said. "They can get it on the plane."

And as I think of Elliott Roosevelt's dog, it probably was true. I appealed to the general's better nature, and the last time I saw him, which was about two weeks ago, he still had not forgotten.

"That coffee table was the only thing I ever wanted," he said. "It was a great mistake to let it go." Then we went to the bazaar and looked at dried lizards and pottery. We were late the next morning on account of weather. We left at seven o'clock heading straight over the ocean.

"Well," I said to the general. "We're going to see Ascension Island. We mustn't miss Ascension."

"You'd be surprised," the general said. "A great many people have." And he began reading a paper edition of *The Best of Damon Runyan*. There was nothing but water, and there was some talk that we might be going through a "front." Ascension Island was about ten flying hours away, a volcanic peak rising from the Atlantic, about five miles long and three miles wide. The general was right. A good many fliers had missed Ascension when they wanted most to see it. At the end of nine hours the boys in the plane grew restless and began peering out the windows. But there was nothing to see but the water, ten thousand feet below. Yet in half an hour the sensation in one's ears indicated that the plane was letting down. Ascension might be a hundred miles away, and still there was nothing to be seen of it. The first indication of something unusual was a formation of clouds a few thousand feet above the water, the sort that gather about small land masses, and then very suddenly there was the whole island off on the horizon to the left, a single, greenish peak rising above a shoreline of black lava and pumice rocks out of a greenish sea with a white ring of surf boiling all around it. It was four in the afternoon when the plane banked and hovered over an airfield cut out of a rock formation that looked like the portals to Dante's Inferno. We bumped and settled down, and there were the same hangars and repair shops, the same mess halls, barracks, hospitals, and camps of pyramidal tents. A jeep came out to meet the general, driven by a lieutenant colonel, who wore a steel helmet. The commanding officer sent his regrets. He was out fishing, but he would be back in time for supper. Ambulances drove up for the wounded. We had been late in starting because of weather. A plane would not leave until tomorrow morning, as it was better not to approach Natal at night, and if the general wanted we could take a ride around the island.

The airfield was a shelf cut on the sloping side of the island close to the water's edge. Its runways, long enough to launch the heaviest planes, had literally been blown out of the lava and volcanic ash by an outfit of U.S. Army engineers. The field was a gash in a region of volcanic desolation as cheerless as the surface of the moon. Yet. as I say, it was the same army field. Whenever I hear someone say that there is no unified national spirit and no culture in the United States, I think of our airports in Africa, India and the Pacific. It may be true that the Englishman far from home dresses for dinner and has his Number One Boy bring in his gin and tonic, but in all his centuries of colonizing he has never brought his civilization with him wholesale, as our armed forces have brought theirs in this war. Machine shops, plumbing, air-conditioning, outdoor movies, ping-pong tables, boxing rings, *Time*, *Newsweek*, the weekly comics, Pocket Books, Gillette razors, Williams' Aqua Velva, Rheingold beer, Johnson's baby powder, Spam and Planters' peanuts, all followed our army to the war for the edification of dark-skinned men in G-strings and for the shocked amazement of the French and British.

Most of this culture, slightly attenuated but very evident, was there before my eyes at Ascension. The field was very active. Two light bombers were warming up their motors, making those ear-splitting backfiring sounds of cold internal combustion engines. The ground crew was already up in the wings of our C-54. The wounded were checked and in their ambulances. There was nothing in the external details of the Ascension airfield, and nothing in the appearance of the lieutenant colonel, who had been a football man at West Point, and, I believe, was called affectionately "Hippo" something in the army, to give any illusion of peace. Yet for the first time in weeks I felt relaxed and peaceful. The breeze which blew across the airfield was soft and air-conditioned, absolutely clear, without a trace of dust or smoke. There were no starving natives worshipping strange gods, no danger of air attack, no poisonous snakes, no bloodsucking leeches, no Bagdad boils, dysentery or cholera, no sand flies and no malarial mosquitoes, not even a poisonous plant, nothing but weirdly shaped lava rocks and pumice stone and the sea. We were standing in the innocent beginnings of creation there on Ascension Island. Our pasts had been left behind us on the west coast of Africa. There was nothing but the monotonous present.

The general was looking inland across the stretches of arid lava to the single volcanic peak, greenish with vegetation, its summit hidden by a misty cloud. He asked if we could drive up there, and the lieutenant colonel hesitated. But then, it was just as well to do what a general wanted.

"We have restricted installations at the top," he said, "but I guess it'll be all right as long as you have number-one priorities. It isn't everybody who goes up there. Most people just stay on the field while the planes are being gassed."

I know now that we were very lucky. Not everyone has had the chance to go up the mountain of Ascension, and I doubt whether many will have the chance in the future. The jeep bounced over a road our engineers had built across the dry lava field of the coast past a conventional hospital, past supply dumps, mess halls and groups of tents. Ascension was guarded by a regiment of infantry, and there were also the medical detail, the patrol fliers and the ground crews — perhaps in all between four and five thousand men. The lieutenant colonel spoke as we climbed to the edges of the jeep, mechanically but politely retailing the rather timeworn history of Ascension. It seems, in case you do not know it, that the island was discovered by a Portuguese ship some time in the 1500's on the day of the Catholic feast of the Ascension, and hence its name. For obvious reasons it was uninhabited. There was no rainfall on the lava fields of the small coastal plain. Only the mountain in the center collected the passing rain clouds. No one wanted Ascension Island for a century or so until the British, who seemed to have an instinctive passion for collecting odd pieces of real estate, took possession, presumably toward the end of the eighteenth century in the days when Napoleon was world enemy number one. There seems to have been some talk of putting him on Ascension, but the authorities thought that this was too close to solitary confinement, and they settled on St. Helena, six hundred miles to the southeast. When the South Atlantic cable was laid Ascension became more important, and for years a cable station has been established there, and a small settlement on a shallow bay containing a score or so of homesick British and a few St. Helena natives for servants. The water for the settlement had to be brought down from a few springs or reservoirs on the mountain peak. And there on the mountain the governor had his residence, and there were a few resthouses for the British. We were climbing up the mountain now, and the air was growing cold enough so that we put on our trench coats. All at once we were in a zone of rainfall, and clumps of grass and bushes began to appear which grew progressively thicker and more luxuriant. Finally, at perhaps a thousand feet, the whole aspect of the land changed. The sun shone only hazily through the clouds above us upon a cool, rolling country that looked very much like the Scottish moors, and the illusion was increased when we saw a flock of sheep grazing beside the road.

The lieutenant colonel said that there could not have been much indigenous vegetation, but that British scientists had imported seeds and plants from all parts of the earth in the hope of finding something to grow. As far as I could see they had not had much luck. The mountainside was too windswept for heavy vegetation, but the final results were most peculiar. You could see a few stunted fir trees in a few low valleys, and at the lee of a cliff beside the road was a grove of eucalyptus, and then on one slope was a mass of wisteria which seemed to have become so successfully established that it was running wild over acres. There were also stray hibiscus plants, and at one point where the road made a hairpin turn there was a clump of spiny African trees out of which flew a small flock of birds that looked like sparrows. I was still wondering how these tiny birds could have got there when the jeep pulled to the edge of the road, because another jeep was approaching from the mountain top.

"That's the governor and his wife," the lieutenant-colonel said.

The governor stopped when he saw us, and we were introduced in the lee of a hibiscus bush and a tangle of ginger flowers. The governor was a brisk man in his sixties, looking like all British civil servants. He was dressed in shorts and a Cheviot sweater. They were frightfully sorry that they were going down to the coast to the settlement, but we must be sure to stop at the bungalow up by the farm and have a peg. Just call for the houseboys, and please be sure to sign the guest book.

I asked the governor's wife one of those obvious questions that come into your mind when you try to make conversation. I first said it must be a relief to be up here where everything was cool and green, and then I asked her if she were lonely.

"Oh, hardly," she said. "Hugo and I are never lonely. We have been here for ten years and it is rather jolly. Before that we were at East Africa, and that was quite a poky place, but it's jolly here with the books and flowers. You must be sure to see my garden. And then Hugo is governor of St. Helena. We spend six months there. It's very gay in St. Helena."

They moved on down the winding road and we continued up. We passed a small barn and a tiny farmhouse, and across the road we could see the governor's bungalow on a neat lawn on the edge of a cliff, and we discovered that the governor owned three cows and two hogs.

"We've been having a little trouble with the governor," the colonel said. "Those hogs collect flies, and they get right down the mountain and breed in the mess hall." We passed the house, and a short way beyond it the road narrowed to a path. We dismounted and climbed to the peak. There on a little shoulder just below the summit was a new shack with a huge radar above it.

"I may get my ears pinned back for taking you here," the colonel said. "This is all dead secret."

But now that we were there under the twisting arms of the radar, whose antenna groped blindly into the foggy air, he told about it. The radar was for submarines. It could pick them up at a distance of some sixty miles off shore, but there were blind spots eight miles off the island. The great excitement was the brushes that they had with submarines. Word would be flashed to the field when one was sighted and the bombers would go out for it, and they had already sunk an unspecified number. Yet there was always a danger of a German sub getting close inshore, and for that reason all the coast was patrolled to prevent sabotage. As we stood by the radar installation we could see the whole arid coastline, and twice we heard machine guns. They were always working out ranges and problems, the colonel said. The island was always alert for a raid.

We were standing on the rim of a crater of volcanic ash, the sides of which had disintegrated so that the mountain dropped away from us in all directions down to the sea. We were standing among rain clouds surrounded by lush, green vegetation. But at the base of the mountain we could see the sun beating down on the area by the seacoast where it never rained at all. It reminded me of what I had read of the Galapagos Islands, a band of arid lava, and then a mountain where it rained. Later, when I once had a talk with Admiral McIntyre, the late President's physician, I discovered that I was right, we also had installations in the Galapagos group, and we built a road through the lava to the mountains.

Ascension was a queer place, the colonel said. You have a lot of time to think, and there was so little to see that you noticed almost everything. The water supply was the most difficult problem. Even the rain on the mountain disappeared quickly through the porous ash. They were piping a little water down from the mountain springs, but most of the water for washing and drinking had to be distilled from the sea. When our troops first landed, we had brought our water with us in 250-gallon drums, and there was still a pile of them dumped down by the shore. All supplies, of course, came by ship. All the food and heavy materials, and millions of gallons of gas had to be landed on lighters at the small bay near the small English settlement. We could see the roofs of the settlement's stucco buildings shimmering in the sun. Ascension was a queer place, the colonel said. You never could tell about the sea. Sometimes even when it was very calm, great waves would appear out of nowhere as high as forty feet, and these would dash on the rocks without warning. A number of men had been caught by these waves as they wandered along the shore. Then there were the rats. The whole place was full of rats, descendants of visitors from some ancient ship that thrived in these benign surroundings where there were no cats or hawks or foxes. But the sea birds were the worst problem. They nested everywhere in the rocks by the shore, and their population must have run up into the high millions. They were out fishing in the daytime, but at sundown they would come back in clouds. Though we had cut down the sea-bird population, it was still dangerous for a plane to approach the field at night, for the sound of the motors would arouse the gulls and there would be such clouds of them in the air that more than once their dead bodies had stalled the engines of a bomber. The birds and loneliness were the main problems at Ascension.

As we walked down from the peak we saw again the white walls of the governor's bungalow perched on the edge of the crater's rim near a cliff that dropped a great many hundreds of feet. A neat white gate opened on a lawn. It might have been a cottage in Torquay. The colonel felt we ought to sign the guest book, but he seemed hesitant about accepting the drink which had been offered, until I pointed out that it was reverse lend-lease. A houseboy from St. Helena, who I think was mostly Portuguese, brought us a Scotch and soda on the veranda of the little house, and we looked at the dining room and the living room, furnished in a stuffy, rather Victorian manner. Then we looked at the garden. It seemed to me that everything in the world grew there in a most disorderly manner. Cabbages and papayas, for instance, grew together beside a hibiscus hedge. There were exotic tropical

ferns, and forget-me-nots and snapdragons. You had the idea that
Nature herself was puzzled and hesitant about the biological balance on
a place like Ascension.

Then we were back in the jeep again winding down the mountain
to the settlement, those few buildings grouped around a cable office
and a civilian clubhouse where a single palm tree grew, which people
who had never been up the mountain erroneously said was the only tree
on Ascension. An army truck was standing on a small pier, and some
troops were unloading fish from a small launch, one of the few craft
in the bay. They were the fish the commanding officer had caught, and
it certainly was fine fishing. There were some small ones all colors of
the rainbow, and two were bluish-green monsters which must have
weighed three hundred pounds apiece. The colonel did not know the
names of any of the fish, but he thought that the large ones were called
wahoos. I always thought that this was a joke until I took up the matter
later with Admiral Ross McIntyre who knew all about such things,
having fished often with our late President.

"Yes," the admiral said, "those big ones were certainly wahoos, a
very sporty fish. Too bad you didn't stay and get one." But we ate
wahoo steak in the officers' mess that evening.

It was sundown when we reached our quarters, one of a group of
tents perched on black rocks on the side of a hill, each with an open
piazza and easy chairs. We used tin helmets for wash basins, and having
done so we were escorted to the commanding officer's quarters a few
yards up the hill. This gentleman, a full colonel, had a blonde moustache, the ends of which were carefully waxed. I remember it distinctly because it was the only waxed moustache I saw in all my
travels. He was delighted to see the general and wished that we might
all have gone fishing. But he was obviously puzzled as to where I
fitted into the picture, since insignia and uniform are the only means
by which you can place anyone in a war theater, and one becomes dependent on them after a few years of war. Personally, I was wearing
a pith helmet and a British bush jacket, and I wore no insignia at all.
Thus I was an intellectual puzzle, with no social position until we
walked down the hill for supper at the officers' mess shack.

"We have a big surprise," the colonel said. "Frederic March, you
know, the big motion-picture actor, is going to entertain the boys
tonight. He's on his way to Africa."

And there, sure enough, in the mess hall, eating fish, was Frederic March, and fortunately Frederic March remembered me and we began to talk of personalities in Hollywood. It seemed to me at this moment that the colonel breathed a sigh of relief. At last he was able to place me in a category. In fact, after dinner he took my arm in a friendly way.

"Why didn't you tell me you were a friend of Freddie's?" he asked. "Why don't you stay for a day or two? We can go and catch wahoos tomorrow."

I only stayed for a little while at the March show. It was held in a natural amphitheater where lonely boys sat in the dark on jagged rocks and laughed uproariously at what seemed to me like very corny jokes, and listened to two very nice, but tough, little girls of the March party, who played rather aggressively on the accordion. They were very brave girls. They had just finished playing their accordions in the Aleutians, and now they were off to Africa and India.

The breeze was blowing hard, and the night was clear as a bell so that you could see all sorts of constellations overhead. But in spite of the stars, I have never known a place where the sky was so completely black. Blackness seemed to close all around us as the general and I moved up the hill to our tent. I remember how the canvas flapped all night, and I remember a sense of being in space. Perhaps everyone on Ascension always felt entirely alone.

Then the next morning after sunrise we were gone, and Ascension seemed to be lost in the rising sun. By the time we were an hour out over the sea it seemed to me that Ascension had never existed except as a sort of abstraction made up of what I had once read of *Robinson Crusoe* and *Swiss Family Robinson*. I could think of Ascension as one of the greatest examples I had seen of the prowess and genius of my country, and I could think of the soldiers I had seen there, ordinary men, who had made a great monument out of nothing. And yet Ascension was already as far removed from my life as the things I had read of Valley Forge or Chancellorsville or the California Gold Rush. There was nothing to connect it with any other human experience.

I remember when I first thought of Ascension in just this way. It was when we landed at the American base in the jungle by the ghost city of Balem, where the birds were light-pink and the butterflies were as large as blue saucers. As usual, the commanding officer of the airport, this time a lieutenant colonel in the reserve, had come to meet us and had taken us to his quarters. But he excused himself immediately, because the secretary of the navy and his party were coming in. The general felt that this was natural. But when the general and I dined at the mess alone without being asked to the dinner given to the secretary, the general paced back and forth on the comfortable veranda in front of our rooms listening to the music and revelry in a building opposite, oblivious to the beauties of the tropical night.

He said that he was not going to take any backwash from a conceited reserve officer. The very least he could have done was to have asked us to sit at the same table with Secretary Knox. I told him in my personal opinion we were missing absolutely nothing, and he said this was not the point. We had been treated with discourtesy. At this juncture an orderly appeared carrying a bottle of Scotch and some glasses of soda.

"General, sir," the orderly said timidly, "the colonel sent out this in case you should care to refresh yourself."

The general looked very coldly at the Scotch.

"We don't want any, son," he said.

The orderly left, but fortunately he also left the bottles behind him on a little table. It had been a hard, rough day flying from Natal to Balem, and Scotch has a high spiritual value.

"Do you mean to say you're not going to take any of it?" I said.

"No," the general answered, "I'm not going to touch one damn drop, and you're not either."

I realized he was very deeply moved, for in all the months we had traveled together this was the first time he had ever given me an order.

"Have you ever heard the story of Paul and Virginia?" I asked him.

"No," the general said, "I haven't, and furthermore I don't know what it has to do with that reserve officer."

So as we sat in the dark I told him the plot of that eighteenth-century French romance and ended with that touching scene of Virginia on the wrecked ship just off the island of Martinique and of Paul waiting on the beach. I told of the kindly sailor who offered to swim with Virginia to the shore, but who stated it would be impossible to make the trip if Virginia did not take off her clothes, and I told of Virginia's preferring death to nudity. Then I pointed to the whisky on the table and asked the general if he did not think that he was acting like Virginia.

"I see what you mean," the general said.

"And furthermore," I told him, "if you really want to give this officer pain, the best thing to do is to try to finish the whole bottle. Scotch is pretty scarce in Balem."

The general was always able to make up his mind quickly.

"Orderly," he called. "Bring us a bowl of ice, Orderly. I can take care of half of it, if you can take care of the other half."

It occurs to me in this narrative that most of it has been concerned with whisky. I can only say without apology that it is an important factor on such a trip as ours, after months on bucket seats and after risings before dawn. At any rate, we were near the end of our journey, and we were feeling relieved that so much was behind us. We sat there for a long while talking of all the places we had seen, of Iceland and London, of the English country inn where the waiter explained to us that hare was game, but rabbit was vermin, of the Arabs in Tunis, of the German raid at Bizerte, of the Jews at Jerusalem, of the heat at Basra, and of the Indian Untouchables. Then we were silent for a while.

"What's on your mind now?" the general asked.

"I was wondering," I told him, "what they're doing at Ascension."

"That's funny," he said. "I was thinking about Ascension. They ought to be able to control those flies in the governor's hogpen. I wonder how flies ever got there." Then he was silent for a moment and then he thought of something else.

"By God," the general said. "You shouldn't have discouraged my bringing back that coffee table."

"What coffee table?" I asked him.

"That coffee table in Accra," the general said, "made out of a mahogany elephant."

We were both having the same trouble. Ascension Island was gone from us both. It was nothing more than a safety square in some gigantic game. We had stopped there and now it was gone.

Good Morning, Major

(1926)

This story is, I think, the oldest in this volume by several years. It has appeared in a number of anthologies, including a volume compiled by that indefatigable short story critic the late Edward O'Brien enti-tled Fifty Best Short Stories *— or words to that effect. At first I was pleased that Mr. O'Brien considered this piece of work of sufficient stature to place in this anthology, but later I was deeply hurt when in his foreword to the story he referred to it as "commercial." Of course he was right. Its climax is based on a brittle and improbable coinci-dence. Its construction, while not bad, was obviously intended for a magazine of large circulation.*

Between the day it was written and the present, an avalanche of change has swept over "Good Morning, Major," including an economic depression that brought in its wake a great revision of social thought and values, and another even more devastating war. Thus, time has made the story dated in both characters and weapons. The snobbish and supercilious young officers seem much less plausible now than they did a quarter of a century ago. One forgets that their boyhood and youth were spent in the comparatively static security of the Edwardian Era, when schools still prided themselves on bringing up "little gentle-men." One forgets also that the Military Mind was much more of a phenomenon then than it is, alas, today. At the time I wrote the story, I, too, was much more amazed at this phenomenon than I am at pres-ent. Consequently the cleavages of thought and habit between the gen-eral and the boys are more overdrawn than perhaps they should be, but a part of this, I am afraid, is due to the story's shortness.

At this point perhaps I should apologize for the rather inordinate number of generals appearing in this collection. The truth is that, like most of my contemporaries, I have seen more of generals in my life-

*time than I may have wished, and they always have fascinated me as
social specimens. The brigadier general appearing in this story is as
dated as his staff, less suave and more ignorant of public relations, less
well-educated militarily than his World War II successors. Let us not
forget that War I generals, too, had been brought up, rather obscurely
then, in their own Edwardian security. They were apt to be rougher
around the edges and more arrogant than their 1940 counterparts. If the
story is still readable it is because some values remain constant in a
changing world. War is still war. Boys will be boys, and generals are
still (essentially) generals.*

SURELY Billy Langwell, in spite of a certain polite indifference
toward things which he considered of no importance, had been with
brigade headquarters long enough to know that the general was not a
funny man. Surely Billy must have known that the general hated all of
us, for anyone could have read uncomplimentary sentiments in the
general's harsh green eyes and in the way his hard lips, straight as a
disciplined platoon, moved when he spoke to the young gentlemen.
Perhaps, in part, it was the natural dislike and contempt of a disciplined
old man who had spent his life in the service for parvenus like us, but
anyone could tell there was something else.

"Young gentlemen" was what he used to call us. It is easy still to recall his voice those times he came into the mess room late for breakfast, when all the young gentlemen snapped hastily to attention. It was
not a pleasant voice, General Swinnerton's — slightly thick, and of a
suppressed timbre that made you wonder how it would sound when
he was angry. Down in the mess room, one can imagine him walking
still, heavy, but straight as a post, and aggressively shaven in that way
peculiar to old soldiers risen from the ranks, that way no civilian can
imitate; so closely shaven that you would think his epidermis must
have been removed by the razor's edge, revealing a pinker, thinner skin
beneath. Without a word, he would walk to his place at the table, while
the young gentlemen listened to his boot heels hit the floor. *Snap* they
went, as inevitable as regulations. *Snap* — and then a pause, a military
pause, and it was up to me to say, "Good morning, General." It was
my part of the drill that he had taught me.

"Good morning, Major," he would answer, and we would shake hands there in the mess room, stiffly, like pugilists posing for the Sunday supplements.

"Good morning, Major," he would say, and sometimes there seemed to be a note in his voice of a lonely man, and sometimes it seemed like the voice of a man slightly puzzled by a changing world.

Then he would pause, and then his heavy neck would move deliberately within the circumference of his stiff white collar — you could almost hear it grate — as he stared down the mess hall. Of course, all the overnight lieutenants would be watching him, stiffly trying to look military and knowing that they could not. They were young, so young, without a trace in their faces of any blow from life. They were so fearless, so serenely sure of themselves. Was that what General Swinnerton could not understand, and what he resented most? There was Billy Langwell in his whipcords, much more expensive than the general's; one of those nice New York Langwells, slender and almost delicate, with his yellow hair still moist from his morning bath, and smiling at the general. Billy was always smiling as though he had encountered some amusing private thought. And then there was — what was his name? Sometimes faces are so clear and names so hard to remember — Edwin Bryce, the general's other aide, one of the Philadelphia Bryces, with a gentle voice, but always with a look that was slightly supercilious. Then there were those other ones, faces new and pleasant voices. Sometimes in our mess hall you might have thought it was a college house party and not a brigade about to sail for France.

As the general looked at those faces before he pulled back his chair, his own face would assume a slightly peculiar expression, almost of bewilderment, you would sometimes think, and then he would speak, precisely still, but somewhat differently.

"Good morning. Sit down, young gentlemen. You won't get any rations like this a month from now."

Then he would seat himself stiffly and raise his coffee cup with exaggerated ease, and grasp his spoon in his awkward fingers. What was he thinking of as he raised his cup and stared silently above its brim? Was he envious or sad? Was he thinking that he was not and never would be quite like the rest? Was he thinking that we knew it? I wonder. Perhaps he always thought that we were laughing.

What strange intuition or trick of caste made Billy spot the general for what he was? The first time Billy's eyes met the general's eyes he knew, and the general knew he knew.

Of course I can remember — anyone can remember those first days when uniforms were new, when Camp Abraham Hicks was just beginning to rise out of its wilderness of yellow pine, a hideous checkerboard of order, when the first men of the draft were herded in, in cheap, baggy clothes which they took off, never to wear again.

Those were the days when brigade headquarters seemed a place of mystery — a veritable religious shrine, in which one could imagine strange rites marching in the night. Headquarters was almost the only wooden house in Camp Abraham Hicks in those days. Typewriters were clicking through the half-open windows; an orderly was standing at the door, one of those jaded Regular Army orderlies, passive yet sneering, whom the War Department doled out, one to each of our companies.

In front of that wooden shack, the stumps of yellow pine still obtruded themselves, making you stumble in your new boots. And a set of awkward men in olive drab were grubbing at those roots while a young second lieutenant, who had been a lieutenant no longer than they had been soldiers, kept saying, "Now, fellows, make it snappy! Make it snappy!"

The orderly at the door had a reason to grin sourly. It was probably the first time in his life that he had heard enlisted men addressed as "fellows." He was still grinning when I saw him.

"Yes, sir," he said, "the general's expecting you. He'll see you in a minute." Then he stopped grinning and stared wearily beyond me and wearily saluted, and then I heard a voice behind me that I knew. It was Billy Langwell, hopping adroitly over the pine stumps, and only stumbling once over an upthrust root.

"Oh, now, George," he said, "are you here too? How did you pull it? By writing to your congressman?"

"I don't know," I answered. The army ways were as strange to me then as they are today. "I just got an order and came here to report." Billy grinned and flicked at his boot with a swagger stick that he twirled self-consciously, in nervous knowing arcs.

"Now don't be so upstagy just because you have those what-you-may-call-'ems on your shoulders," he suggested. "They got you because you can ride, of course. I bet we're the only people in this place that can mount without a ladder. It's just as well. I don't want to be a nurse to those East Side criminals in my outfit, and anyhow, the family wanted me to be an aide."

The orderly interrupted us, saluting languidly. "The general sends his compliments and says he'll see you now."

"Both of us?" I asked.

A round solid mass of something moved in the orderly's beefy cheek. "Yeh," he said, "both of you, sir."

As we entered, from the corner of my eye I saw the orderly expectorate furtively. It was my first experience with the regular enlisted personnel, and still I do not know how some of them chew tobacco and yet appear not to chew it.

The general was standing in a stuffy little room, with a table and two chairs, and a map showing the squared barrenness of the future Camp Abraham Hicks pasted on the cardboard-composition wall. He wore the marching shoes of an enlisted man — broad and dusty, like two solid cornerstones, necessarily large to support his weight. His leather leggings, of an inferior type, were also covered with the camp's red dust, and over his heart was that curious array of ribbons and bits of masonic jewelry that we were even then beginning to stare at with fascination, not to say with envy. They began with the Indian War ribbon and ran the whole gamut of ribbons — Spanish War, the Philippines and Boxer. Also hanging among them were a silver medal and a pair of crossed rifles. But you needed no service badges to spot him. You could read his service on his face. His jaw and his mouth, without speaking, fairly shouted Regular Army. His eyes were the eyes of the Regular Army, typical and peculiarly like the eyes of the orderly who sinned in secret by chewing tobacco at the door.

"When you come into my room," said the general, "take off your hats. Good morning, Major." And he held out a stubby hand to me and looked me in the eye.

"Good morning, sir," I answered.

He stood motionless, still looking at me. "Say 'Good morning, General,'" he replied. "I consider it better etiquette."

Then, precisely as a machine gun turns on a pivot, his head veered, rising from his white collar, to Billy Langwell.

"Lieutenant," inquired the general, "what's that in your hand?"

"A swagger stick, sir," said Billy.

There was no expression of contempt, no change in the general's face. "Throw it out the window," he said.

Without moving from where he was standing, Billy threw it. It made a little whistling arc through the room and was gone.

"Who told you," asked the general, "to carry one of those things?"

"Why, no one —" began Billy.

"Sir," said the general.

"Sir," said Billy.

The general folded his hands behind his back and rocked backward and forward from his toes to his heels. "Now listen to me, both of you," he said. "Where did you go to school?"

"To Harvard," I answered. The general's lips contracted.

"Sir," he said.

"Sir," I said hastily.

You could tell what the general was thinking. His eyes again met those of Billy Langwell, who began to smile.

"I am just as effete as he is, sir. I come from Harvard, too, sir."

"Yes?" said the general. "Well, it's no joke, being effete, young man, not when there's a war. Now listen to me, both of you."

He paused and once again rocked from his toes to his heels as though the rocking might give impetus to his thoughts.

"You won't like me," he said. "Neither of you will like me, but that makes no difference in the service. In '75 I was a private in Arizona, before either of you was born. There used to be real fighting in '75 and the service used to be a real service. I got my corporal's stripes when I pulled Chief Three Horns off his pony and choked him, back in the Navaho war. I got my majority for going out ahead of my detachment and killing three brown brothers with a bayonet in Mindanao. I'd rather have a bayonet in my hands now than this confounded job. But as long as I'm a general, I'll be a soldier's general" — he scowled slightly and his voice began to sharpen — "and not one of these bootlicking, dancing-party generals with a pull back in the War Department. And the men on my staff will be soldiers and they'll act like soldiers, and not like military attachés. I haven't been to Harvard. I haven't been anywhere except to military schools. That's why you won't like me. But you'll be soldiers just the same. That's all. Sit down at that table, Major, and go over those reports. And you, Mr. — I've forgotten your name —"

It was a new experience to Billy to have anyone forget his name, once it had been mentioned.

"Langwell, sir," he said. "William Langwell."

The general looked at him for a moment in silence. Then for the first time I became aware of that curious, baffled expression in his eyes — half puzzled, almost diffident.

"Langwell? There used to be — where was it? — back in the 65th — a shavetail named Langwell. Mr. Langwell, go out and tell that low-lived, no-account orderly that he'll be making little ones out of big ones if I see him chewing tobacco again the way he's chewing it now. If he'd been in the cavalry in '75 he'd know how to stow it in the back of his jaw when he's on duty. Little ones out of big ones — he'll understand if you don't. And then go to the stables and get my horse and one for yourself. And by the way, Major, you'd better go out with him and see that he speaks properly to the enlisted men. There's nothing more important than speaking properly to enlisted men. Salute when you go out. And rightabout! One! Two!"

Then we were outdoors again where the men were grubbing at the pine stumps, and Billy was speaking to the orderly.

"My boy," he said, "the general has just sent me out to tell you he'll have you making little ones out of big ones if he sees you chewing tobacco. Personally, I can't perceive that you're chewing. But just as a friend — strictly as a friend — I'd advise you to cut it — or shall I say spit it out? — because you didn't serve in the cavalry back in '75."

I seized Billy hastily by the arm and pulled him out of earshot.

"Don't make an ass of yourself," I hissed. "Can't you watch your step?"

Billy smiled at me and blinked. "Tut-tut, George," he said. "Now don't be so continually upstagy because you've got those fig or maple leaves on you! Can't we be boys together once in a while? All right, I'll promise not to do it again. All right, but I somehow couldn't — George" — his smile grew broader and he patted me softly on the arm — "do you know what I perceived? Really my perception has grown remarkably keen since I embarked on this military business. I perceived, or it seemed to me I perceived" — his voice grew lower, but was very careless, very playful — "I actually perceived that the general isn't quite a gentleman!"

And there you have it — that stupid inexorable conventionality we all of us have when we are young. Billy Langwell was too young, always too young, to have perceived that a man could be a man and still not quite a gentleman.

Billy was smiling at the tree stumps, but you could see that he was thinking, for his eyes had a curious distant look, and suddenly he tapped my arm again. "George, my boy," he said, "the more I think of it — do you know what I think? Seriously, George, I've got a mission to perform."

"What sort of a mission?" Somehow you could not help but be amused, for he was never more than half serious even at his worst.

"I feel it devolves upon me," said Billy, and tapped my arm again, "as a representative — I'm hanged if I know of what, but — well, I feel it devolves on me, under the circumstances, to put the general in his place."

"To what?" I gasped.

"To put the general in his place," repeated Billy. "Oh, not crudely; of course, not crudely; but watch me. I'll find a way."

The egotism of it! It's the sort of thing that always rather shocks you, but Billy Langwell did it. There was that unyielding, curious sense of pride, of decency or position or something of the sort. It took Billy Langwell four months, but just the same he did it — and nicely — oh, so nicely.

It was an afternoon when the thick mud of Camp Abraham Hicks was baking into the clay of spring. You remember those afternoons, dreary as a misspent life, with the weight of a badly cooked dinner resting like a sin upon the conscience. The general was at his table in the orderly room, licking his thumbs the better to turn the papers before him. His blunt thumbs went snap with grim steadiness; his hair was like a gray rat's nest; his coat was unbuttoned at the collar and his eyes were slightly protruding. At the sound of a gentle tap on the door, he muttered something beneath his breath and sighed. It was Billy Langwell in his whipcords, walking delicately in his new custom-made riding boots and silver spurs, with his garrison cap pulled smartly over his eyes as he had seen in pictures.

The general cleared his throat, and Billy spoke at once with his inevitable slight smile: "Excuse me, sir."

The general looked at him coldly for a moment before he answered. "Mr. Langwell," he said at length, "when you come into the orderly room, take off your cap."

The slight smile did not leave Billy's lips. His cap was instantly in his hand.

"Certainly, sir. But the general said — "

Of course the general interrupted him at once, but not unpleasantly — rather with a sort of triumph. "Don't argue. I can appreciate the way you feel, but don't argue. I won't make pets of second lieutenants because they're aides of mine. Do you remember I told you that?"

"Yes, sir." Billy had not moved from attention, and his voice was perfectly respectful. "But the general said — "

"Well, what did I say?"

"The general told us to keep our hats on when we carried side arms."

Of course the general had not noticed. There was a moment's pause, and you could almost feel sorry for the general. Of course it was a little thing, but Billy Langwell had the general right on the hip, the way he said he would.

"Side arms?" The general cleared his throat. "Who told you to put on side arms?"

Yes, he had put the general in his place. Billy's face had the innocent triumph of youth and something more, that indefinable expression that made the general know what Billy thought.

"The general," he replied, "told me to report at three with side arms."

Right on the hip — that was where Billy had him. The general pushed back his chair, but did not rise. The chair creaked and grated beneath his weight, and you could have laughed almost to see his embarrassment. He had made a mistake and he knew he had made one. It might seem little, but not to a Regular Army man.

"Then why" — his voice was thicker — "then why didn't you tell me in the first place, without all this confounded argument?"

Against the thickness of the general's voice came Billy's answer, pleasant and conventional, devoid of any emotion. He did it nicely, very nicely. "I tried to, sir," he said.

"Well," said the general, "you didn't try hard enough."

"No, sir," said Billy. It was almost sad to watch them. Why could the general not have left it there? Billy was speaking so quietly, leading the general slowly beyond his depth. It was childish, so absurd you could almost laugh, though the pulses were beating in the general's temples.

"Well, you should have," said the general. "See here — you put your hand over your holster. You hid it. Did you try to make a fool of me on purpose?"

Billy's answer came at once, perfectly certain, perfectly controlled, and that eternal trace of a smile still flickered on his lips. "I'm sure I beg the general's pardon," he replied. "If the general thinks — "

General Swinnerton rose slowly from his chair. His voice was chilly, his hand trembling. Something within him, the thing that was always there, burst loose for a moment before he could stop it. "Can't you speak to me like a man?" he roared.

Why is it that youth is so obtuse and can never understand?

That very evening Billy came into my tent with a stiff parody of a walk and held out his hand.

"Good morning, Major," he said softly, and giggled beneath his breath.

"Stop it!" I whispered. "Don't be such a fool!"

Billy giggled again. He always had a most engaging way when his friends fell out. "Don't be such a fool yourself. Just because you've got those fig leaves, or whatever they are, on you — you can't forget we used to go on parties. Oh, I know we're in the army now, but maybe I didn't have the general dead to rights! What? Didn't I?"

"You ought to be ashamed of yourself — " I began, but he stopped me with a delicate shrugging gesture.

"Why the deuce should I be ashamed?" he demanded. "Do you think I'm going to sit still and have the life ragged out of me, my boy? Do you remember what I told you? He isn't a gentleman, George, my boy. I said he wasn't — remember?"

"If you aren't a West Pointer" — I can still hear the general's voice, as he paced about the orderly room one evening when we were there alone — "if you're not a West Pointer, young man, or if you haven't come from the ranks like me, there isn't any hope for you. You don't know what the army is, that's all."

And I suppose in a hundred other barracks, a hundred other old men with ribbons on their chests were holding forth in the same grim strain. Of course you can't understand; no civilian can fathom the eccentricity of the military mind. That ridiculous affair of the garrison cap and the side arms did something to General Swinnerton.

It has occurred to me sometimes that a monk's life and a soldier's life are really quite the same, for they both have their eternal round of order in which the smallest thing that moves against the methodical current becomes great enough to shatter all existence.

If anyone had come to Camp Merritt to see the general off, it might have been a better thing, because I think he would have liked a kindly word; but no one came. No one sent him a box of cigars or candy. No one but the camp commandant said good-by.

He was a short, asthmatic little man, too old to go across, who could only sit and watch others go. He took us down to the Fort Lee ferry himself, and shook the general's hand. It was what the general had said — you couldn't understand the army unless you were an army man.

"Good-by, Swinnerton," he said. "Give 'em hell."

Billy Langwell was opening the automobile door.

"So long," said General Swinnerton. "Don't drink yourself to death. You needn't help me, Mr. Langwell. I'm still young enough to walk. Run aboard there and give the colonel my compliments and tell him to see his men below and stop their singing. This isn't a Y.M.C.A. social. It's a war."

And that was all the general said as he left his native shores. Yet he seemed to want to talk that night. He called the young gentlemen to his cabin on the boat deck after dinner, where all the portholes were battened tight, and gave them a short lecture.

"Now don't forget," he ended — and for once that day he seemed almost happy — "don't forget we're through with *thés dansants*, or however you say it, and pink teas and kissing the girls good-by at those hostess houses, or whatever you call them. Don't forget we're going to a war. Don't forget that tomorrow morning or a month from now we may all be dead." Then he paused, looked a little puzzled at the young gentlemen.

Of course he could not understand the way they took it, and his voice grew louder. "You don't believe me, do you? You think you've got a return ticket because you're on the staff! What do you find to smile at, Mr. Langwell?"

There was a slight sound of shifting feet above the churning of the engines, and we looked at Billy Langwell. He was standing in the center of the cabin. He was scarcely smiling; certainly not broadly enough to merit a rebuke. And he answered at once, without embarrassment, as he always did: "I'm sure I beg the general's pardon. I wasn't smiling at the general."

"Then what the devil are you smiling at?" General Swinnerton demanded. "Tell us, Mr. Langwell, if it's funny."

If Billy Langwell had only blushed or stammered, but he neither blushed nor stammered, and he answered right away: "It's not exactly funny, sir, but I was only thinking — "

"Go ahead," said the general. "It's obvious that you're thinking."

"I was only thinking," said Billy, "that the general's room used to be the bridal suite, not so many months ago."

The general looked at the brass bedstead and at the velvet hangings before the portholes, already tawdry from the army, reeking with stale cigar smoke.

"Major," he said, "send my compliments to the gunnery officer and tell him my aides will be on submarine lookout with the other young men from the regiments. Tell him to put them in the bow. Good evening, young gentlemen."

The general was alone when I returned. He was pacing up and down the bridal suite, and in spite of the slight pitching of the boat, his step was as accurate as ever. His boots went pit-pat on the heavy carpet. In his right cheek was a slight spherical bulge which he caused to disappear when I came in, in the manner of a good cavalryman back in '75.

"I don't understand them," he said. "I'm damned if I understand. Young men didn't used to be like that when I was young. Don't they ever think of anything serious?"

I tried to pass it off lightly. Somehow I knew he was oppressed and lonely, and suspected his dinner was not setting right that first night at sea.

"It's their tradition, General," I said. "They don't mean anything by it; they're only following the tradition — being *toujours gai*."

But the general stood stock-still and folded his hands behind him. "Two joor?" he inquired. "What does two joor mean? Oh, it means always, does it?" He coughed and moved his jaw hastily, and continued his walk about the bridal suite.

I moved toward the door, was just about to say good night, when he said the most peculiar thing, that made me stop and look at him.

"Just a minute, Major." Was it possible that his voice sounded dif-

fident? "Would you mind — have you got time — Here, I wish you'd
read this letter. It's written to my son."

It was the first time that I knew — the first time that any of us
knew — that General Swinnerton had a son. And why he told me of it
then I never could understand. Perhaps he was thinking of his farewell
from Merritt that morning.

Perhaps he knew that among us all he was a being apart, and for a
moment did not want to be.

He handed me a sheet of foolscap paper from a field clerk's box that
was set upon a rosewood writing table.

"Dear Earl," I read. Now you might have known his name would
have been Earl! "Dear Earl: The old man has got off in a cloud of
dust. I am sitting in a bridal suite, surrounded by a lot of college boys
and a Y.M.C.A. secretary, with a bunch of city boys in the steerage
who don't know how to wear their OD breeches. God knows how we
can ever fight a war with a lot of college boys and city boys who
think they're soldiers. I'm glad you're not a college boy. See if you
can't be a soldier even if you are a half-baked shavetail. Do what they
tell you and don't grin about it. So long, Earl. I wish I was going with
you to the front line where there isn't all this damn funny business.
Remember what I said — always keep two biscuits and a clean pair of
socks, old army issue if you can get them, in your back breeches
pocket. And be sure to take along a .45 revolver. Good night, Earl.
Your Old Man."

I handed the letter back. What was there to say? What could I
possibly have said?

The general looked at me curiously, trying to read my comment
in my face.

"You think it's a bum letter, don't you?" he inquired. "But you see
the way I feel."

"I don't blame you," I said. I forgot to call him sir.

"Good night, Major," said the general. "Go round the decks before you turn in, and if you find anybody smoking a cigarette or showing a light outside, take his name for a special court. That's all. Good
night."

As I turned to close the door I had a glimpse of him standing alone
in the bridal suite, staring at the curtains, and I never told anyone
about the letter. Somehow I could never even smile about it. If it was

not a letter from Lord Chesterfield to his son, at least it was a letter from an army man.

As one thinks of it, it becomes inevitable that Billy Langwell should have laughed at General Swinnerton. And yet it's so hidden now that one can scarcely recall all those little things leading to that end.

Take the history of the Umpty-something Brigade, for instance. You know those stories printed on smooth shiny paper by some local printer and pathetic from their sheer inadequacy. There is only a sentence in it that brings a picture back.

"On the evening of September eighth," it read, "the Umpty-Something Brigade was carried in trucks to Je Ne Sais Quoi and marched on foot to Ca Ne Fait Rien, where it relieved the Umpty-Something-Else Brigade of the Fig-Leaf Division at 10:40, occupying a front extending east from and including the town of Quelque Chose along the line of the Quelque Chose highway, through the farm of Petites Chausettes and thence to the woods and Je Ne Sais Quoi." There it is, in black and white, written with all that singular lack of imagination which is characteristic of all things military.

And yet it brings back pictures—a dark, startled obscurity, and noise as constant as silence to the ears, muddy columns of men, sweating startled horses, and a grim shape riding on his horse in silence, without a hat.

It was like the general to throw his tin helmet away. "If they get me they get me," he said. "What's the use of all this funny business?"

Those are the sort of things that those pedantic words bring back — even to the shadows of the town of Quelque Chose.

When we took over the brigade P.C. and the front line, of course the enemy specialized on the town of Quelque Chose. You could see its houses two miles off, as it stood there on the hill. They only had to say a number, that was all, and let the guns turn loose.

You should have heard the general swear when those first shells went by. It was enough to have made you laugh, if it had been a time for laughing. You should have seen him scramble in the mud among the wounded horses and have heard his voice, not frightened, only angry, as he shouted to a runner from the Umpty-Something Division: "Where are we? This is a hell of a place!"

"We're just getting in, sir. It's Quelque Chose," said the runner. But he was a green man. He had a catch in his voice. "Damn their hides!

Them Jerries know we're moving out tonight. You mighta knowed those Blanks 'ud know it."

Then the general's voice came out of the dark. It really was a funny thing he said, and I felt Billy nudge me in the ribs as the general said it. "Damn your own hide!" roared General Swinnerton. "Cut out that swearing!"

We were stumbling over a heap of rubbish that had once been a street. Billy Langwell tripped and grasped instinctively at the general's arm to keep his balance, and I heard him draw a sharp quick breath.

"What is it, Mr. Langwell?" said the general. "Can't you keep your feet?"

"A man!" said Billy. His voice was a little high. "General, I stepped on a man!"

You would have known the general was a soldier even in the dark. "Did you hear Mr. Langwell, young gentlemen?" he inquired. "Mr. Langwell stepped on a dead man. Don't be surprised. There always are dead men in a war."

"Here we are, sir," said the orderly. "Mind the step, sir. It's in a cellar. Lord! What's that?"

"A heavy gun, you ass," said the general.

And we were in the headquarters of the town of Quelque Chose. I can still hear the general's voice. It goes with candlelight and the damp and reeking smell of night. "Give me a map. Where the devil is that map? Are the telephones installed?" And then it is all a nightmare, nothing more.

Quelque Chose I called the town. It isn't its real name, but every town was Quelque Chose in the stretches of those nights. Every town was something that makes you sit up still and stare into the black. As a matter of fact, it was Ouchy or Coulchy-sur-the-Something-or-Other. The way the old general spluttered and coughed as he pronounced it was enough to make you laugh. It's not so long ago since I saw the place, but though eight years or more have passed, there is a shocked silence, and you can almost think it was the day before yesterday, the time those names meant nothing.

I can remember the general glaring at the French artillery map. The rest is dim, but that part of it seems almost the day before yesterday. There were two candles in that cellar hole where headquarters P.C. were located, shining mellowly upon his face and making the silver stars glitter on his shoulders. And the yellow light gave his face a most peculiar reddish tint which was almost like old copper.

He was in the center of that cellar, quite calm, standing in a welter of equipment that had not been cleared away, between the box where the field telephones were already going and the muddy curtain of blankets by the door. The mud from the road — that strange gray mud of France — came off his stubby fingers on the map he was holding. He was staring at the map with reddish eyes, running his forefinger slowly across it.

"What the devil's the name of this place?" he inquired, looking up for a moment. The young gentlemen were standing around trying to look perfectly calm. "Oozy — Coozy? What the devil is it? And what the devil are those little gimcracks up ahead?"

It was not peculiar. Maps of all kinds always annoyed the general. He did not have time to get an answer, for the telephone operator interrupted him.

"Call from the division, sir," he said.

"Confound the division," said the general. "Can't they leave a man alone?" And he sat down by the instrument.

His two aides were just behind him, straight and quiet; Billy Langwell a little paler than usual, and Edwin Bryce playing at his belt with his long fingers.

"Stop that noise," said the general. He seemed to forget that no one could stop that noise until the war was over.

"Hello! Is this what? Is this what? — What? Brewery One? Are you crazy? What do you mean by Brewery One? This is General Swinnerton speaking. Headquarters of the Umpty-Umph Brigade."

Billy Langwell looked at me and winked. The color had returned to his cheeks.

"Oh! It's a code word, is it? The Germans will hear me, will they? How many peanuts have I got? What do you mean by peanuts? . . . Oh! Every man has got a hundred rounds, if the fools know how to fire them. . . . What's that? The Germans will hear me? Don't make me laugh, sir. You used to talk sense before you got those two stars on you. A hell of a mess? Of course it's a mess. They're turning on everything they've got. Have I got my front line located? No. How can I be sure when all the wires are out? Well, hold the wire."

The general tossed the instrument to the telegraph orderly and seized the map again. Of course he knew we all were watching him. Of course we knew he was in a strange position, not knowing where the front line was, not knowing anything — just stumbling in the dark.

"What the devil's the name of this place?" he repeated. "Oozy? Coozy? Why the devil can't they make sense? And what's that little gimcrack? That's where the Umpty-Umph ought to be, isn't it? No, not that. That's a brook. That little square thing. La Ferme? What the devil's a ferme? I came here to fight a war, not to learn French! Confound this light! La Ferme de la Sainte? Sainte?" The map crumpled beneath the general's fingers.

He looked around at the young gentlemen almost stupidly, with his mouth half open. "That's a deuce of a name to call anything! It isn't a name at all. It's like a piece of underwear. It's like one of those things women put on themselves when they don't wear corsets."

There was a moment's silence. The word "corsets" in that place seemed to have a magic sound. The orderly at the telephone looked up. The runners at the door with red bands on their sleeves looked up. And all the rest of us looked at him helplessly, as we listened to the noise outside. Then there came the most incongruous sound. The general's head flew up. Billy Langwell had not meant to laugh. You could see it on his face. It was a reflex of strained nerves, when everyone's nerves were strained. But General Swinnerton heard him. For an instant his face went scarlet, and his lips moved without a sound. For an instant even the noise outside seemed to lessen. And then the general spoke — quietly — much more quietly than he had spoken all that night. "You're laughing, Mr. Langwell?" he inquired.

It was the first time I ever saw Billy startled. In spite of the shadow his helmet cast over his face, his whole face looked drawn and startled.

"I beg the general's pardon," he said hastily. Even then he did not forget the etiquette he had been taught.

"Well, what were you laughing at?" The general's voice was louder. "You're laughing at me, Mr. Langwell. You've always been laughing at me! Now tell me what's so funny."

"I beg the general's pardon," began Billy again.

General Swinnerton stared at him. He seemed to have forgotten everything — even the noise outside. "Don't be so damned polite!" he said. "You're always laughing. Now tell me what's so funny."

Billy's answer came quickly. He wasn't frightened exactly, but he was embarrassed: "I'm awfully sorry, sir. I had no business to laugh. I — I don't know why I did, except what you said about the name — the corsets. I — "

Billy stammered and stopped, and the general nodded. "I understand," he said. "You like to see the old man make a fool of himself."

You couldn't help but be sorry for Billy Langwell then. Just to see the color in the general's face and the glazed look in his eyes was enough to make you sorry.

For the end of everything was there, or the ultimate result. All that had gone before — the little things, memories of sly glances and half smiles, everything which was hidden beneath courtesy and manners flashed into the general's cheeks and forehead, as though some unseen caldron had boiled over and had completely spilled its reddish-purple contents even over the general's nose. He blushed and stammered, as though he were fighting against something that had grown too strong at last.

"You second-chop shavetail!" You would hardly have known it was the general, his face had grown so dark. "Did you think I haven't watched you? Do you flatter yourself I haven't seen you and the lot of you sneering at me because I can't hold a fork? Don't lie to me about it! You think I am a mucker, don't you? — you damned dude! I may be a mucker, but I've got eyes and ears. Don't think I am fit to order you! You don't think I'm a gentleman, do you? I've seen the bunch of you whispering at Hicks and on the boat. You don't think I'm one, do you? Answer me — you! D'you hear?"

The words poured out of him as suddenly as the color had poured into his face, just as ugly and as horrid, and with them came all the pain and the resentment he must always have harbored, for he was not under control. No one was under control unless it was Billy Langwell. I saw Edwin Bryce's face flush and his lip curl angrily, but Billy Langwell maintained the most irritating poise — that poise which the general had always hated — and stared at the general placidly.

"The general," he said, "has me at a disadvantage. I can't say what I think — what I should have to say — without going under anew. Perhaps some other time — "

The general interrupted him as though the sound of Billy's voice was more than he could bear: "Say what you mean for once in your life — to my face — like a man — you sniveling coward!"

He was not a sniveling coward. The general ought to have seen that from the way that Billy stood and answered.

"You want me to?" he inquired. Everyone must have wanted to catch him, to pull him away, but no one did, and his voice continued meticulously distinct. "You want me to? All right, then. I've stood enough. I think you're a bully and a windbag. Stop it! Put down your hand!"

There was no doubt the general was not himself. Edwin Bryce sprang in front of him just in time, and you could almost have been proud of Edwin.

"There, sir," he said, "we'll apologize, of course. But let me remind you — the division is on the wire. They want the coordinates for the front line."

"The division is still on the wire, sir."

The general looked at Edwin Bryce and then back at Billy Langwell. His hand trembled so that the map moved uncertainly in his fingers, and his voice was as unpleasant as I had ever heard it.

"You know everything, don't you?" he remarked. "You two young men? Orderly, tell headquarters that I'm sending runners up and I'll telephone the coordinates when I get them. And now, Mr. Langwell, do you know that word? Can you read it for us?"

Billy leaned over the map. His voice trembled slightly. "Certainly, sir. It's La Ferme de la Sainte-Hilaire."

"De la Sainte-Hilaire," mimicked the general, suddenly grotesque and terrible. "Is it now? And can't you read all these other names, Mr. Langwell?"

Billy looked at the general. Billy no longer looked exactly nonplused. He took a corner of the map in his thumb and forefinger. "Certainly — easily," he answered; "in fact without any trouble at all."

The general made no comment. He looked at Edwin Bryce. "And you, Mr. Bryce?" he inquired with that same unpleasant parody. "Of course you can read them, Mr. Bryce?"

"Of course," said Edwin shortly.

And then Billy said something that finished it. Although he was perfectly cool, you could see he was angry — as angry as the general.

"The general must remember," he said gently, "that we haven't had — the benefits of an army education."

The fool! What a fool he was! The coldness and the silence of the general were what made it terrible. He looked at them both with that slightly puzzled expression which changed into something else, and swayed back and forth from his toes to his heels before he finally spoke.

"How fortunate," said the general, and swayed again from his toes to his heels, "we've got someone who can locate the front line. Rise and shine, young gentlemen." They didn't understand him. None of us exactly understood. "Do you hear me?" The color of the general's face seemed to choke his voice. "Get out with you both, if you know so much. Go up and find that farm. Go up and see if the line is in front of it, behind it or in it. And come back and let me know."

And he knew what he was doing. That was what made it worse. He was sending them up to the front line in the dark, under heavy shelling, on the first night that they had ever heard a shell go off — in the dark — without their ever having known the road. Was there any wonder Billy Langwell looked a little sick?

"Of course you'll send us a runner who knows the way?" he said.

"Knows the way?" said the general. "Can't you see the way — on that road past the little gimcrack and by the thingumajig? What are you standing arguing about? Go up and find that front line and come back and report. Do you think you're any more valuable than anyone else because you're on the staff? My aides are expendable. Go out with you! Forward march!"

Even as the general spoke, he must have known how he appeared, from the way that Billy Langwell looked. For Billy Langwell was the better man just then — much the better man.

He gave a slight pull to the gas mask on his chest and nodded to Edwin Bryce. "Let's get out of this," he said.

They walked straight to the door, while the general stared at their backs. Once I thought he was going to speak. Once he cleared his throat.

But at the door, Billy Langwell turned and smiled at the general in a most annoying way. "Will the general excuse me if I don't take off my hat?" he said. "I may need it on outside."

Before the general could answer, they were gone. For a moment he stared at the swaying blankets by the door, almost forgetful of where he was.

"Major," he said at length, "make a note on Mr. Langwell's record tomorrow morning — that his manner is insolent toward his superior officers. Send out two more men from the detail with my compliments to the signal officer and ask him why he cannot mend his wires."

Then he hesitated, still standing in the center of the room. You see, he was a soldier — too good a soldier to let his anger carry him away for any length of time. He swayed for a moment from his toes to his heels.

"Is there any runner here who knows the way to that farm?" he asked suddenly. And somehow the tension in everyone relaxed, soundlessly yet definitely.

"Yes, sir." It was the single regular orderly from Camp Abraham Hicks who spoke. "I've been there, sir."

"Is it hard to find?" The general looked relieved. At last he was speaking to someone he understood.

"No, sir. You gotta go in the fields, though. They're shelling hell out of the roads."

"Then you better — " began the general. The orderly was moving automatically toward the door, but the general did not have time to finish.

"The regimental wire's in, sir!" cried the telephone orderly.

The general whirled about. "Which regimental line?" he cried. "Give me the telephone. . . . Hello! Who are you? Baggage? How can you get artillery support if you don't send back your coordinates? Well, send another man back. Send two more. Now read them before you go out again. Write 'em down, major, as I say 'em — 23 point — I've got that. Two-three point." There was a silence. The general set down the instrument and swore.

"The damn thing's out again!" he said. "Orderly, go out and give those lieutenants my compliments and say you'll take one to the farm and send the other back. And the rest of you clean up this mess in here and give me a chair to sit on."

But when he got the chair the general would not sit down. He began pacing up and down instead, listening to the noise outside. And you could tell what he was thinking. He was wishing he was up there. He understood better than any of us his present uselessness. It was making him restless. It was wearing down his nerves. Once he looked at his wrist watch. It was two o'clock in the morning and you could tell he was wishing it was light.

The suspense — the uncertainty of everything — was enough to get on anybody's nerves. The telephone orderly sat tense, fingering the plugs on his board with tense fingers. The orderlies by the door sat with their shoulders slouched forward, looking at their hands.

But the general's shoulders were the ones that should have sagged. Everything was resting on them, and he knew it. But he still kept walking up and down. He was the first one who heard a noise in the passage — a scraping, hesitating step.

"Pull back those blankets!" he cried. "Here comes a message!"

We all saw it at the same time.

"What — ?" began the general. "What — ?"

A private entered — a stupid redheaded farmer's boy, carrying an officer like a bag of meal across the shoulder.

The general was the first person who spoke, for, you see, he was an army man. "Lay him down," he said. "Don't stand there looking at me! Lay him down and put something under his head." Without surprise, without contrition — quite methodically, the general spoke. And he knew who it was. You could tell by the useless spurs and the whip-cords and the exquisite Sam Browne belt, even before you saw his face.

"Break out a first-aid kit, one of you!" he said. "What are you looking at? Haven't you seen any blood before? One of you orderlies go out and call a stretcher."

The red-haired private was scrambling to his feet. His shoulder was wet and dripping. "There was two of 'em," he said. "They was walking up the road just like — just like — "

The general stopped him. His voice was enough to stop anything just then. "And where's the other one?" he said.

The soldier blinked. He was very stupid and startled — almost dazed. "Dead," he answered. And then his voice became querulous and wild. He was seeking relief in words. "I seen him and he yelled at me," he said. "He was coming from here, poor kid, and I was coming here."

"What's that again?" the general's voice stopped his flow of words. "You were coming here? Where from?"

The orderly was still dazed. He had difficulty to think. "From headquarters of the Umpteenth up to that farm with a message."

"Well, why didn't you say so in the first place?" The general took a step toward him. "Where is your message?"

That poor redheaded boy was a stupid sight. He blinked, he swallowed, he fumbled at his belt. "I — I can't remember, sir."

"Can't remember?" roared the general.

"I — I must have dropped it, sir, when I picked him up."

General Swinnerton's fingers closed on his palm and opened. Before he even spoke, that red-haired boy cowered away from him. But we never heard what he had to say.

"Don't jump him, sir." It was Billy Langwell speaking in a curious, dreamy way, as he turned his head on his blanket pillow. "The poor boy did the best he could. We" — he moved slightly and caught his breath — "we can't all be in the cavalry back in '75."

The general turned toward him and bent down. Perhaps it was because the candles were flickering that his face looked gray and that he looked older than he had before — much older.

"Don't talk, Mr. Langwell," he said. "Are you in pain?"

Someone was applying a rude tourniquet to Billy Langwell's leg. Another was cutting open his whipcord jacket and trying to pull off his Sam Browne belt. But Billy Langwell hardly seemed to notice. He was in that state, you see, where pain has ceased to mean anything or where pain itself brought its own peculiar peace. As he stared at the general, he seemed peculiarly delicate, fragile, as fine as a tenuous thought which a word or a gesture might send away. It was not what he said to the general that made the general's face grow gray and still. It was something in his eyes, rather, and the way he moved his lips.

"Don't bother about me, thank you, sir," he answered. "I'm all right — perfectly all right."

The general turned to the telephone operator. His face had become like a stone — as hard, and quite as gray. "Get the division," he said, "and ask why those casual officers they were sending have not come up." And then he turned and looked at me.

Except for Billy Langwell, we were the only officers in the cellar then, for the signal officer was out, the intelligence officer was out, so was the detachment commander. And of course he saw the way I felt. But he was kind about it — surprisingly kind. He put his hand quite gently on my shoulder.

"Don't look so sick, Major," he said. "It's the war, that's all; and the next lieutenant that comes in to report will go out the same way if the telephones are working."

He was not exactly justifying himself, for he thought it was duty, straight duty. Two stretcher bearers had come in, and the two were working over Billy Langwell, talking in low voices. That constant inflow and outflow of people which is a part of any headquarters was beginning again, like a part of the same vague dream.

Some newcomers had appeared, seemingly from nowhere, as people often did in those vague nights. They stood blinking and looking about them until one of them spoke. "Beg pardon, sir. Is this brigade headquarters?"

For some reason, I was startled. They were officers — second lieutenants — those casual officers of whom the general had spoken. The one in front saluted, holding the salute for exactly the right length of time, most like a regular officer.

"Sir," he said, "Lieutenant Swinnerton reports for duty with the detail."

The theater — always the theater! Even up there, we had those close-cut banal phrases. Lieutenant Swinnerton! You would have known he was the general's son without any intuition to make you feel it. He had the same heavy shoulders, the same uncompromising head, and he looked from me to the general without showing any recognition. He knew the old man was a soldier. He knew what the old man wanted, and you had to hand it to the general then, for the thing he did was not what he wished to do. I heard him draw a quick breath, but he spoke at once. He could not hesitate, because he was an army man; and if he had not been, how could he have hesitated, with Billy Langwell lying on the floor?

Billy Langwell had not lost consciousness. You could see he was listening and taking a detached interest, as men sometimes do in spite of pain.

"Mr. Swinnerton," said the general — and once again Billy Langwell had him, though perhaps the general never knew it, or never thought — "Mr. Swinnerton, do you see that thingumajig on the map — the ferme-something-er-other? We can't pronounce it now since Mr. Langwell's got laid out. Well, get up there to the Umpteenth Regiment. Give the colonel my compliments and tell him to give you the coordinates of the front line, and tell him to send every man he can spare to lay out another wire. That's all."

The lieutenant saluted. He must have known the old man well

enough not to argue, and yet he asked a question: "Can you let me have a runner, sir, who knows the way?"

There was a slight tremor in the general's voice, but very slight. "The last one's out, and he hasn't come back yet. But you don't mind a thing like that. You were raised in an army post."

They were lifting Billy Langwell to the stretcher. They were moving with him to the blankets by the door, when the general noticed. "Are you comfortable, Mr. Langwell?" he inquired, and Billy opened his eyes.

"Thank you, sir," he said.

And then there was an embarrassing moment. The stretcher bearers did not know whether to move on or stop; because the general made no sign.

"You don't feel — " The general cleared his throat and seemed to have difficulty with his words. "I hope you don't feel you've been discriminated against in any way?"

Billy Langwell twisted his lips upward. He was quite himself in that last moment, and careless, but not so careless as we had sometimes seen him.

"Lord, no, sir," he said. "It's funny what an idiot I was. I thought you couldn't be real, you know. But now I've seen you working out — " Without finishing his thought, he waved his hand slightly in a curious, airy way. "George, give me a cigarette, will you? Now I've seen you working out — Good morning, general! I don't mean to be rude, sir. It's just a way I have." He had ceased waving his hand, and added the truest thing he ever said: "We're just a different breed of cats — that's all." What else was there to say — now that he had definitely, completely, put General Swinnerton in his place and himself in his place as well?

When did that regimental wire come in? It might have been an hour or less, although it was impossible to think of time in hours or minutes. The general was seated when they called him, staring at the floor, and no one wished to interrupt him. He might have been asleep, for his chin was sunk on his chest, and his campaign ribbons moved with a regular easy motion. As the telephone orderly spoke, however, General Swinnerton started and seized the instrument.

"Have you heard?" he began. "Is there — ?" You could tell what he wanted to say, but he stopped himself. "Well, it's time you hooked up. This has been a hell of a mess. And those signal officers will get a court for it, or I'll know the reason why. What can I expect? Didn't you get any messages? Didn't — "

The general's shoulder moved forward and he cleared his throat. "Didn't a lieutenant report to you with my message? Yes, a new one. His name's Swinnerton. Can't you hear me? Swinnerton. Yes, he's my son, as a matter of fact. But what's that got to do with it? What's that?"

The general's shoulders moved suddenly. He sat up very straight. And suddenly his voice was choked and queer. "Thanks. Thanks. . . . But there's no use saying that. There are others who have caught it. Lots of others. Thanks. Now keep in the wire."

There was a noise. The telephone orderly stooped down hastily. The general had dropped the telephone headpiece on the floor and was standing up.

"Major" — his voice was still queer, but perfectly controlled — "when you get after the morning report, add on Lieutenant Swinnerton. He — he's dead. I — I think I'll turn in now."

Now what was there to say? What was there to do? Absolutely nothing, for, you see, he was an army man. No one said a word, and he stood by himself in the light of the guttering candles — alone, as he had always been alone. And why I did it I do not know, but suddenly I found myself holding his hand, trying to say something, anything at all. But still he was an army man, though I felt his fingers close on mine.

"Don't be a damned fool," he said. "What time is it? Three o'clock? Well, I'm turning in till six. Good night — or rather, good morning, Major."

Lunch at Honolulu

(1945)

Here in this story the big brass appears again, twenty-five years later than in "Good Morning, Major." This time it is navy and not army, but war is still war. "Lunch at Honolulu" is, I believe, a more natural and easy story. It may not have such a wide appeal, because of its local and rather specialized setting and because signs of old missionary families are not very well known outside of the Hawaiian Islands. For all I know it may be necessary actually to be entertained at luncheon in Honolulu by one of the Big Five to appreciate some of the nuances which amused me when I set them down on paper. The strange habit that exists among the dwellers in our Pacific Paradise of dragging the atmosphere of Polynesia into their everyday language perhaps should be observed at firsthand before it makes good fiction. It may even be that only people who know the Islands can see that the story is social satire — but there is still the war and the admiral and the boy, and about war I have never been able to be satirical.

THE house was off Nuannu, beyond the cemetery where Hawaiian royalty lay with symbolic tabu sticks at the corners of their burial plots. It was a fine clear day by the sea, but rain was falling up by the jagged skyline of the mountains. Mr. Huntley knew that in Honolulu they called it liquid sunshine.

The house where he was invited for lunch was built of coral stone and redwood, and a porte-cochere covered the drive. The house might have been in Redlands, California, except for the ornamental planting. It was said that almost anything could grow on the Hawaiian Islands. By the time the taxicab had stopped beneath the porte-cochere, Mr.

Huntley had identified upon the lawns a traveler's palm, an Alexandra palm, a Norfolk Island pine, ginger flowers, hibiscus, and a bed of calla lilies, snapdragons and forget-me-nots. There were also some bamboo and banana. This dizzying combination gave its own horticultural evidence that Honolulu was the melting pot of races and the crossroads of the Pacific.

Even before Mr. Huntley had climbed the steps, a middle-aged Japanese maid had opened the door. Her hair was done in Japanesse convention. She wore the kimona and the obi. When she bowed and took his hat, she looked like a part of the chorus of *Madame Butterfly*. Inside, the long living room was cool and shadowy, paneled with some polished darkish wood. There were reed mats on the dark, highly polished floor. There were comfortable American upholstered chairs and Chinese lacquered tables. There were Hawaiian calabashes filled with ginger flowers. There was a large Capehart phonograph, and on the walls were Chinese ancestral portraits, an oblong of old tapa cloth, and some Malay weapons.

The Japanese maid smiled. Before she put her hand in front of her mouth, she revealed three black teeth and one brilliant gold one. She drew in her breath politely.

"Mr. Wintertree, he waits, on the back lanai, please," she said. "This way, please."

As Mr. Huntley followed her, he had a glimpse of himself in a cloudy ornate Italian mirror. His image was disturbing in that shadowy room that was heavy with the scent of tuberoses. He was a moist, dumpy, middle-aged interloper in a wrinkled Palm Beach suit.

Mr. Wintertree was on the back veranda. The veranda, furnished with wicker chairs, potted ferns and hanging air plants, looked over a deep-green tropical gorge to the darker jagged mountains. To the left, far below, were the streets and houses of Honolulu, and the docks and the Aloha Tower, and the harbor and the sea. Mr. Wintertree was a cadaverous man. He was dressed in an immaculate linen suit. His face was deeply tanned. His hair was as white and as smooth as his coat.

"Aloha, Mr. Huntley," he said. "It's very kind of you to come and take pot luck. Mrs. Wintertree was dreadfully sorry she couldn't be here. It's her day at the Red Cross, so it will be a stag party — just five of us. Admiral Smedley is coming with Captain Rotch of his staff. Henry D. Smedley — you know the admiral?"

"No, I have never met him," Mr. Huntley answered. "I hope I'm not too early."

"Oh, no, no," Mr. Wintertree said. "They'll be here any minute now. Just the admiral and Captain Rotch, and Lieutenant — " A slight frown appeared on Mr. Wintertree's face. "What the devil is his name? Oh yes, Wright. A Lieutenant Wright. He's just off a carrier. Walter Jones wrote me about him, too. He's a naval aviator. Did you ever hear Walt mention him?"

"No, not that I remember," Mr. Huntley said. "It's very kind of you to have me here."

"It's always a pleasure to see a friend of old Walt's," Mr. Wintertree said. "Maybe he told you, we were together in the class of '08 at Yale. When did you last see Walt?"

"In New York last month," Mr. Huntley told him. "Walt told me to be sure to look you up."

"I wish you could see this place the way it used to be before the war," Mr. Wintertree said. "It's the duty of kamaainas to make malihinis like the islands, but Honolulu is a madhouse now. Army, Navy — they're into everything. They'll be taking over the golf club next."

"What's a kamaaina?" Mr. Huntley asked.

Mr. Wintertree smiled.

"That's a Hawaiian word. Roughly translated it means 'old-timer,' " Mr. Wintertree said. "I'm an old-timer and you're a malihini. This is a kamaaina house. Father built it in 1880. Honolulu was just a small town on a small Pacific island then. My God, how it's changed!"

"You have a beautiful view from this porch," Mr. Huntley said.

"Lanai, not porch," Mr. Wintertree told him. "I suppose we're eccentric the way we cling to Hawaiian words. This is a lanai, and that couch over there is called a hikkiai. It's a real Hawaiian hikkiai, not just a couple of mattresses the way they make them now. You can see it is made out of lahala mats, the woven leaves of the pandanus tree."

"Hikkiai," Mr. Huntley repeated.

"Good," Mr. Wintertree said. "That's the way to say it."

"What do you do with it?" Mr. Huntley asked.

"Why, you lie on it," Mr. Wintertree said. "Do you want to lie on it?"

"No thanks, not now," Mr. Huntley answered. "You do have a beautiful view from here."

"Those light-colored trees that you see on the side of the mountain are kukui trees," said Mr. Wintertree. "They have small round nuts called kukui nuts. In old times the Hawaiians would string those nuts on a reed and use them for candles. My father used to say when he was a child that his father — we come of missionary stock — used to say, 'Children, one more kukui nut and it's bedtime.' "

Mr. Huntley glanced at a low table, hoping to find a cigarette.

"When my father was a boy," Mr. Wintertree said, "he spoke of seeing a little crowd of native Hawaiians on the docks, about where the Aloha Tower is now. We were all friends in those days. Those Polynesian boys were looking at something and laughing — two bluebottle flies. Yes, they had never seen a fly, and now we have everything — flies, marines, planes, battleships. I suppose you're out here for the government, Mr. Huntley."

"Yes," said Mr. Huntley. "I'm out for the OWI."

"What's the OWI?" Mr. Wintertree asked.

"That's a native American expression," Mr. Huntley said.

"Now, now," Mr. Wintertree told him. "Don't forget that we're just as native American here as any other part of America." He looked at his wrist watch. "I've never known Admiral Smedley to be so late. Wait — I'm wrong, I think I hear him now."

Brisk and somewhat heavy steps sounded on the floor of the living room. It was Admiral Smedley, followed by Captain Rotch. The admiral's glance was sharp and direct. His face was set in tranquil lines, like the bust of a Roman emperor. His gray hair was cut very short. He was dressed in fresh khaki. He wore two tiny silver stars in his shirt collar. On his finger was a Naval Academy ring.

"We're just waiting for one other guest," Mr. Wintertree said. "A friend of a friend of mine. He is just off a carrier — Lieutenant Wright."

"That must be the *Great Lick*," the admiral said. "She ran into a little difficulty. What did you say the officer's name was?"

"Wright," Mr. Wintertree answered.

"I don't know him," the admiral said. "Rotch, did you ever hear of anybody named Wright?"

"No, sir," the captain said.

"Well, it's a big navy," the admiral said. "And the Pacific's a big ocean."

"We might have something to drink while we're waiting," Mr. Wintertree said. "Would you care for something, Admiral? Sherry or a Martini? — or a little of our island drink, Okulehau?"

"Okulehau, I haven't had any of that since I was stationed here in '32," the admiral said. "We used to call it Oke. How about you, Rotch?"

"If the boss falls off the wagon, I guess I can fall, too," the captain said, and he laughed.

"I hope you'll excuse me if I don't join you," Mr. Wintertree said. " I very seldom indulge in the middle of the day, but Taka and Togo will give you anything you want. Would you care for a Martini, Mr. Huntley?"

"Thank you," Mr. Huntley said.

The Japanese maid came through the door on the far end of the porch, which evidently led to the dining room. She carried a large tray of dark wood, upon which were small plates of olives and other appetizers. Behind her came an old Japanese in a white coat, with bottles, ice and glasses.

"Taka and Togo have been with us for thirty years," Mr. Wintertree said, and he lowered his voice. "They were very unhappy on December 7th."

"So was I," the admiral said. "Do you live out here too, Mr. Huntley?"

"Oh, no," Mr. Huntley said. "I'm with the OWI. I've only been here about a week."

"Oh, a writer, are you?" the admiral asked. "Well, there's a lot to write about."

"You have a beautiful view from this veranda," Mr. Huntley heard Captain Rotch say to Mr. Wintertree.

"Yes, we think it's a very pleasant lanai," he heard Mr. Wintertree answer. "You see it faces both Mauka and Makai. Those are the old Hawaiian words for the sea and the mountains, Captain Rotch. They form two of the cardinal points on our island's compass. Those light-colored trees on the mountainside are called kukui trees."

"Let's see," the admiral said to Mr. Huntley. "I think I have read something that you have written. Didn't you write an article for the *Saturday Evening Post* about trailers?"

"No, sir, that must have been someone else."

"Yes, maybe it was someone else. Did you fly out, or come by boat?" the admiral asked.

"I flew out," Mr. Huntley told him.

"You can get places flying — anywhere in the world in two days' flying," the admiral said. "It's a great place, Honolulu. We're certainly lifting its face for it. Give us another year and we'll make it look like Pittsburgh. No one's ever going to say again that America can't fight a war. Thank you." He took a glass from the tray the old Japanese was passing.

The Japanese houseman bowed and smiled. He was a very polite old-time Japanese.

"This is like old times," the admiral called. "This is real Oke, Winter-tree."

"It comes from the big island," Mr. Wintertree answered. "They used to make it in the old days — that was during prohibition — but there were only two kinds of Okulehau, the right kind and the wrong kind. This is the right kind. It was made from the root of the ti plant. You've seen its leaves on dinner tables, Admiral. In the old days the Hawaiians would break off a ti plant and sit on it and slide down a mountain slope. It was one of the old royal sports."

"Yes, I've heard they did," the admiral said. "In my spare time I've been making a little study of the Polynesians. I've got a dictionary of Hawaiian words."

"It will be useful to you," Mr. Wintertree said. "Hawaiian words still crop up in kamaainas' conversations."

"Some of the words are very expressive," the admiral said. "Do you know the word for cat?" But Mr. Wintertree did not answer. He was moving to the living-room door, to shake hands with the last of his guests, Lieutenant Wright. Lieutenant Wright had a piece of adhesive tape above his left eye, but even so he looked very fresh and young. His voice was loud and mellow.

"And how do you do, sir," Lieutenant Wright said. "Thanks for letting me aboard. I hope I'm not too late to snap onto a drink."

"Oh — not too late at all. I am very glad you could come, Lieutenant," Mr. Wintertree told him. "As soon as I heard from your Uncle Walt . . ."

Lieutenant Wright laughed so loudly that Mr. Huntley saw the admiral's forehead wrinkle.

"Uncle Walt would have given me hell if I had passed you up," Lieutenant Wright said. "Uncle Walt told me if I ever hit this rock to look you up, sir, and now I've hit it." He looked at Mr. Huntley's glass. "Is that a Martini I see him drinking?"

"Yes, that's a Martini," Mr. Wintertree said. "And this is Admiral Smedley, Captain Rotch, and Mr. Huntley."

"How do you do, Admiral," Lieutenant Wright said. "Sorry I'm late, but I don't mind catching up." He took a Martini from the tray. "Make me another one, boy," he added gently. "Maybe you better make me two. This is really a nice place you've got here, Mr. Wintertree."

The conversation had died. There a silence while Lieutenant Wright picked up another Martini. The admiral cleared his throat.

"I hear you're off the *Great Lick*," the admiral said.

Lieutenant Wright laughed loudly, although there appeared to be no reason for his laughing.

"Yes, sir, the old *Lick* and promise. That's what the kids call her, Admiral, sir," Lieutenant Wright answered. "And she's mostly *Lick*." Lieutenant Wright laughed again. "She really is, sir. She really took them aboard, sir, but we knocked off one of their BBs."

The admiral turned to Captain Rotch. "How many did you say she took?"

"Three of them, sir," the captain said.

"She really took them," Lieutenant Wright laughed again. "Oh, boy! she really took them."

The admiral glanced at Mr. Huntley and then at Mr. Wintertree. He seemed to feel that the occasion compelled him to say something but not too much.

"Occasionally," he said, "in the course of an air battle a Japanese plane crashes on the deck or superstructure of one of our ships — a suicide plane. It naturally causes considerable damage."

Lieutenant Wright whistled. He was on his third Martini, and as far as Mr. Huntley could see, rank did not disturb him.

"Did you say damage, sir?" he asked.

The wrinkles deepened on the admiral's forehead.

"Just one minute, please," he began, but the lieutenant raised his voice.

"It's really rugged when one of them comes in at you," the lieu-

tenant said. "Now this first that hit us — it was about eighteen hundred
and thirty hours — he came in from the port side. We gave him everything we had. You could see the 40s going into him like red-hot rivets."

"Just a minute," the admiral said. "Just a minute, son —" but the
lieutenant's voice was louder.

"That kid must have been dead, but he still kept coming in. You got
the idea there was nothing you could do but stand and take it. It was a
very rugged feeling."

"Rotch," the admiral said to the captain. Captain Rotch's manner
reminded Huntley of that of a kindly policeman. He rested his hand
on Lieutenant Wright's shoulder and whispered something. As he
listened, the lieutenant's face looked blank and his thoughts seemed to
drift away from him and he was back again where he had started, right
on Mr. Wintertree's lanai.

"I'm sorry, sir," he said. "I didn't know it was restricted."

"That's all right, son," the admiral told him. "That's all right."

"Down in Numea we had a song about it," the lieutenant said.
"Some of the kids made it up at the club. 'I'm forever whispering
secrets.' "

Mr. Wintertree's voice interrupted.

"I think luncheon is ready now," Mr. Wintertree was saying.

"Well, let's skip it," Lieutenant Wright said. "As long as pop here
says luncheon's ready."

"If you'll just lead the way, Admiral," Mr. Wintertree said.

In the dining room a narrow dark table was set for lunch. There was
a center decoration of breadfruit and green leaves. There were Chinese
plates and small wooden bowls filled with a gray pastelike substance,
that Mr. Huntley knew was a native food called poi. The admiral
was at Mr. Wintertree's right, Mr. Huntley at his left. Captain
Rotch was beside Mr. Huntley and the lieutenant was beside the
admiral.

"I'm forever whispering secrets," the lieutenant was singing beneath
his breath. He lifted up his plate very carefully and set it down. Then
Mr. Huntley saw him staring at his bowl of poi. The servants were
passing plates of clear consommé.

"I'm sorry there isn't a sixth to balance the table," Mr. Wintertree
said. "This is Mrs. Wintertree's day at the Red Cross. I see you looking
at the table, Admiral. Do you know what wood it's made from?"

"Yes," the admiral said, "koa wood."

"No, no," Mr. Wintertree said. "It's made from the monkey-pod tree."

"Have they got monkeys on this rock?" the lieutenant asked.

Mr. Wintertree went on without answering.

"Now, the chairs we are sitting on are koa. They are our best wood, very close to mahogany. The koa is a very handsome tree, Mr. Huntley, long, graceful, curving leaves. You still find specimens in the mountains, but our most beautiful wood came from the kou tree."

"I never heard of the kou tree," the admiral said.

"As long as it isn't the cuckoo tree," Lieutenant Wright said and he began to laugh.

"The old calabashes were all made from the kou," Mr. Wintertree said. "You can see one of them — a very handsome one — on the sideboard, but the kou is nearly extinct. When ants appeared on the island, they ate the kou."

"What did they want to eat it for, pop?" Lieutenant Wright asked.

"They ate the leaves," Mr. Wintertree answered.

"Well, bugs do eat the damnedest things on islands," Lieutenant Wright said. "At Hollandia something ate the seat right out of my pants. Maybe it was ants. Ants in my pants, pop."

"Mr. Wintertree," the admiral asked, "do you know the Hawaiian word for cat?"

"Why, yes," Mr. Wintertree said. "Poopooki."

"I suppose you know how the word was derived?" the admiral asked.

The soup was finished. Mr. Wintertree glanced at the servants and they began to take away the plates.

"Oh, yes," he said. "Of course I know." But the admiral went on telling him.

"Well, Huntley ought to hear it," the admiral said. "Mr. Huntley can write it down sometime. It seems that there didn't use to be any cats in the Hawaiian Islands."

"No cats, no ants," Lieutenant Wright said. The admiral glanced at him sideways.

"And no Naval Reserve officers," the admiral said. "It seems the missionaries brought the cats."

Lieutenant Wright smiled.

"And the Navy brought in the reserve officers, Admiral, sir. They had to, to win this war."

Captain Rotch cleared his throat.

"Perhaps the admiral would like to finish what he is saying," he said gently.

"Sorry, sir," Lieutenant Wright said quickly. "Aye, aye, sir. The missionaries brought the cats . . ."

"You see, none of the kanakas had ever seen a cat. They didn't have a name for it," the admiral went on. Mr. Huntley saw that Mr. Wintertree winced when the admiral used the word 'kanaka.' "Then they must have heard one of the white missionary women call her cat 'poor pussy' and that's how you get it — poor pussy — poopooki."

"By God, what do you know," the lieutenant said, and he whistled. "You come to an island and it's like every other island and all the native Joes and Marys are just alike. Coral, palm trees, a lagoon, and then out come the canoes — and there you are, like that." He snapped his fingers. "Pretty soon you beat a drum and start singing."

"You have never been to Honolulu before, have you?" It seemed to Mr. Huntley that Mr. Wintertree's voice was sharp. "I think you'll find it different. These fish are mullet. The old kings used to keep them in the royal fish ponds."

"There's nothing better than good mullet," Captain Rotch said.

"Back out there " — the lieutenant waved his hand to illustrate back out there — "we used to chuck a stick of dynamite in a lagoon and get mullet, and did the natives go for those fish? You ought to have seen them go for them. Once when I was out with a sub over in the Zulu Sea — all right, Admiral, sir, security."

"I'm sorry we can't hear about it," the admiral said.

"This is one-finger poi," Mr. Wintertree told the table. "There's a shortage of good poi, like everything else, but some of my native friends help me."

Mr. Wintertree stopped, because Lieutenant Wright had begun to laugh for no apparent reason.

"You know, they tell a story about me out there, pop," the lieutenant said, and he waved his hand again, to illustrate out there, "and I guess I can tell it to you without breaking security. It's rather a funny story." He laughed again as he remembered it and pushed his plate away. "One of the CPOs who was working with me came up to me one day and he said — 'Lieutenant, sir, I ought to get a little leave. This country here is getting me queer.' Well, I didn't blame him. So I just told him to relax and tell me what was the matter. And he said: 'It's this way, sir. All these dark women begin to look to me as though they were white.' And do you know what I said to him? At least, it's what they say I said to him." The lieutenant paused and beamed at everyone. "I said to him — 'Kid, what dark women?' " The admiral smiled. Mr. Huntley laughed, although he had heard the story several times before.

"We are having papaya for dessert," Mr. Wintertree said. "It isn't quite the season, but I'm proud of my papayas."

They had small cups of very black coffee out on the lanai. Mr. Wintertree explained that it was kona coffee, so named because it was grown on the slopes of the Kona coast on the big island of Hawaii. There was an island too big to be spoiled, Mr. Wintertree said. The ghosts of the past still lingered over the Kona coast. You could still see the old burial caves in the cliffs that fringe the bay where Captain Cook was killed. You could still see the black walls of lava rock that marked the compounds of the native villages.

As Mr. Huntley sat listening, he was thinking of the irrational accidents that threw people together. In a few moments this party on the lanai would be breaking up. The admiral would return to his office. Mr. Huntley would return to his hotel. He wondered what the lieutenant would find to do. Very little, he imagined, now that Honolulu was a garrison town.

"They still sing the old meles on Hawaii," Mr. Wintertree was saying. "Those old word-of-mouth songs have been passed on for centuries."

The lieutenant looked at his small cup of coffee.

"Would it be out of order to turn this in for something else?" he asked.

"Turn it in?" Mr. Wintertree repeated.

"For a Scotch and soda," the lieutenant said. "If you wouldn't mind, pop."

"Oh, certainly," Mr. Wintertree answered. "A Scotch and soda, Togo."

"Double," the lieutenant said. "If you wouldn't mind."

"Sometime you should hear an old Hawaiian chant — a mele," Mr. Wintertree told the admiral. "It's a living page of history."

The lieutenant clapped his hands together and drummed his foot on the floor.

"Boom-boom," he said. "Yai, yai, boom-boom. One night at Tanga those Joes began singing — Oh, thanks."

Togo was back with a double Scotch and soda, but the lieutenant had grown restless. He prowled back and forth across the lanai, withdrawn from the conversation, but Mr. Huntley could still hear him, muttering beneath his breath, "Yai, yai, boom-boom." This must have gone on for several minutes while the rest of them were talking before the Japanese maid appeared. She said some officers in an automobile were calling for Lieutenant Wright. Lieutenant Wright looked very much relieved.

"I thought those boys could wrangle some transportation," he said. "You've got to see these rocks when you hit them. Well, I'd better be shoving. Thank you, Mr. Wintertree. Good-by, Admiral, sir. So long, Captain. So long, Mister."

There was a moment's silence when Lieutenant Wright left. They could hear him cross the living room.

"Boom-boom, boom-boom," he was still chanting. "Yai, yai, boom-boom."

The admiral looked at his empty cup, and then he looked at the captain.

"That was a pretty fresh kid," the captain said.

"Yes," the admiral answered. "It's quiet, now he's gone."

"You never can tell about a new guest," Mr. Wintertree said. "I'm sorry."

The wicker chair in which the admiral was sitting creaked as he leaned forward to set down his cup on a little table.

"That's all right," he said. "Every now and then they act that way. You and I would, too." The chair creaked again as the admiral rose. "Will you see if the car is outside, Rotch? It's only that boy was glad — and that's natural — just glad he is still alive."

Return Trip to the Stone Age
(1949)

RECENTLY I happened to be conversing with a man whose family had accumulated large sums of money in the general vicinity of Pittsburgh, at an epoch when such a thing could be done quickly, comparatively easily and even with a modicum of public applause. It had happened, as was then customary, that certain fractions of this fortune were set aside for eleemosynary and other worthy purposes, including a large institute of scientific research. My friend had recently visited this family memorial and had brought back with him in his pocket a sample of a substance which had been perfected there after years of painstaking study.

This substance, when he removed it from his pocket, resembled a lump of modeling wax or ordinary putty, but when he placed it in my hand, it obviously had a lower specific gravity. After assuring me that it would not explode, he suggested that I mold this malleable lump into a ball. When this was accomplished, as easily as a pellet could be made from a bread crumb, he asked me to drop it on the floor. To my amazement, this lumpy sphere did not fall dead like clay or putty, but instead bounced upward in a resilient and disturbing manner. Furthermore, its tensile strength was almost nil. It could be broken in two as easily as a corn muffin.

It was not difficult to express admiration for this scientific wonder, but it appeared that there was one catch to the thing that was vexing the scientific institute. They had made it, and, now that it was made, they could think of no conceivable use for it.

Sometimes on a restless night when I think of my journeying about the world, I am reminded of that bouncing piece of putty. I have never been able to make any use of travel experience, although I have been to a number of interesting and out-of-the-way places. I have seen the

Assam Valley, Bushire in Persia, the Gobi Desert, the Sahara Desert, the Andes, Iceland, Ascension Island, Lake Chad, the Amazon, the Nile, the Ganges, the Coliseum and the Taj Mahal, and a few volcanoes, and yet I have brought back no photographs, no notes, no material for a book or travelogue — and no stuffed animals.

Of course I have collected a few memories, because you can't avoid bringing back assortments of impressions from thousands of miles of travel, but there is a catch here also. If you have moved about long enough, these memories and impressions, once so vivid and indelible, begin merging into each other, until it becomes difficult to recollect whether it happened in Peking, Tokyo, Cairo or Lima. And finally all that is left, at least from my own experience, is a spirit of restlessness, an impatience with all travel literature and a passionate desire to see it all and do it all again.

This sense of confusion is greatly intensified by air transportation. A few long trips and everything about them becomes so indelibly blurred by the shrinkage of distance, that all that is really left is a recollection of airfields, each approximately the same as the other. At a conventional cruising altitude of eight or nine thousand feet, most mountains are inclined to level out, and most terrain, even unexplored Arabia, Central Africa and the Amazon Valley, has only a map-like appearance. About all one finally learns from extended air travel is that there is a very great deal more water than land on the planet.

I only bring up these facts to show how little fitted I am to make a report on a little-known island that was once widely discussed in the Pacific war news. I should not dream of mentioning a quick trip of mine to the Carolines in a navy plane, and my four-hour stay on the atoll of Truk about a year and a half ago, if many other people had ever been there. As a matter of fact, only a very few have. Some fliers, some crews from naval vessels, and a comparatively small number of marines and other naval personnel have visited Truk, usually for brief periods, since the close of the Japanese war. Also some scientists have called there under government auspices a year ago last summer, but aside from these few and usually casual visitors, scarcely an American appears to have set foot on any land of this atoll since whaling ships used to winter in the general region in the '70s and '80s.

Arellano, the Portuguese navigator, who discovered the island in

1569, sailed off rapidly on other business; and the Spaniard Miguel Lopez de la Gaspi, who touched there in 1569, was more interested in the conquering of the Philippines and the founding of Manila. From those remote dates there is no record of a European intruder until 1820, when it is casually mentioned in a German magazine article that "the Frenchman Duperry" stopped there. Who M. Duperry was and why he stopped appears impossible to determine, at least from American sources, because there is no bibliography of Truk, save for casual mention in a few magazine articles and in scientific periodicals, many of which are of German origin. Occasional Spaniards, both traders and missionaries, must have stopped there also, since Spain acquired the island group in 1885, but no attempt was ever made to colonize or develop it. The Germans bought Truk after the Spanish American War and held it until the Japanese moved in in 1915, but the rugged character of its seventy islets offered no opportunity for exploitation, except for two or three modest coconut plantations.

In spite of its magnificent sheltering lagoons, it would seem that only a few whalers ever lingered at Truk, because the main fleet wintered off the lusher islands of Kusaie, Ponape, Jaluit, or the Marshalls. In fact from its original discovery it appears improbable that many Europeans have lived there for extended periods.

With the arrival of the Japanese such a heavy veil of secrecy descended upon Truk that the impression grew that a great naval base was building there. Actually, serious military installations were begun after World War II had started. Though the lagoon afforded a fine, safe anchorage for the Japanese fleet, and though some twenty or thirty thousand troops who could throw up some of the hottest antiaircraft fire anywhere in the Pacific were there at the time of the surrender, when it emerged from behind its iron curtain, Truk was largely another example of the overextension and the basic feebleness of Japanese imperial domination. The Japanese have been shipped away now and all that is left is the original Micronesian population, somewhat scarred and battered by their contacts with various exponents of Western culture.

To assist the island's inhabitants, a small unit of navy government and a hospital unit are about all that is left now on Truk. The airstrip is closed. Truk's only communication with the outer world is now by water; the only vessels apt to touch there are rare U.S. Navy supply craft. Truk is a very lonely place again, and this is a pity from a tourist's point of view. The climate, though somewhat warm, is genial and on the whole healthy, and the Truk atoll and the islands, the tips of submerged mountain tops appearing above the blue waters of the lagoon, make one of the most geologically interesting and esthetically beautiful island groups to be seen in the Pacific, or for that matter, anywhere in the world.

It would take many months to explore the scores of small islands in this group. Their geology, their flora, and especially the varying cultures of their population pose a series of problems and fascinating fields of speculation. I regret that I only stopped for four hours on Moen, one of the main islands in the atoll, but the shortness of my stay gives the whole place a romantic, dreamlike quality.

"Out of this world" is an expression which I deplore, but it can be literally applied to Truk, which is still waiting for a Burton Holmes or an Agassiz to do a better account of it than the intelligence data assembled by the U.S. Navy.

Much more vivid than my recollections of Truk itself is the transportation that brought me there. Instead of traveling on bucket seats as I had previously on crossing the Pacific, I accompanied five naval officers aboard a plane formerly assigned to Admiral Nimitz, and no private car could have been more comfortable. On reaching Kwajalein before dawn, it was a pleasant change from past experience to be one of a party met by the commanding officer of this island and to be taken to his quarters for an adequate breakfast. In spite of this innovation, Kwajalein was obviously going downhill. It had been a boom town when I had seen it in the early months of 1945, one of the main crossroads of the Pacific, and it was a ghost town now. The temporary barracks, which except for the runways and roads, crowded nearly every available square foot of this coral islet, were not built for the moist and humid air of the central Pacific. Every bit of metal on the island was already in advanced stages of corrosion. Water coolers and letter files were crumbling. Typewriters only had a few months' life span. Even a bronze plaque in the island chapel, placed to commemorate the dead in the island invasion, was already almost illegible. Worse still, the hardware, the nails and screws holding the buildings together, the locks and doorknobs, were all beginning to give way. In the sudden rainy dawn that followed our arrival, all these facts became dramatically evident. They gave a sense of impermanence of a vanishing civilization because our mechanized installations on Kwajalein already had something of the antiquity of the Roman Wall in Britain. You had a definite conviction that nothing built by civilized man would remain for very long on the Marshalls. What would last longest was obviously the pandanus-thatched house with beams held together by fibers, and one could not escape the feeling that the Marshallese were waiting hopefully for a new Dark Age which would permit them to put up their huts again.

It all looked much better from the air. Shortly after the take-off, the sun burnt away the overcast, permitting one to look down from a great height on an occasional coral islet. Anyone who has seen one from the air or sea must admit that a Pacific atoll is the loneliest sight in the world, but from the air it is one of the most beautiful, because from a height one can perceive all the opalescent color gradations created by the sun, the sand, the coral and the startlingly clear Pacific water as it touches the first bench of the outer atoll reef and merges into purples and violets and whites around the coral heads and then into the more delicate greens and blues in the shallower lagoon. The ringlike atoll itself, with its dazzling-white sand, its dots of coconut palm and its untidy shrubbery of pandanus, is thus always surrounded by a mass of changing color. From the air it becomes a punctuation mark in an interminable waste of ocean.

There were several of these punctuation marks between the main Marshalls and the Carolines, but they were only a preview of the Truk formation. Truk, as we approached it in the late forenoon, was completely in the clear, without a wisp of vapor to hide it, rising from the midst of a cobalt and silver sea. Unlike those atolls of the Marshalls, which seldom could have stood more than eight feet above high-tide mark, Truk seemed like a part of a submerged continent. As our plane began letting down, the lagoon became a large round lake, protected by a circle of barrier reef as perfect almost as if it had been drawn by a geometric compass. There was room for ten world navies to anchor in the Truk lagoon, and three good channels through the reef. Rising nearly in the center of this clear and beautifully sheltered body of water were five ancient volcanic peaks, now islands, covered with a deeper, richer, emerald verdure than is common with Pacific islands farther north, and, like freckles, there were tinier islands scarcely to be noticed from a circling plane, both inside and outside the coral barrier.

The Truk islands, which shelter about eleven thousand natives, have names that sound as remote from civilization as they really are — Moen, Duplon, Fefan, Udot, Fala, Toi, Polic, Onamuc.

As the plane headed toward the island of Moen, which was Truk's administrative center, as it lost altitude and as the flaps came down, it was possible to see a concrete pier, a crane and a few abandoned buildings. These were left by the Japanese and except for some rusted hulls of shipping, were the most impressive signs I saw of the earlier occupation. The airstrip on which we landed a minute later was also Japanese, but the control tower and the Quonset huts and the Quonset roofs of the administration buildings a little way up the hill gave it the customary American look. Ours was the last plane to come into Truk before the strip was closed, but there was no sign of abandonment that morning. The naval island commander and his staff and the native constabulary and even some boy scouts were out to meet the plane. The constabulary were dressed in shorts and wore bluish helmets and were armed with what appeared to be salvaged Japanese weapons. They were well turned out and stood at stiff attention, but they looked no more military than the Marshallese. Their features were irregular but agreeable, their eyes dark and intelligent, their height only medium. None of them had the Grecian, athletic build of the Polynesian, and none possessed his coordination or physical beauty. It was warm on the airstrip, too warm for clothing, and yet I was just as pleased that the Trukese constabulary were not turned out in G-strings. Not one of them would have looked like a beach boy on Waikiki.

When we rode in jeeps from the airstrip to the administration building and the hospital higher up the hill over a dusty, glary, coral road we were to encounter an experience almost unique in postwar history. Moses Arkana, the chief of the Truk atoll, emerged from his office building — another Quonset hut set up by naval government — to greet us. The chief wore khaki trousers, a khaki shirt and sneakers. He was a short, stoutish man in his late fifties, and he had a quiet and moderate command of English because in his youth he had shipped before the mast aboard some tramp steamer that had anchored off the atoll. When we asked if there was anything that he and his people wanted, he made the surprising statement that his people were comfortable and doing very well and that they wanted nothing. When he was asked again if he was sure about this, he said that they would like a few fishhooks. His people had nearly forgotten the art of fishing.

The chief, whose life had been spent under Spanish, German, and Japanese domination, explained that the Trukese had been discouraged from fishing by the Japanese, possibly for reasons of security. Their canoes had been taken from them, and Japanese fishermen had been imported from Okinawa, and had carried on a commercial industry until the outbreak of the war.

It must not be assumed, however, that the Truk islanders follow the hardy seafaring tradition of other Caroline natives. Captain Walter Karig, USNR, who has recently traveled extensively in these regions, has pointed out to me that the Trukese have always been exporters rather than sailors, using boatmen from Puluwat to carry their processed goods through the Carolines — a yellow vegetable dye called turmeric still used on the atoll and a fragrant cosmetic oil composed of coconut and frangipani blossoms, not to mention tortoise shell and pearl shell. They had only done lagoon fishing and had purchased outriggers for the purpose from such canoe-building islands as Moril. Now that the natives wanted to fish again in the lagoon, they no longer had boats. They had almost forgotten the fishing grounds, and besides, the Japanese, in the months of starvation that had faced them immediately before they surrendered, had dynamited portions of the lagoon and had thinned out the fish considerably. However, Chief Moses was sure they could get some if they could get fishhooks.

We then walked to the small hospital that cared for all the natives on the Truk islands. The naval doctor in charge was a young man with great enthusiasms. His wife, who had come with him, was a trained nurse. Together with a very few enlisted personnel, they had trained a group of Trukese girls for nursing and Trukese men for orderlies. They were also conducting a general school for health and sanitation, which was designed to send intelligent natives to teach hygiene to the outer islands. These efforts, the doctor said, were already beginning to bear fruit. Tuberculosis was common in the atoll, but their main problem was the familiar tropical yaws, a filth disease, which was now being controlled, largely by the graduates of his school. Infant mortality and death from childbirth were also a Trukese problem. An effort was now being made to bring expectant mothers from the outer islands to the maternity ward, where they would have proper care, but sometimes this was difficult because the outer islanders still had taboos and prejudices and still lived without clothes and other benefits of civilization. The prize patient in the hospital was suffering from elephantiasis. He had been picked up by a health team from an outer island and he seemed pleased to exhibit his monstrous deformity, which was going to be fixed in a few days by an operation.

There was a road, a circumference of perhaps five miles around the base of the island, built by the Japanese, and very badly built indeed. The jeeps lurched through it dustily. The conelike hills of Moen rose sharply to the right and mangrove swamps and beaches met the lagoon on the left. The foliage on the island was thick, a preview to the heavier foliage of the southwest Pacific. Fine, large breadfruit trees grow in the valleys, their shiny intricate leaves making rich blots of dark green against the lighter foliage, and there were also luxurious stands of coconuts and dense growths of plantain. The doctor said that the natives' diet was much like that of any other Pacific islanders; fish, plantain, breadfruit, coconut, taro root, and yam. Since the departure of the Japanese, the food situation had been bad because the starving troops had cut the hearts from thousands of coconut palms. There was also a second agricultural menace in the form of a land snail imported by the Japanese for food from the island of Madagascar. This giant African snail, apparently freed from the natural enemies which controlled it in Madagascar, was multiplying itself in huge numbers, and devouring the new leaves of breadfruit trees and attacking the yam patches. Nevertheless, life was not hard for the Trukese. In their genial climate, no great efforts at agriculture were necessary. Food in the main still dropped from trees, if one waited long enough beneath them.

Invasions from the outer world may have threatened the balance of life on Truk, but even from the front seat of the jeep, it was possible to lapse into one of those daydreams, so apt to overtake visitors to Pacific islands, and to think of the Truk atoll as it must have looked before the first European ships discovered it, bringing such gadgets as iron nails, Christianity and disease. The lagoon, the steep mountain slopes and their luxurious verdure, must have looked very much as they still did. The influence of the West was superficial, yet curiously blighting. There were no outrigger canoes, no villages of thatch on Moen. On a causeway running through a mangrove swamp some Trukese were making minor repairs on the road surface, and all were sedately dressed in shirts and trousers in spite of the steamy heat of midday. The doctor explained that missionaries had indoctrinated all natives on the main islands with such a sense of modesty that bodily exposure was most uncommon, that workmen seldom removed their shirts. The missionaries, it seemed, had done an exceptional job on Truk. There was a story that in 1934 when the Japanese were staging some sort of celebration, they asked if the Moen natives would oblige with their songs and dances, only to discover that these had been forgotten long ago. It was wrong to dance and the only songs the Trukese knew were some moldy European hymns.

On the far side of the mangrove swamp stood a Trukese settlement. The buildings of this tiny village looked worse than any in an American hobo jungle. They seemed to have been constructed principally from tin cans and packing cases, but after all there was no lumber industry in Truk and boards and nails were at a premium. Rickety as the buildings were, the natives evidently preferred them to pandanus thatch. The main building was a Catholic church, recently constructed, framed with the wood of the breadfruit tree and roofed with gasoline tins. Two black-gowned Portuguese priests conducted us through it, but barriers of language forbade communication.

Then we climbed halfway up the mountain on a rocky, washed-out road to the island commander's bungalow, where we had lunch. Sitting on his veranda, looking out to sea, we all seemed like transients. The head of the island government told of other islands on the atoll and showed us handcrafts, baskets and mats woven from pandanus leaves and a fine cloth woven from vegetable fiber and wooden masks and models of outrigger canoes. In spite of the closeness of the islands in the atoll to each other, many, he said, were seldom visited and in many there was still a Stone Age civilization. The truth was that Truk had no great natural resources, nothing much a predatory white man would want, except the harbor facilities of its beautiful lagoon, and it might well be that even this would not be wanted either, now that the strategical areas were shifting north. It was too bad, an officer was saying, that this magnificent anchorage, large enough for adequate dispersal in case of air bombing, could not be towed six hundred miles north, for then it would make a better base than Guam, but there seemed to be no use for Truk in its present situation.

Since the American occupation there is only one Trukese product that has achieved any wide sort of popularity. This is the native love stick, which may still be used on the outer islands, but surely not on Moen. The love stick is an intricately carved piece of wood whittled by a native suitor and shown to the girl of his choice, who becomes so familiar with its individual carvings that if the stick is pushed through the thatch of her hut on a dark night, she knows that it belongs to the man of her choice and is glad to join him outside in the starlight. The naval personnel landing on Truk had carried the story of the love stick over most of the Pacific, so that even when we were there, even the sedate natives of Moen were manufacturing them in quantities, and they could be bought for twenty-five cents apiece.

It was necessary to leave Truk shortly after luncheon, as we were due in Manila in time for dinner. I can remember the languid heat, the acute sense of loneliness and my feeling of disappointment at the sight of that jerry-built village. I can remember wondering too what would be more practical than that village and what could possibly be done by an enlightened civilization to make the life of the Trukese happier and more fruitful. Aside from some medical attention, I was not able to think of much. I could even imagine that the kindest thing the outer world could do for Truk would be to leave it alone. If this idea has any value, perhaps happier days are coming to the atoll, because as one reads the news from China and listens to the rumblings of revolt in the East Indies, it may be that a silence will settle over the Central Pacific, that a curtain of neglect will fall again over Micronesia, and that if you want to see Truk, it might be well to lay your traveling plans sometime for the near future, for as history is moving, every day makes Truk more remote and further off the beaten path to anywhere.

The End Game

(1944)

Mr. Herbert Mayes, who, next to George H. Lorimer and Maxwell Perkins, is the best editor I have ever met, once thought highly of this story, and I hope still does. He may have been partial to it because he gave me the idea of a chess player in a Sixth Avenue (I mean Avenue of the Americas) Arcade. I recall that Mr. Mayes personally took me to see one of these places, but aside from this the machinery of the story was my own — and so was the motivation, except, naturally, that I wanted Mr. Mayes to buy it.

Mr. Mayes says it is good narrative and I sincerely hope he is right. I can venture to say one or two things for it myself. I knew, for one thing, what I was writing about, in the main. I had played chess. I had lived in Honolulu. I had encountered the military mind, I had traveled in China and of course I knew something about New York. I was also familiar with unhappy persons too young for the first war and too old for the second. These facts all form essential parts in the story.

As I read "The End Game" after ten years I approve on the whole of my narrative and dialogue. I cannot discuss it as a short story because it is a size now known to the trade as a "one shot." I do not know what Henry James would have called it but it must approximate in length his Daisy Miller, *which I hasten to say is the better work of the two. I can only add in the light of my own experience that it is dangerous to attempt to write a narrative of this size, which is neither a short story nor a novel. Such a fictional form can fall over itself more readily than any other I have ever known. For some reason unity and coherence drop by the wayside and the result is often either too abbreviated or much too long. I like to think that "The End Game" has cleared some of these hurdles. It holds the attention as it moves through various areas of time and place without undue stress and strain. Its*

characters, except for our unbelievable chess player, are reassuring be-
cause all of us have known them, and I like the Honolulu atmosphere
because I like Honolulu.

THERE would be only a few people, Elsie Bacon had said, and it would not be one of those parties that start at five in the afternoon and keep on until two in the morning. There would be only a few people, who would talk intelligently — no noise or shouting. There would be just a few friends of Bill's up from Washington, and the So-and-So's, who were attached to the British Embassy, might come in, and old General Peyton, who Elsie said was really an old sweetie, and there might be some young officers with him. After all, you had to do something for the boys. Bill was going to be up from Washington for only the day, and they all would be people who had something to say, if they would only say it. That was why she wanted Henry to come; and, besides, Henry had been in Hong Kong.

It was one of those things that you went to from a complete contradiction of motives. Partly you want to get away from yourself for a little while and to avoid reality, and partly you want to face reality in the company of friends. It was April, and Henry Ide always had enjoyed April more than any month in New York; but in 1943, April had assumed an enigmatic aspect. There was a disturbing blandness about the afternoon sunlight on Park Avenue; there was a deceitful sort of glitter in the shops, reflecting the effort he, and everyone else, was making to prove that everything was going on as usual. The taxi driver was talking to him, as taxi drivers often did. The driver had served overseas in the last war, with the 27th Division. Yes, mister, he had served overseas, and in spite of that they were cutting down on his gas quota.

"Now, that isn't right," the taxi driver said. "I say it isn't the right way to treat someone who fought for his country. Am I right or am I wrong?"

"I wouldn't know," Henry said. "You see, I was too young for the last war and I'm too old for this." Somehow in these new days you told taxi drivers almost everything.

"Is that so?" the driver said.

"Yes," Henry said, "that's so. I was sixteen at the time of the armistice."

"Is that so?" the driver said. "Well, that makes you six years younger than me. I was twenty-two at the time of the armistice."

Henry did not answer. They came to a traffic light and stopped, and the driver sighed. "Well, it's a tough world," he said. "A lot of things can happen to a guy in this world."

"Yes," Henry said, "that's so."

"What I say," the driver went on, "the best thing to do is to forget it."

"Yes," Henry said, "that's so."

"The best way to forget it," continued the driver, "is to have a hobby. Mine is dog racing. Do you follow the races?"

"No," Henry said, "not very much. It's the building with the awning, the next one."

There was nothing of any importance in that conversation. Henry Ide felt a little like the bar drunk who confides to any stranger all of his domestic and most of his financial difficulties. It was that queer human desire for confession. It was not consoling to realize that if the driver had been a more sympathetic type, more of a listener than a talker, Henry Ide would have told him a great deal more. It was like talking to space and yet at the same time to a person. It was the sort of talk you had on a ship or on a lonely station platform while you were waiting for a train. It was almost the way people talked when they thought they did not have long to live.

A week or so after Henry had got back to America, almost the same thing had happened; but there had been more reason for it that time. There had been a basis of mutual respect then that came from the intricacies of a game. They had been playing the Czech variation of the queen's gambit, and the end game had been interesting. It was only natural to ask, "When did you first play chess?"

That was the sort of question that might lead to anything. If you were a fair player, it made your thoughts go a long way back. You first played chess with your father or your brother, or you learned it from someone at school or during an ocean crossing. You liked chess for a number of reasons, none of them particularly valid, but you did not treat chess as a hobby. It always annoyed Henry Ide to have chess called a hobby.

. . . And then he realized that he was thinking about something that had nothing whatsoever to do with the present. He was standing in the hallway of an apartment house, and he was going to the Bacons' for a cocktail.

When the maid opened the apartment door, the voices from the living room down the hall were quiet and decorous. It meant the party would be so small that he would have to be introduced to everyone.

"Hello, dear," Elsie said.

"Well, well," Bill Bacon said, "if it isn't Henry."

Bill was working in Washington; but they were in the same boat in a way, because they both had been too young for the last war and were too old for this one.

"Now," Elsie said, "you must come and meet everyone."

There were only six or seven people there — the couple from the British Embassy, a lieutenant commander and his wife, a man from the Office of War Information, and a major general.

"This is Henry Ide, General," Elsie said, and he remembered that over the telephone Elsie had told him the general was an old sweetie. It occurred to him that all women, nearly all, had this same preconceived idea about generals, and that generals hardly ever fell into that category. "Henry went to college with Bill," Elsie was saying, "and he was Bill's best man" — there was no reason for explaining, but Elsie was explaining — "and he worked for the Standard Oil in Hong Kong."

"Oh," the general said. "Hong Kong."

Henry moved uneasily, but Elsie was still explaining.

"He was caught there," Elsie was saying. "He was in a Japanese concentration camp. That's why he's so thin. Henry's an Old China Hand."

Then when Henry looked at all the faces, he saw that this was what Bill and Elsie called one of their China parties, and Bill and Elsie considered that they, too, were Old China Hands because they once had lived for three months in a rented house in Peking not far from the Forbidden City. A Number One Boy had come with the house, and yard boys and rickshaw boys and everything.

"Did you come out on the *Gripsholm?*" the general asked.

"Yes, sir," Henry said, "on the *Gripsholm.*"

"It must have been quite an experience," the general said.

Henry straightened his shoulders and put one hand in the side pocket of his coat. Everyone in the room was talking about China. Someone was speaking about the bund at Shanghai, and about the country club. They were recalling the past of China, perhaps because the past was comfortable and tangible.

"Oh," Elsie said, "and here's someone else you haven't met. This is Colonel Blair. Colonel, Mr. Ide was caught in Hong Kong. He can tell you all about the Japanese. Colonel Blair is leaving for China."

One advantage came from living in the Far East. Out there, against a background of customs and language so complex as to be nearly incomprehensible, Europeans were dependent upon one another's society. You learned more about your own fellow countrymen than you ever did at home, and you became familiar with all types. When Henry Ide shook hands with Colonel Blair, he thought of evenings in the East, where he had seen so many other officers — American, British, German, French, Italian. He thought of dice and cards and of the white-gowned Chinese servants moving softly in their slippers. He was able to place the colonel perfectly. He knew even before he saw the colonel's West Point ring — simply by the colonel's face and posture — that Colonel Blair was not a civilian poured into uniform, but a professional army man. Colonel Blair must have been approximately his own age — not much over forty — but he was not too old for this war, because he always had been a soldier. His face was like his uniform, made exclusively for the army; but once Henry Ide accepted it as a soldier's face, he discovered there was something disconcertingly familiar about the features. The colonel's nose was short and straight; his forehead was high and narrow. The eyes were pale blue and the sandy hair was crew cut. In civilian life his mouth would have been good-natured, but the army had given it an uncompromising look.

"Haven't I met you somewhere?" Henry Ide asked.

Colonel Blair looked at him carefully. It was the look of an officer who was used to remembering the names and faces and characteristics of hundreds of enlisted men.

"Have you?" he answered. "Maybe, but I don't think so," and he smiled. His reddish face broke into hard, pleasant creases when he smiled, and his voice also was familiar — flatly incisive, but agreeable.

"You remind me of someone," Henry said, "but I can't remember who."

Colonel Blair smiled again and picked up his glass from a low teakwood table. "I'll tell you what it is," he said. "Foreigners say the Chinese all look alike. Maybe it's the same with the uniform. It may have been one of my brothers. You may have seen one of them somewhere — Tientsin or Manila or Honolulu. We all look pretty much alike."

"I don't think so," Henry answered, "but I can't remember."

Then there was nothing more to say, and so he stood beside Colonel Blair in one of those strained pauses that sometimes come between two people who feel they must talk agreeably and who have nothing in common to discuss.

"I met Bill and Elsie in Peking," the colonel said. "They had quite a house in Peking, part of an old Manchu palace. Did you meet them in Peking?"

"No," Henry answered, "I've always known them. Almost always."

"Oh," the colonel said. "I met them when I was at the language school in Peking."

A maid gave Henry Ide a Scotch and soda. Henry drank half of it quickly, but it did not help him to think of anything else to say.

"If you're going to China," Henry said, "I suppose you're going to Chungking."

"Yes," the colonel said, "Chungking. Do you know Chungking?"

"I've been there," Henry answered. "I guess it has changed a lot, what is left of it."

"Do you know Honan?" the Colonel asked.

"I haven't been there for quite a while," Henry answered.

"There's a general in Honan," the colonel said, "one of the old war lords, Wu Lai Hsung. Did you ever hear of a General Wu?"

"General Wu?" Henry said. "There used to be a Wu in Jehol. He was poisoned in 'twenty-eight. It couldn't be the same Wu." Henry looked into his half-empty glass, and they were silent again.

"This is a nice apartment, isn't it?" the colonel said.

Henry became conscious of the Chinese carpet and the lacquer tables and the ancestor portraits, which Bill and Elsie had brought back from Peking.

"Yes," he said. "Bill and Elsie brought back quite a lot of stuff."

The lacquer and the pictures were of the humdrum sort that represents a stranger's naïve and uneducated enthusiasm — things a dealer would sell to tourists — and the same was true of the porcelains in the glass case near the window.

"That's a nice ivory chess set," the colonel said. He was looking at some red-and-white carved chessmen arranged on a chess table.

"Do you like them?" Henry Ide asked, and he felt pleased. "I gave them those. They're not old, but there was an ivory carver in Canton — "

"Do you play?" the colonel asked.

"Yes," Henry said, "a little."

"Well," the colonel said, "how about a game?"

"Those ivory sets are hard to play with," Henry said.

"I know," the colonel said, "but you can use them."

Those Chinese men had a personality European chessmen lacked. The pawns were advancing foot soldiers equipped with spear and shield, with each tiny face contorted in an angry grimace. The rooks were forts on the backs of elephants. The knights were like the horsemen of Genghis Khan. The bishops were high court officials clad in elaborate ceremonial robes. The queen stood on a pedestal, an austere lady holding an ivory fan. The king was a tall, somewhat emaciated gentleman, looking like one of the weak emperors toward the end of some great dynasty.

Henry Ide picked up a red pawn and a white pawn and shuffled them behind his back.

"Right hand," the colonel said. He had drawn white and the opening move, and they sat down at the table.

From the way the colonel moved his men, he obviously enjoyed chess, and the game, with its necessity for concentration, was a good substitute for talking. The colonel followed his opening pawn to king four with pawn to bishop four, and on the fifth move sacrificed the knight at bishop three. It was the risky but devastating Muzio gambit, an opening that is like an attack in modern war, a thrust in force to smash the lines and paralyze communications in the rear. When they reached the twelfth move, the colonel looked up and shook his head.

"You know the reply," he said, "but I've always liked that opening."

Henry Ide had the conviction again that he had known the colonel somewhere. "Would you mind telling me," Henry asked, "where you learned to play?"

"The whole family learned," the colonel answered, "before we took the exams for the Point. It's an army game, you know. Our people have gone to the Point since before the Civil War. The old man always said you couldn't be an officer unless you could play chess."

Henry Ide drew in his breath. "I said I thought I'd seen you somewhere," he said. "I remember now."

The colonel's forehead wrinkled as he looked at Henry Ide across the tops of the carved chessmen. There is something deadly literal about the military life. The colonel's expression showed he never had been bothered by any lack of memory.

"It isn't you," Henry said. "You reminded me of someone, that's all."

"Oh," the colonel said. "As long as you've got it off your mind."

"Yes," Henry said. "It's all right."

It was like working out an intricate algebraic equation and having it balance perfectly just at the very end.

"If you knew the Watkinses," he heard Elsie saying, "you must have been to their temple in the Western Hills."

He could speak of his conclusion or keep quiet; it was entirely up to him. He put his hands slowly into his coat pockets. "Your name's Johnny, isn't it?" he asked. "Johnny Blair? You were the one who had the brown-and-white Welsh pony, and there was a Japanese house-boy named Mori."

The colonel sat up straighter. Henry was certain he was Johnny Blair. The other two boys would be Tom and Edgar. Tom was the one who could sing and play the ukulele. Edgar was the oldest.

"Well," the colonel said, "which Blair brother did you know, and what made him mention Mori and the pony?"

"I suppose he wanted to talk to someone," Henry answered. "Sometimes you see a stranger and you talk."

"Which one was it?" the colonel asked. "Tom or Ed?"

Henry Ide leaned back in his chair. It was none of his business, and perhaps he should not have told; but it was too late now. "There were four of you, weren't there?" he asked. "The one I know is called Joe, but I don't know whether that's his name."

But it must have been his name.

"Good God," Johnny Blair said, "Joe."

Henry Ide leaned back in his chair, and all at once the whole conversation was out of his control. It was too late to consider whether or not it was kind. "There's a penny arcade off Sixth Avenue," Henry Ide said. "Joe's down there every night."

Johnny Blair pushed back his chair and stood up, and Henry Ide stood up, too. "Just what in hell is Joe doing in a penny arcade?"

"He used to be down there," Henry Ide answered, "playing chess for twenty-five cents a game."

Johnny Blair did not speak for a moment. He stood very still, and then he smiled. "Well," he said, "that's that. What I need is another drink. Will you have another drink?" Colonel Blair must have been thinking of all sorts of things he could not speak about. Then he asked: "Did he ever talk to you about a girl named Ruth? Ruthy Postley? A girl in Honolulu?"

"Yes," Henry said, "he did."

"That's Joe, all right," the colonel said. "It must be Joe. When did you see him last?"

"About a month ago," Henry said. "He was going away somewhere, but he said he would come back."

"I ought to see him," the colonel said. "Somebody ought to see him. Would you mind? If you're not busy, could you take me there to-night?"

II

New York, in Henry Ide's opinion, in spite of its size, in spite of its polyglot population, is not a crossroads of the world like London. It is understood in London if you go away for a term of years to Africa or Asia. The servants and the members of your club know exactly who you are when you come back, and it is possible to pick up life where you left it. It is different with New York. Henry Ide always had found, when he had returned to New York, that even his best friends had almost forgotten him.

He usually felt like a stranger, but never so much as after the fall of Hong Kong. Previously he could feel that a part of his life with all his interests was waiting for him safely in the East as soon as his leave was over; but now his house on the Peak at Hong Kong was gone, and his clothes, his books and papers were scattered in the wreckage like his friends and his associations. There was nothing tangible left of all his active years except a bank account, for he always had saved his money.

New York was a bland, uncomprehending city untouched by death, disease, or starvation. The few friends he had there could not understand his loneliness, and it always seemed to him that he was speaking in a foreign language when he tried to tell about Hong Kong. Murder, fear, insult, hunger, and disease were only set expressions in New York. People would sit and listen to him when he tried to describe it. "It must have been a gruesome experience," they would say.

Somehow he suspected that they did not quite believe him. They never had seen death or street fighting. They were not familiar with the low value Asia always had placed on human life.

He had found himself, as time went on, more and more reluctant to see people he had known. He knew it was unhealthy, and he knew, too, that he would get over it in time; but for a while he preferred being by himself. In those first weeks in New York he was not well, and he was always tired. He wondered where he ought to live. He had a way of waking up in the middle of the night and not being able to sleep again. The days were not much better, for there was nothing for him to do. He usually left his hotel room at noon and walked slowly in Central Park. Then he would have lunch alone at one of the restaurants in the East Fifties, and after lunch he would walk for a while, and then he would go to his college club to read the papers. When he had read the papers, sometimes he would go to the club library and try to read one of the books describing the fall of France or the Battle of Britain, but he could not keep his mind on the pages. And then he would dine somewhere in another restaurant. He always took a single cocktail before dinner — only one, although he wanted several, for he had lived in the East long enough to be distrustful of liquor. Then the evening would stretch ahead of him. If he went back to his hotel too early, he could not sleep, and if he tried to read, he could not keep his mind on it. The best answer to the problem was to walk on Broadway after dark, although he always was disappointed by the dimness of the streets now that the electric signs were out.

It was eleven o'clock the night he first saw the penny arcade. He was drawn to the place by the sound of rifles in the shooting gallery. He liked it because nothing there had any purpose or much meaning. There were machines to try your strength and machines to test your skill. There were mechanical baseball games and hockey games, there were submarines you could shoot at, there were antiaircraft games, and downstairs there were bowling alleys and chess and checkers.

The chess and checkers tables stood behind a wooden railing close to a booth run by a Chinese, where you could roll rubber balls into little cups — ten cents a try, with inexpensive prizes. Above the noise there was the tinny sound of phonograph music, and the single Chinese face and the music brought back to Henry Ide all the sights and sounds and ceaseless motion of a Chinese street. There were five tables of checkers and two of chess. Henry Ide leaned on the rail for a while looking at the play, and for the first time since he had come home he was able to get his mind off himself, because each game was a little struggle of its own. It did not matter who you were or what you had been while the game lasted — you simply played with what intelligence you had.

Henry Ide supposed that he must have been standing near the rail long enough to have been conspicuous, or it may have been that he looked different from the rest of the crowd. The house player at the second chess table looked bored, and his glance traveled occasionally over the heads of the crowd; but Henry Ide did not notice him particularly until the chair in front of him was empty.

"How about a game, mister?" the man asked. "Come inside. You don't have to wait out there." Henry did not realize that he was being spoken to until the man spoke more loudly. "Come in, mister. Maybe I can teach you something. Come inside."

There was a swinging gate in the railing, and Henry pushed it open. It was the first time that he had played a game of chess publicly. He felt embarrassed, but it took his mind off everything he had been thinking. Sitting beneath the bright electric light, the player who had spoken to him looked pale and at first like any of those men who preside at gaming tables anywhere in the world. He had the same accuracy and watchfulness, and his features had the same intellectual, chiseled sharpness. He was a man in his forties. His hair was thinning and receding from his high forehead. His eyes were pale, and his lips were pressed very tightly together even when he smiled. But what impressed Henry Ide most was his voice. In spite of the words, the voice was cultivated and precise, and it did not fit with any of the sounds around them.

"How much do you charge?" Henry Ide asked.

"Twenty-five cents, brother," the man said. "And nothing if you beat me and nothing if we draw." The voice did not go properly with the words. "You can have white. Sit down. You look tired, brother."

"Well," Henry said, "I'll tell you what I'll do. I'll give you white, and I'll give you a dollar if you beat me."

The man smiled the same tight-lipped smile. "Pleased with yourself, aren't you, brother?"

"No," Henry answered, "but I want a good game, that's all."

The man's hands were thin and white and delicate. He was setting up the pieces very quickly as he talked. "There's nothing like chess," he said, "to take your mind off your troubles, is there, brother?"

"Maybe you're right," Henry answered. "I haven't played much lately."

They were silent through the first moves of the opening, and then Henry smiled. "You shouldn't have tried the Muzio," he said. "If he's careful, black always has the better game."

"Brother," the man said, "it's nice to know you. There hasn't been anyone in tonight who knew how to play."

Some years back, when Henry Ide was managing a lonely station in the interior, he had taken chess quite seriously, because it had happened that a medical missionary, one of the few Europeans in that place, had been devoted to the game. In the hours out there when there had been nothing else to do, Henry Ide had read and reread a half-dozen books on chess. It had gone so far that he and the missionary could sit outdoors in the mission compound on a summer night, and while they listened to the songs and the voices of the Chinese in the street beyond the compound wall, they could play a game without a board or men simply by calling out the moves. In those days Henry had been a good player: so good that most of the opponents he had met later at the European clubs in the treaty ports bored him by their ineptitudes and by the simplicities of their mistakes, and so for several years he had done very little about the game.

A great deal of it came back to him quickly. If your opponent is worth anything, you have to learn something of the order of his thoughts. The man he was playing against, he realized after a few minutes, was a strong player who had been so careless and overconfident that he had overextended himself, but now he was not afraid to sacrifice his pieces to consolidate his position.

"Brother," the player said, "this is quite a game."

"I don't think you're going to get my dollar," Henry said.

"I'll bet you ten dollars I get your dollar," the player answered.

Henry looked suspiciously across the table. The mention of the sum reminded him of card games in the smoking room of an ocean liner, but there is no luck or cheating in chess. The man was betting on his skill, and his threadbare suit and his frayed necktie showed that ten dollars was a heavy bet.

"You're in too bad a way," Henry said. "If you want to put up ten dollars, we'd better start another game."

"We'll play this one," the player said. "Try to get it if you can."

And then his glance grew sharper. "And I'll know if you try to lose. I don't need charity, brother."

Once when Henry looked up, he could see a crowd bending over the railing, and the players at the next table had stopped to watch. It was after midnight now, and the game had taken more than an hour. Henry became conscious of the sound of a guitar.

"Don't mind it," the player said. "That's a guy who always comes in after midnight."

The guitar player was a fat man with a greasy, perspiring face. He wore a pink sports shirt open at the neck, and he sang any song the crowd downstairs wanted.

"From the legion of the lost ones," he was singing. "From the cohorts of the damned." He was singing Kipling's "Gentlemen Rankers." It sounded fusty and dusty and mid-Victorian in the penny arcade. It became a snobbish, sophomoric, and rather whining song about the English gentleman who had fallen on evil days and all the world was kin when you had the ready tin. The game was ending on the chorus. Henry Ide had queened a pawn, and there was no use going farther.

"Yah, yah, yah," the player said, and he laughed. "All right, brother, I resign."

He drew a battered wallet from the inside pocket of his coat, peeked inside it, and shook his head. "Yah, yah, yah," he said.

Henry felt acutely embarrassed. "Never mind it now," he said. "Some other time."

"No, no," the stranger answered. "Little gentlemen always pay their debts. Nice little gentlemen." Then he turned sideways in his chair and spoke in dialect to the Chinese conducting the game with the rubber balls. The Chinese held out a ten-dollar bill.

"So you've been on Pearl River," Henry said. He was not very familiar with it, but he was very sure that it was the water-front dialect of Canton. Henry was pleased by his own acuteness, and he waited for the stranger to express surprise, but the other's face showed nothing.

"That's right," the chess player answered, "Canton. Jake over there used to run a string of flower boats in Canton. Here's your money, brother."

Henry did not want to take the money, but he had to. "How about coming out and getting a bite to eat?" he asked.

"Trying to pay some of it back, are you?" the man asked.

"Yes," Henry answered, "of course I am. Wouldn't you?"

"Yes," the other answered, "that's right. I wouldn't mind a beer. There's a steak joint around the corner."

He stood up, and as he did so his face made a grimace of pain, and then it composed itself. "It's in my side," he said. "I'm sorry. It's all right now."

When the man stood up, Henry saw that he was tall and very thin. He took a frayed black overcoat from a hook on the wall and put on a soiled gray felt hat.

"This is the first time I've been whipped for quite a while," he said.

All sorts of misfits constantly drifted to the Far East, but you minded your business west of the date line and let other people mind theirs. That was why Henry Ide was not particularly surprised to encounter someone who could play chess and speak a southern Chinese dialect and who showed signs of having lived quite differently.

"My name's Ide," Henry said when they were out on the street. "Henry Ide."

"Joe's my name," the other answered. "The rest of it doesn't matter much. That's all anybody ever calls me."

"All right," Henry answered, and he thought of other people who had not cared to tell their names. "All right, Joe."

When they were sitting in a booth in a small restaurant, Henry realized that he was more comfortable than he had been for a long while — comfortable and no longer restless. Perhaps it was because each had seen so much that he was not deeply interested in the other's past or present. They sat drinking beer for a long while, doing nothing more than discuss the game they had played and indulging in conjectures of what might have happened if each had played differently.

"If you hadn't sacrificed the bishop as well — " Henry said.

"Yes," Joe answered, "I know, but I don't blame myself. *L'audace, toujours de l'audace.* It pays, you know, when things are going bad." He spoke the French with a good accent and crumbled a bit of bread between his fingers.

"Will you have another beer?" Henry asked.

Joe nodded. "Thanks," he said. "It's nice that you don't ask questions, Mr. Ide."

"I don't," Henry answered. "Not very often."

"You act as though you were quite a way from home," Joe said.

"I shouldn't," Henry answered. "I was brought up in New York."

"Just the same," Joe said, "you act as though you were quite a way from home. Now, me — I never had a home. I only had a family."

"I don't see exactly what you mean," Henry said.

"I mean, we always moved around," Joe answered. "You'd never know where you'd be next, but there always was the family." He was looking straight ahead of him and thinking about something he did not put into words. "For instance, I first learned chess at Fort Bliss, when I was twelve. I wasn't good with the Muzio gambit until I was in Honolulu, when I was sixteen. I beat my brother Ed with it. Ed always was a bastard." He might just as well have been alone and talking to himself. Then his pale eyes focused on Henry Ide. "It's time to turn in now. If you're lonely, come around any night and play a game. I'm always there till midnight."

It was two o'clock in the morning when Henry Ide got back to his hotel room. It was as devoid of personality as when he left it, but he no longer felt as alone and uprooted, because he was thinking of something besides himself. He was not thinking of the man named Joe as an interesting type. There had been too many of that type on the beach in the East, but his speech and even the cut of his clothes showed that once he had belonged somewhere else. The only thing that was puzzling was his manner. Those other men Henry Ide had known who had been washed up on the beach were sly or arrogant or sensitive or fawning, and they all gave a final impression of being finished.

There are, of course, a good many ways of ending on the beach, and plain hard luck never is one of them. There are the obvious ways that pop into anyone's mind. There is liquor, for instance, or women. Then, of course, there are all sorts of other causes, those mysterious threads of self-destruction and failure that are woven into the character of nearly everyone; but such people always show certain signs of furtiveness and unhappiness and unbalance, and as far as Henry Ide could see, this stranger had shown none of these. He had shown no anxiousness or shame. Instead, he had seemed absolutely happy, as though he were satisfied with everything he had done; as though he were glad to go ahead with whatever he might be doing, without resentment and without regret. As Henry thought of him, he did not think of the shabbiness of his clothes, or of the sallow thinness of his face, but rather of a sort of inner serenity, the reflection of a state of mind that everyone living must have desired. That was why Henry Ide went to see him again — not once, but a good many times.

III

It was a problem he never had attempted — the task of piecing together out of allusions and indirections the details of someone's life. Henry Ide was sensitive, and he respected reticences — and besides, none of it was his business really. This may have been why Henry Ide was surprised to find that he told his new acquaintance a great deal more about himself than he ever had told anyone else. In a polite, impersonal way, each must have been curious as to how the other had got where he was. Both had keen, logical minds, and both must have been piecing together those casual half-confidences that come up in any conversation. It was like betting on a card and throwing more chips on the table. Sometimes you would win and sometimes you would lose. His companion's casual remarks were like chips, which Henry stacked carefully in little piles. "There always was the family." It became necessary to discover what sort of family would have no home. "I learned chess at Fort Bliss, when I was twelve." It was necessary to learn what Joe was doing at Fort Bliss when he was twelve. "Ed always was a bastard." It became necessary, a part of the game, to find out why, and all that time he knew Joe was doing the same, storing up remarks and piecing them together. Sometimes he would venture more than was wise, to the extent of risking that peculiar shy confidence that was growing between them, in order to find out more.

"Sometimes when you move too quickly," Henry said, "something hurts you. What is it?" It was one of the few times he had asked a direct question.

"A bullet in my side," Joe said. "It gets me now and then."

"It's none of my business," Henry said. "I'm sorry."

"That's all right," Joe answered.

"But you ought to see a doctor," Henry said.

"I've seen one," Joe answered. "He knows gunshot wounds. That's all right. It's part of the end game."

"What?" Henry asked.

"A part of the end game," Joe answered. "Life is like chess."

"You oversimplify it," Henry said. "You've got chess too much on your mind."

"That's not my fault," Joe said. "I had it licked into me when I was a kid. Ed licked it into me. I wanted to beat him at it. That's how I learned to play."

The name stood between them, like a face detaching itself from a crowd.

"Ed?" Henry asked.

"My brother, the oldest," Joe said. "Ed — but it doesn't matter. With chess it's like living a whole life every time you play, and you know what I mean."

"No," Henry answered, "I don't know what you mean exactly."

"It has a beginning," Joe answered, "and a middle and an end. You have everything in the beginning, and it's up to you. But it's the end game that counts. I like my end game pretty well. Better than you like yours, I guess."

Joe rested his thin forearms on the table and clasped his hands carefully. His hands were long and delicate, and Henry noticed that his cuffs, which projected from his shiny coat as he folded his hands, had been neatly mended where they had begun to fray.

"Nice mending, isn't it?" he asked.

"Yes," Henry answered, "very nice."

Joe leaned his weight on his elbows very carefully, as though a sudden move might hurt him. "You aren't happy, are you?" he asked. "Why aren't you happy?" He must have known that it was impossible to answer such a question concisely. He must have known that no reason would be enough.

"Very few people are," Henry said. "You're one of the few I have seen."

Joe raised his shoulders and leaned his weight more heavily on the table. "That's so," he said. "Have you ever been in love?"

"Yes," Henry said. "Everybody's been in love."

He knew it was time then to talk about himself. There had been a girl in New York years ago whom he did not mind telling about, because she was an abstraction in that talk, like Joe's brother Ed. He had met her once when he had come home on a six months' leave; but when the time had come to go back to the East, she had not wanted to go back with him. In fact, he had been so sure of it that he had not asked her. He was living upcountry, and it would have been no place for her. That was when he had learned chess — when he got back. He did not mind in the least telling about it now. She had married one of his best friends a year or two later, and he had been home on leave again when it had happened. He had been best man at the wedding, and they were good friends now. He did not mind telling about it.

"They went around the world," he said, "and what do you think they did? They rented a house in Peking for three months, servants and everything, and now they're Old China Hands." Henry never had seen their house in Peking, but he might as well have, because they talked about it all the time.

"And they brought back lacquer tables," Joe said. "They always do."

"That isn't what bothers me now," Henry said. "What bothers me is being here like a refugee."

He never would have made such a confession to anyone he had known well. He would not have wanted to admit that he was sorry for himself or that there was no real way for him to fit into the lives of people he had known years before. But with Joe it did not matter. There was nothing Joe could do for him, and there was no danger of Joe's being sorry.

"I've tried the army," Henry said. "I was too young for the last war and too old for this one."

Joe still rested his weight on his elbows. While he had been listening, he had been looking at the darn on his shirt cuff, and once or twice he had touched it gently, but he looked up from the table quickly when the army was mentioned. "The army," Joe said. "You wouldn't have liked the army. You see, you're not the type — not any more than me."

"How do you know?" Henry asked.

At first he thought Joe had not heard. Joe sat there looking at nothing, and when he spoke he seemed to be speaking to himself. "I know," he said, "you've got to be the type. I know all about the army. I ought to know."

Nothing about him reminded Henry Ide of a soldier, and he must have seen what Henry was thinking. "I was brought up in it," Joe said. "You had to be in the army." He stopped again, sitting very still and looking straight ahead of him. "You had to be. There wasn't any other answer, and once you have something licked into you, you can't ever get away from it. You always come back to it. Well — " He stopped, still looking at nothing, and you could see that he was moved by whatever it was that he was thinking. "I'll tell you about my opening game, when all the pieces were on the board. I don't mind telling you.

"You don't have to," Henry said.

"I know I don't have to," Joe replied.

Henry Ide never could understand why he should have been told that story. It must have been the desire that everyone has at one time or another to have his thoughts turned into words. Joe spoke very slowy at first, as though it were difficult to bring back memory.

"Tradition," he said. "There wasn't any home, but there was tradition. It was all right if you were made for it. Johnny was made for it, and so was Ed, but me, all I wanted was to get away. Did you ever hear about the Battle of Bull Run?"

"No," Henry answered, "not very much."

"That was where it always started, with the Battle of Bull Run. Three of us were in Bull Run, and two of us were killed — the family, I mean, the family. The family had been going to the Point since before the Mexican War. The family always went to the Point, and if there were any girls they married into the army. Mother was Southern, but she was army, too. She died when I was five, but the CO carried right along. It was an army family."

His pale-blue eyes grew brighter as he spoke, and his whole face was mobile and seemed younger. It made Henry Ide think of boyhood and youth, and somehow that friend of his named Joe was young again, and Henry Ide was young, too, a friend of Joe's living a life he never had known. Sometimes it was Texas, sometimes it was a year in Washington. Once it was the Philippines. The boys went everywhere with the CO, and the army wives were kind to them. Everyone always stuck together in the army.

"That was Father," Joe was saying. "We always called him the CO — commanding officer to you. You should have seen him. He was quite a boy. He always looked as though he had just come out of the barber shop — haircut, shave, shine, everything. You learn how to dress if you have it licked into you. The CO was quite a boy."

Finally, when he put the words together and set all the occasional allusions into order, it seemed to Henry Ide that he had known the CO. He could see him — always neat and active, with every button exactly right, with every line in his face exactly right. He could see all his campaign ribbons. There was the Boxer ribbon, and the one for the

Philippine Campaign, and the World War Victory ribbon with three battle stars on it, and the Army of Occupation ribbon, and the one for the Croix de Guerre, and for the Distinguished Service Medal. He could see the silver eagles on the CO's shoulders, and the three gold V's on the left sleeve for service in the A.E.F., and the single wound stripe on the right, that came from the Argonne near Montfaucon. Henry Ide could even hear the click of the colonel's boot heels, and the tone of the colonel's voice, when he used to say: "I take the kids with me whenever I can. It's the best way to beat it into them if they're going to the Point."

He could see the officers' quarters. He could hear the bugle calls that told the time of day, and the talk on the veranda in the evening. He seemed to be there, sitting quietly with the boys, listening to the endless army gossip. He seemed to be tiptoeing softly up to the CO's room, where everything was in exactly the right place. The room must have been like the mind of the man who slept in it — uncompromising, untroubled, austere, and wrapped in a deadly sort of orderliness — equipped only with what was necessary for direct action.

It must have been a world of changing scenes, but the ideas were never new. A child endeavoring to adjust himself to his surroundings must have thought of this world as a series of army posts, guarded by sentries presenting arms at the entrances to straight driveways, with barracks and parade grounds and artillery parks and stables and officers' houses, the club and the bachelors' quarters. On the outskirts of that army world lay Panama, Hawaii, the Philippines, and China. There would be new faces and new sights, but once the sentry had presented arms and you were inside, the world was just the same. It was divided, of course, into the enlisted men and the commissioned officers, and the enlisted men were always kind to the colonel's boys. There were the bandmasters who let you beat a drum, and the stable sergeants who taught you how to ride, and the orderly who taught you the manual of arms. While Joe was talking, Henry Ide was able to see it all as though he had been part of it.

IV

Then there were the friends who came and went, and relatives whose photographs stood upon the mantel in the living room at their quarters. There was Uncle Jack, a major in the cavalry, whom you saw now and then, and Uncle Robert, to whom, the CO always said, the boys must listen carefully, because Uncle Robert was a very brilliant officer and slated to be chief of staff some day. It always made Joe happy when anyone told him he looked like Uncle Robert, and perhaps in a way he did. Uncle Robert was slender and pale, and his hair was thin on the top of his head, and he was not so neat as the CO. In fact, Joe once heard the CO say that Bob was careless about detail because he was too brilliant. Even at the Point no one had jacked him up hard, on account of his mind, and he understood the line of command but did not respect it. Still, when he quieted down, he would be chief of staff some day. Uncle Bob was the only one who could put the CO on the carpet, because Uncle Bob was older. Joe remembered once when Uncle Bob dropped in — it must have been the summer they were at Fortress Monroe — and had had words with the CO. The boy could not remember the reason, but he could recall some of the words. Uncle Bob had come down from Washington, and there had been an inspection and a war-game problem, and in the evening before dinner there were highballs in the CO's living room. Uncle Bob had taken off his tie and had unbuttoned his shirt collar, because the evening was very hot.

"Bob," the CO said, "the general is coming in."

"All right," Uncle Bob said. "All right, George."

"Then I wouldn't be too comfortable, Bob," the CO said. "The general likes amenities."

"I know him," Uncle Bob said. "He's a damned boiled owl."

"Bob," the CO said, "the boys . . . It's time you were back with troops."

"And it's time you got away from them," Uncle Bob said. "There's such a thing as being too much with troops."

"You can't be with them too much," the CO said. "Bob, the boys — "

"Oh, yes," Uncle Bob said. "Hello, boys." Then Uncle Bob put down his glass and shook hands with the boys.

The colonel had sent for the boys, and they had come running to the house. You ran, not walked, when the CO sent for you. Edgar came in from tennis. He was blond and handsome and going on seventeen. They had found Tom at Barracks F, where he had been playing his ukulele. Joe had been in his room reading, and Johnny, the youngest, had been at the stables. Now they all stood near the dining-room door, and each one stepped forward smartly, without slamming into any furniture, and shook hands and looked Uncle Bob in the eye, just as the CO had taught them.

Ever since they had been old enough to appear in the living room at all, the CO had been very careful of the amenities. Being the eldest, Edgar stepped forward confidently, because he knew he was a very accomplished boy. That was what Joe remembered best about him — an impregnable sort of self-assurance. It was not exactly conceit, but a sort of exterior obliviousness.

"How do you do, sir," Edgar said.

"Thank you," Uncle Bob said. "I'm doing quite nicely, thank you, Edgar."

"I'm very glad to hear it, sir," Edgar said.

"Thank you," Uncle Bob said. "I hear you're off to the Point. I think you'll find it interesting there."

"Yes, sir," Edgar said. "I'm sure I shall."

"I'm sure, too," Uncle Bob said.

"Edgar," the CO said, "go fetch some more ice and soda."

"Sir," Edgar said, "can't Joe or Johnny go?"

"No," the CO said. "Ice and soda."

The room was momentarily silent while Edgar turned smartly and left.

"Quite a boy, isn't he?" the CO said. "He's well set up, isn't he?"

"Yes," Uncle Bob said.

"I'd pick him ahead of the rest," the CO said, "for a soldier."

The other boys stood listening silently. The CO always discussed their points frankly before visitors, particularly before the family.

"He's got strength," the CO said. "He never gets tired. He gets that from me. I don't think Tom's going to have the stamina. Tom, what have you there?"

"My uke, sir," Tom said.

"Your what?" the CO asked him.

"My ukulele, sir," Tom said.

The CO glanced from Tom to Uncle Bob. "Put it down," the CO said. "You'll be wearing a grass skirt next. Shake hands with your Uncle Bob."

"Are you musical, Tom?" Uncle Bob asked.

"No," the CO said. "He just makes noises. He's outgrowing it."

"Hello, Joe," Uncle Bob said.

"How do you do," Joe said.

"How do you do — what?" the CO asked.

"Sir," Joe said.

"All right," the CO said. "Now, then, Johnny. And look at his eyes and not at your feet."

"Yes, sir," Johnny said.

"Don't get rattled," the CO said, and his voice was more kindly. "Never be rattled before a superior officer. They don't bite as a rule. Have you ever seen me bite anybody?"

"No, sir," Johnny said.

"All right," the CO said. "Sit down. Quite an outfit, isn't it, Bob?"

"Yes," their uncle answered. "Are they all going to the Point?"

"Naturally," the CO said. "Where else should they go?"

Uncle Bob settled himself more comfortably on the sofa. "Sometimes," he said, "I wish I'd never gone."

"Don't mind what Uncle Bob says," the CO said. "He was number one in his class. Which one do you like the best, Bob?" It was the way the CO always talked before the family.

"I've told you," Uncle Bob said, "if you go on this way, George, you'll have trouble with the boys."

"We were always talked over, weren't we?" the CO said. "Jack and I were the boneheads, and you were the boy wonder, and we've always stuck together. The boys don't care what we say about them. We're in the family."

"How do you know they don't care?" Uncle Bob asked.

"They don't," the CO said. "It does them good to be talked over."

"George," their uncle said, "you've been with the troops too long."

"No one can be with troops too long," the CO said.

"You're the type that gets the God complex," his brother replied. "I know, you don't ask the men to do anything that you can't do. You can do anything better than the men. You can solve their problems for them. You can manage anything."

"Bob," the CO said, "the boys!"

"All right," Uncle Bob said, "but isn't it fair to talk you over, too? You're a good line officer, and you'll never be anything more."

"I never went to be anything more," the CO said.

"All right," Uncle Bob said. "Ed and Johnny will make good soldiers, and Tom will be all right." Uncle Bob's glance moved slowly about the room. "But Joe — I wouldn't be so sure of Joe. Joe's like me. He's the brightest of the lot. Joe will end up on the general staff if he doesn't run away from home."

"And just why," the CO asked, "should he run away? He likes it here. They all like it."

"I don't know why they should," Uncle Bob said. "Why should they?"

"Because they like me," the CO said.

"Do they?" Uncle Bob said. "Why should they?"

Then the CO laughed. There was one thing you could say for him — he was absolutely fair and he never lost his self-control. "You see, boys," he said, "your old man can take a bawling-out when he has to. Your Uncle Bob ranks me, and I can take it."

"Now," Uncle Bob said, "take it easy, George. Joe, come over here. I want to look at you. Do you play chess?"

"Of course he does," the CO said. "They all play chess."

Uncle Bob's mind always moved very rapidly from one point to another, and sometimes it was hard for the CO to follow him. "Well, let's see what you've taught them," Uncle Bob said. "Let's see you play a game with Joe."

The CO looked puzzled; but young as Joe was then, he could guess at his father's thoughts. The CO must have suspected that he was being put in an undignified position. Yet at the same time it was a question of seniority, and he had obeyed superiors too long and too unquestioningly to argue.

"Joe," he said, "didn't you hear what your uncle said? Get out the board and the men."

It was a good English Staunton set — battered, but entirely serviceable. The two older men were looking at the board seriously, as though the pawns and the pieces were military units and the squares of the board the terrain of a battleground.

"Give the boy black," Uncle Bob said. "Let him defend, George."

"Joe," the CO said, "remember what I've taught you. Keep your mind on it. Don't get rattled."

There must have been two points that worried the CO. It was a test of discipline more than a game. It was necessary for him to demonstrate how well he had taught the boys. He wanted Joe to play well, but he wanted the game over quickly. Joe could tell it from the opening. It was the Muzio his father was using, with its quick and devastating attack. It was an opening his father had not taught him, and Joe realized suddenly that the CO was confident that he did not know the proper replies.

"Careful," the CO said. "Careful, son."

It was an opening Joe had watched Lieutenant Haskell and Captain Bragg work over in the bachelors' quarters. It was the CO who was not being careful, because the CO's mind was entirely concentrated on his own plans and not on those of the enemy.

"Support your pieces," the CO said. "I've told you to support your pieces. You shouldn't have lost that knight."

It was a very curious position for a boy as young as Joe. He could see that his father was being careless, and somehow he could guess it was what his uncle wanted. The CO had begun to improvise instead of following the conventional moves. His attack had no foundation behind it. He was already overextending and not prepared for the counterattack that would follow. It put Joe in a strange position, for suddenly he knew that he could beat his father. He wanted to, and yet he hesitated. . . .

In spite of all the years between that moment and the present, Joe still could set up all the pieces on the board again exactly as they had been in that game. It had been simply a matter of moving the king's bishop — and there it was. If he did so, the CO's attack would be finished and the CO's queen would be certain to be lost in a few succeeding moves. His father did not see it, but Joe knew his uncle did.

"Go on," the CO said, "Play cheerfully. Don't wait all night."

But Joe still waited. He looked up, and his eyes met his uncle's, and he looked at the board again. His hand moved toward the king's bishop, but he never made the move. He moved a pawn instead, and the CO moved his knight, just as Joe knew he would.

"Now you're in for it," the CO said. "Let's see you squeeze out of that."

Anyone could see that there was no way of getting out of it.

"I'm not so bad, am I, Bob?" the CO said.

"Not bad," Uncle Bob answered. "Why didn't you move the bishop, Joe?"

"The bishop, sir?" Joe repeated. He tried to look as though he had not thought of it, but it did no good.

"You threw the game," his uncle said, "because you didn't want to hurt your old man, didn't you? Well, don't do that again. Never throw a game."

"What do you mean?" the CO asked. "What are you talking about, Bob?"

"That boy has a good mind, George," Uncle Bob said. "He'll be a staff officer if you treat him right. See that you treat him right."

There were footsteps on the veranda. The CO stood up, and everyone stood up. The major general and his chief of staff were coming. The general walked with a deliberate, heavy stride, and Joe could see the two stars glistening on his shoulders.

"Well," the general said, "hello, boys." But he was not addressing the boys. He was speaking to Uncle Bob and the CO.

"It's kind of you to drop in, sir," the CO said. "Boys — if you don't mind, sir."

"Oh," the general said, "the next generation."

"Good evening, sir," Edgar said, and they stepped forward, one by one.

"All right," the CO said. "That's all. Dismissed." And then the boys were out on the lawn in the dusk.

"So you're going to be on the general staff, are you?" Edgar said to Joe. "Listen, baby — "

"Oh," Joe said, "shut up."

Joe was only fourteen at the time, and Edgar had the CO's build. Edgar took him by the shoulders.

"So you want me to shut up, do you, baby?" Edgar said.

"Leave him alone," Tom said.

"Go sing a song," Edgar said. "So you're going to be on the general staff, are you? Listen, baby — "

"Oh, go to hell," Joe said, "and to hell with the army!"

It was the first time that he ever had said, "To hell with the army."

V

Of all the army posts he knew, Joe told Henry Ide, he liked Hawaii best. He liked the sunlight and the trade winds and the color of the sea. That was where he met the Postleys, when the CO had a house on the water near Diamond Head. In that last year of the CO's tour of duty in Honolulu, Joe was going on eighteen. In a few months more he would be at West Point, if he passed the requisite examinations. The

CO was not bothered by these examinations, but he was not taking any risk of what he called a "bust." In the hours when he was off duty he gave Joe more attention than he ever had. Joe was the ranking member of the family then, for Edgar and Tom were already at the Academy. It was the CO's idea to be as much as he could with every boy just before he took his examinations. Yet, even so, the CO did not have the time he wanted. The war games and the tactical problems on the island were very demanding during the CO's tour of duty.

"I don't want you to think I'm ducking out on you," the CO said. "I'm giving you all the time I can."

There was a certain element of pathos, Joe sometimes thought, in the CO's intense vicarious excitement. When one of the boys was going to the Point, it was just as though the CO were going back there himself — he could remember every minute of his years there and all the experiences of relatives who had gone before him.

"Don't let it worry you," the CO said. "You'll love it. Soldiering is in the family."

The CO was not missing any tricks. He brushed up on French and mathematics, so that he could be sure that there was no sloppiness and that Joe was well-grounded; and it never did any harm for boys to know the infantry-drill regulations and the field-service regulations and orientation and a few principles of simple tactics and a little equitation before they went to the Point. The CO did what he could himself, and when he did not have the time, he found younger officers and noncoms who were glad to help on Saturdays and in the afternoon, when Joe came back from school at Punahou. On Sundays he liked to take Joe on toughening walks through the mountains, just himself and Joe.

"An officer is no good if he can't do twenty-five miles a day under a full pack," the CO said.

It seemed to Joe that the CO was always watching him those days and that he could see everything at once.

"Stand on the balls of your feet," the CO said, "and not on your heels, and never forget your guts."

There were all sorts of similar, odd bits of advice the CO used to give.

"And I want you to stay with the army crowd," he said. "It's lucky there are so many boys and girls your age here in the army crowd." The CO never had approved of civilian society. "You have to learn how to get along with civilians," the CO said, "but see them too much and they give you wrong ideas. And when you marry, marry a girl in the army crowd. Don't worry, one of them will come along."

Sometimes Joe thought the CO was proud of him, and on occasions in that year when they were in company the CO would slap him on the shoulder.

"He's shaping up," the CO said. "I've licked it into him. Isn't Joe shaping up?"

Yet, even so, Joe had time of his own that year, and Honolulu was quite a place if you had time on your hands.

"It won't hurt you," the CO said, "to travel around a little and see the black and tans. You'll have to learn to handle them when you're stationed here." The CO always referred to the mixed population on the islands as the black and tans, whether they were European or Polynesian or Japanese.

Joe never tired of walking along King Street or through the crowded streets along Nuuanu Stream. Everyone he met was gay and friendly. There was the Chinese temple on Vineyard Street, where old men burned incense before the god of business, and there were the neat Japanese Shinto shrines, and the Chinese shops, and the Polynesian women in their Mother Hubbards, selling leis of gardenia and ginger flowers at the docks, and there were the beach boys at Waikiki, and the fishermen with their spears and torches on the reefs. It all made him realize often how little he knew and how little he had seen. It made him half lazy and half restless, but it always made him happy.

This was the only time in Joe's boyhood that the CO had rented a house outside a military post, and the first time that Joe had been in any close contact with the civilian world. Later the CO realized that Honolulu had been a dangerous place for a boy like him. Later Joe realized that a military post was one of the most protected places in the world, free from most temptations and removed from most economic laws. Now he found himself thrown into the stream of conflicting thoughts and desires that one always encounters at a crossroads of the world. Honolulu was made up of everything: it had the utilitarian mechanics of the West, the sun and flowers and the songs of Polynesia, and the mystery of China, and the infinitely detailed and introverted ingenuity of Japan. A little of all the world was there, and all that little moved each day into changing, restless patterns; and because there was a little of everything, those patterns created a peculiar sort of tolerance. Ships would touch there on their way to Far East, and other ships would tie up for a day on their way home. The water front of Honolulu and its business districts with their rows of palm trees and their fine buildings of coral rock were all very neat and modern; but beneath that veneer and in the cool shadows cast by the almost continually shining sun, there was the scent of ginger flowers, of tar and oil, of sugar and dried fish and spice. There was a constant gentle chatter of unknown tongues, the musical languages of Polynesia and Malaya, the chattering monotony of Japanese, and shifting syllables of English and Portuguese and Spanish, and the pidgin English that embraced them all. All these sights and sounds calling to the imagination had an unsettling effect on tradition and common sense.

The CO himself was occasionally aware of it. You had to be careful, he often said, when you were in a place like Honolulu. There was a danger of going sour if you stayed too long in the Islands or in Panama, or in Manila or Tientsin. There was danger not only from warm weather and poor sanitation, but also from the bad habits of the population. You needed to watch yourself and take plenty of exercise and do plenty of hard work if you were an army man.

Sometimes when the CO and Joe and Johnny sat at supper on the veranda just as the dark began closing over the sea, the CO would ask Joe sharp questions. "Where were you this afternoon?" the CO would ask.

"Down at the beach, sir," Joe would answer, and he would see Johnny looking at his plate. Johnny knew what Joe had been doing on the beach, and so did Mori, the houseboy; but neither of them told.

"What were you doing?" the CO used to ask.

"Playing volley ball, sir, at the Outrigger Club," Joe used to answer.

"Good," the CO would say. "That's a fine game, volley ball."

In spite of the hotels and colored umbrellas and all the Europeans and the coconut oil and the shops and the motorcars along the boulevard, the beach at Waikiki was still a South Sea beach. The beach boys still played along its edge, just as their ancestors had before the missionaries had come, and nothing had driven away that atmosphere. There was a sort of friendliness, an amoral sort of innocence at Waikiki.

The CO must have understood some of this, for he had a way of seeing more than you thought he saw. Joe must always have realized that a time would come when the CO would learn too much about him.

One evening when Joe came home from Waikiki, Mori was setting the table on the veranda, and the sunset by the coral reef was turning the ocean into patches of red and violet, and there was that familiar sound of the breakers on the reef and of the clatter of the trade wind through the palm trees in the yard. Johnny was sitting in the living room in one of the Chinese wicker chairs, studying his French.

"Hello," Joe said to him, "where's the CO?"

"He's not back yet," Johnny answered, and then he closed his book and wriggled so that the chair creaked. "The CO was down at the beach this afternoon. He was at the Outrigger Club watching the volley ball."

"Was he?" Joe said. "I didn't see him."

"I know you didn't," Johnny answered, "but he saw you."

"Did he?" Joe asked.

"Yes," Johnny said, "he did."

"Where is he now?" Joe asked.

"He went to the barracks," Johnny said, "for retreat. Joe —"

"What?" Joe said.

"You'd better cut it out."

"Cut what out?" Joe asked.

"You know what," Johnny said. "He saw you."

"All right," Joe said. "But suppose he did see me?"

"He'll find out," Johnny said, "what you do when you go out."

"Suppose he does," Joe said. "What do you know about it? What do I do?" Then he stopped. He could hear the wheels of the CO's car on the drive.

When the CO came in, he set his garrison cap carefully on the table. "Well," he said, "hello, boys."

"Good evening, sir," they said.

The CO glanced toward the veranda. "And a very nice evening it is," the CO said. "Same old sunset, same old breeze. I'd like to see a snowstorm. Mori, get me a drink." Each evening the CO drank a single measure of the local bootleg liquor, known as "oke," which he mixed with ginger ale. When Mori handed him the tall glass, the CO sat down in one of the wicker chairs. "Joe," he said.

"Yes, sir," Joe answered.

"You were taking things sort of easy this afternoon, weren't you? Down on the beach, I mean."

"Yes, sir," Joe answered.

The CO shook his glass gently, listening to the tinkling of the ice. "Quite a place, that beach," the CO said. "Wikiwiki, the beach at Waikiki. The ragtag and bobtail always end up there."

"Yes, sir," Joe said, "everybody's always there."

"You mean everybody," the CO said, "who can't get anywhere else. You ought to wear shoes there so you won't get athlete's foot."

"It's a lot of fun on the beach, sir," Joe said.

"I know," the CO said. "I know. I was a kid myself once, Joe. Who was the girl you were with? She's white, isn't she?"

"Yes, sir," Joe said.

"Well, it's hard to be sure when they strip down like that," the CO said, "and get a coat of tan on. You can't tell a *haole* from a *hapahaole*, and she had black hair."

"Why didn't you speak to us, sir?" Joe asked. "I didn't see you."

The CO gazed at Joe and smiled. "I didn't think you'd want to see the old man just then. That's all right. At ease, Joe. At ease. I was a kid once myself. There's a time and place for everything, as long as you do your work. Just don't forget you're here studying for the Point, that's all."

"No, sir," Joe said.

"Well, loosen up," the CO said, "and tell Johnny and me who she is. Is she staying at the hotel?"

"No, sir," Joe said. "She lives here."

"Oh, she's an Islander, is she?" the CO said. "Well, tell us, what's her name?"

"Postley, sir," Joe said. "Ruth Postley."

The CO looked at the ceiling and frowned. "Not one of the Big Five families, is it?" he said. "Who are they? I never heard of any Postleys. Where do they live?"

"Off the Boulevard," Joe said, "near the beach. They're nice people, sir — Mr. and Mrs. Postley and Ruth."

"Postley," the CO said. "I never heard of any Postleys. What does he do?"

"He works in a printing shop downtown, sir," Joe said. "I play chess with him sometimes."

The CO set down his glass carefully and took a notebook from his pocket. "How do you spell it?" he asked.

"Spell what, sir?" Joe asked him.

"Postley," he said. "Now, listen, son, just be at ease. It's just as well to check up. A lot of ragtag and bobtail drift out here to the Islands — people who can't get on anywhere else. It's just as well to check up, Joe."

"Yes, sir," Joe said.

"Well," the CO said — and he snapped his notebook shut — "that cleans it up, I guess."

Joe's mouth felt dry. There was something in that conversation that was important and quite different from any other he had known.

"How did you meet her, Joe?" the CO asked.

Joe felt his face redden. "On the beach, sir," he said.

"I know it was on the beach. But how?"

Joe's voice was thick and awkward, and he cleared his throat. "We were just swimming. We just spoke to each other. It's all right to speak to someone, isn't it?"

The CO nodded and rattled his ice in the glass. "Of course it's all right," he said. "How did it happen? What did you speak about?"

"I told her to look out, a wave was breaking," Joe answered, "and she asked me who I was."

"Funny how those things happen," the CO said. "She's got a pretty figure."

"Don't," Joe said. "Don't talk about her like that."

The CO's chair creaked as he leaned forward. He set his hands carefully on his knees. "What's the matter with you, Joe?" he asked.

"She's a friend of mine," Joe said. "Please don't talk about her like that."

The CO did not move, and Johnny did not move. All three of them seemed to be waiting for something to happen, but nothing happened.

"All right," the CO said. "All right. I was a damn fool once myself."

Joe had come to learn that certain moments could never be entirely erased from memory. Later perspective might reveal their clumsiness, and he could see himself and Ruth in just that light; but those first hours they spent together never dropped entirely into the past. He could still see her in a yellow one-piece bathing suit, pushing her wet hair from her forehead, and she was always asking that old question: "Who are you? I've seen you lots of times."

And he could hear himself answering: "Army. Just the army."

They often would go over the details of that meeting very, very carefully.

"You loved me already, didn't you?" she used to say.

It had not occurred to him at the time, but of course he must have loved her.

"Why did you say the army — just the army?"

"I don't know," he would answer. "I guess I had it on my mind."

"And then what did we do?" she would ask. "Let's just pretend we're doing it all again."

"We got out of the water."

"Of course we got out of the water. I was afraid you would go away."

"Were you? I was afraid you would."

"And then what did we do?"

"I took you home. I didn't want you to go away. But you didn't know it, did you?"

"No. I didn't know it."

"And we sat on the lanai and told about everything."

They would talk about it, remembering this and that. The CO had been right. She was a very pretty girl. Joe often had wondered how he had dared to speak to her. Her nose was straight, her eyes and hair were dark. Yet none of this really mattered. It was hard to remember how she looked, hard to judge her as other people might, because all the awkwardness and the poignancy of first love added to the confusion of memory; but there was something more to it than looks. She was able to share his restiveness and his discontent, though her mind was more direct than his, and her directness had an influence on his own thoughts. He never had known that his feeling toward his father was one of rebellion or dislike until he saw her face light up when he told her about home. He never had known anything could be different from home, until he met Ruth Postley. That was why it was more than a boy-and-girl affair. She was actually a year younger, but she seemed very much older and very much wiser than he. It may have been because she had lived for six years in the Islands. Girls in the tropics mature earlier, and life moves faster.

VI

She lived, Joe understood later, on that vague social borderline where the races of the Islands mingle in a new and unanalyzable democracy. She had been brought up with all sorts of children, and they were all her friends, the offspring of queer people on that side street where the Postleys lived. There were a Japanese veterinarian and the leader of a Hawaiian orchestra and a mate of one of the inter-island boats and a Hawaiian beach boy — he was called a beach boy, although he had a son who was just about Joe's age. Mr. Postley in those days was about the only *haole* on that street; but race made very little difference there, where everyone wandered into everyone else's house through doors that were always open.

"Check," Mr. Postley said.

It was five o'clock one afternoon, and the chessboard was on a soap-box on Mr. Postley's lanai, which is the name they give to front porches in the Islands. The living-room door of the Postleys' one-story wooden house was open, just as it always was, showing the dining table and a few chairs and the couch where Ruth slept. The plates on the table were still unwashed, and the floor had not been swept, but Mrs. Postley did not mind. Mrs. Postley was on the lanai, a stoutish woman dressed in a gingham housedress. Her bare feet were pushed into a pair of soiled mules, her rocking chair grated on the sand that had accumulated on the lanai, her hair was done up in a loose knot and held by some large celluloid pins.

"Ruthy, dearie," Mrs. Postley said, "get out of your bathing suit and put on something fresh. Joe won't think you have nice clothes, only a bathing suit, will you, Joe?"

There were all sorts of people on the lanai watching the chess game. Mr. Mitsu, the veterinary, was seated on the porch swing, and three boys from next door in bathing trunks were squatting on their heels near the soapbox, chewing gum and breathing noisily.

"Ruthy, dearie," Mrs. Postley said again. "Put on a dress, dearie, and put some music on the phonograph."

"Joe," Ruth said, "what dress do you like?"

"Why, Ruthy," Mrs. Postley said. "Joe doesn't know all your dresses."

"Yes he does," Ruth said. "I've shown them all to him."

"My," Mrs. Postley said, "what a thing to do. When I was a girl in Saint Louis, I never showed boys my clothes."

"They're all around here, everywhere," Ruth said, "so everybody sees them. What dress do you want, Joe?"

"The blue silk," Joe said, "with the flowers on it."

"My," Mrs. Postley said, "Joe has good taste. You can have my shell comb, and put a flower in your hair, and don't forget the music when you go."

"Violet," Mr. Postley said, "will you please stop talking? It makes me dizzy how everybody chatters on this street. Check. I said check with the queen."

Mr. Postley's linen suit was wrinkled like his face. He wore a pair of steel-rimmed glasses with bifocal lenses, and now he took them off and wiped them with a soiled handkerchief. When he took his glasses off, his face looked pink and startled. Joe moved the box he was sitting on a little nearer to the board.

"You shouldn't have done that, sir," Joe said.

Mr. Postley put on his glasses again and looked at Joe in the surprised way he always did when Joe called him "sir." The phonograph in the living room was blaring a song that was old even then, a song about wearing them higher in Hawaii.

"Why shouldn't I have?" Mr. Postley said.

"I'll take your queen in three moves," Joe said.

From the hammock Mr. Mitsu began to laugh heartily.

"What the hell are you laughing at?" Mr. Postley asked.

"Excuse it," Mr. Mitsu said. "Excuse it, please."

"Well, you play with him," Mr. Postley said. "You go ahead and play."

"Now, Harold," Mrs. Postley said. "Now, Harold, don't get mad."

Then Ruth was calling from the house above the creaking of the phonograph. "Joe, come in here and look at me. Joe!"

"Be quiet in there," Mr. Postley called. "He's busy."

"Now, Harold," Mrs. Postley said, "you let Joe see her dress."

"Why can't he see it out here?" Mr. Postley asked.

"Now, Harold," Mrs. Postley said, "don't be silly."

"Oh," Mr. Postley said. "I'm not stopping anything. Oh, all right."

Of course later it had not been hard to see exactly what Mr. and Mrs. Postley had in mind; but even when Joe knew, something about that memory was always gay and pleasant. If he had been the Postleys, he would have done the same. They were all smiling at him, the boys and Mr. Mitsu and the Postleys. Everyone always understood everyone else on the Postleys' lanai.

Ruthy was in the back kitchen, standing near the sink with its un-washed pots and frying pan. Ruthy was in her blue-silk dress with the red flowers on it. Her hair was done up with her mother's tortoise-shell comb, and close to the comb was a red hibiscus flower; but her feet were still bare.

"I couldn't find my slippers," she said. "They must be around some-where. You don't mind, do you, Joe?"

"No," Joe answered.

"Darling," Ruthy whispered, and she kissed him. "Let's go outside."

They walked down the rickety back steps with their arms about each other, and it did not matter who saw them. No one cared if you loved each other on that street. There was coarse tropical grass in the yard and two algarroba trees and three hibiscus bushes.

"Joe," she said, and she looked up at the clouds above the algarrobas, "you'll take me away sometime, won't you?"

"Yes," Joe answered. "Yes."

"You won't forget me when you go to the Point?" she asked.

"No," Joe answered, "I won't."

"I'd like it," she said, "being married to a soldier. Joe, what would he say, do you think?"

"Who?" Joe asked, but he knew who.

"You wouldn't let him stop you, would you?"

"No," Joe answered. "No, I wouldn't."

"He doesn't know about us, does he?"

"Yesterday," Joe said, "he saw us on the beach."

"Oh," she said. "Did he ask who I was?"

"Of course he did," Joe said. "What difference does it make?"

But she knew more than he did. "He'll send you away," she said, "when he finds out who we are. Suppose he comes here."

There was nothing to answer. Joe could not think of such a thing as being possible. His father had been very busy lately, and he would not have the time to bother. "He won't come here," Joe said. "Why should he?"

The whole thing seemed to him more fantastic than real, for it actually occurred just when he was contemplating the possibility of it. As he stood by the algarroba tree with his arm around her waist, he was aroused by the sound of a car coming down the street, and he had a glimpse of the car from the back yard as it stopped in front of the house. It was the CO's runabout, and the CO was driving. In the moment that followed, Joe had the sensation of living in a bad dream from which inevitably he must awaken.

"Gosh," Joe whispered, "there he is," and he still must have had a belief that it could not be true, until he heard his father's voice from the front of the house, carrying clearly to the back yard where they were standing. The CO was speaking in the tone he used with erring enlisted men, passionless but absolute. Next, Joe could hear a shuffle of feet on the porch. Everyone must have got up to see who it was, and the CO's voice followed again on the heels of that confusion.

"I'm looking for a man named Postley. Is this his house?"

Then he heard the door of the runabout slammed hard, and Ruth held his hand very tight.

"Joe," she whispered, "you'd better go."

He never knew whether common sense told him that his father would know he had been there or whether he stayed from some more courageous motive. He liked to think that he stayed because he did not want her to see him run away and because he had been taught to tell the truth. "No," he answered. "That's all right." He walked slowly with her around the corner of the house.

"I ought to have my shoes," he heard her whisper.

There was a straggling hibiscus hedge in front of the Postleys', with a gap for the weedy path that led to the lanai. The CO was standing midway up the path. He must have motored down from the barracks. There was not a trace of dust on his riding boots, his breeches had just the proper curve, and his Sam Browne belt twinkled in the sunlight.

"I'm looking for my boy," he was saying. "Is my boy here?" Then he must have caught sight of Joe. The CO's face was perfectly composed, as it always was. If you had not known him, you might have thought he was making no effort at control; but Joe knew better. The mouth was too serene, the eyes were too steady. The CO's left hand grasping his Sam Browne belt was too motionless. Everything about his straight figure was too still.

"Oh," he said, "there you are, son, are you? Get in the car and wait. I'll be with you in a minute."

For a second Joe's eyes turned to the lanai. Mr. Postley was walking down the steps, pushing his steel-rimmed glasses more firmly on the bridge of his nose.

"Won't you come in?" he said.

"No," the CO said. "But I'd like to speak to you for just a minute."

Mrs. Postley was standing on the front step. "Ruthy," she called, "come here to me. My goodness, where are your shoes?"

The boys in their bathing trunks had faded into space, the way Hawaiians can, and Joe could see Mr. Mitsu's white shirttails fading into the darkness of the house.

"Sir," Joe said, "I was just playing chess with Mr. Postley."

"Get in the car, son," the CO said.

"Sir," Joe said, "this is Ruthy — Ruth Postley."

"Oh. How do you do," the CO said. "Go out to the car, son, and get in. Don't make me tell you again."

The CO did not raise his voice — he did not change a tone of it — but habit made Joe move as though his father had pushed him. He walked through the gap in the hibiscus hedge and out to the car in the street. He climbed in and sat there waiting.

He could see the CO and Mr. Postley standing midway down the path. He could see Mrs. Postley and Ruth on the steps. But the CO was speaking so gently that Joe could hear only the murmur of his words without distinguishing any of them. He recognized the tone — it was the one the CO used sometimes for reproving younger officers in a military formation in such a manner that the words would not carry to the ranks. The CO's back was toward him. He could see the CO, with his hands clasped behind him, sway gently from one shining foot to the other. He could see Mr. Postley facing him — red, bald-headed, rumpled, with the sun glistening on his glasses — and Joe could hear snatches of Mr. Postley's words.

"If I let him come here to see my girl, that's my business, isn't it? . . . Who are you — God Almighty? . . . You can't say that to me and make it stick. . . . Respectable house . . . decent as you are, by God. . . . I've got my rights. . . ."

But the CO was still speaking gently, swaying softly, and Mr. Postley's voice died down. As it did, the CO's voice grew more emphatic.

"Blackmail . . . And that's enough from you. Any more and you'll get run out of here. . . ."

Then the CO's voice settled back again into its gentlest monotone, and Joe saw him put one foot backward as he did when he was about to turn on his heel.

"All right," the CO said, "that's all." He raised his hands and dusted them together gently as he walked through the gap in the hedge. "Scum," he said as he reached the car, and he climbed in quickly. "I'll talk to you when we get home, son." He stepped on the self-starter, drove down the street unhurriedly, and turned left on the road toward Diamond Head.

Ever since Joe had been five, he frequently had been put on the carpet, as the CO expressed it, and the CO was versed in all the techniques of such an interview. The CO always said you never should jump an enlisted man. You should tell him quietly, but tell him, and it was the same way with one's own family and with boys. You had only to tell them.

Johnny was in the living room studying his French, and just as soon as he saw Joe and the CO he jumped up.

"Johnny," the CO said, "you'd better go upstairs. No, no. Wait a minute. Stay here. Joe, come up to my room."

The CO must have realized that a Hawaiian living room with all its open doors and windows was no place for a talk. The CO's room looked like all his others. There were the same bare walls, the same narrow bed, the same green locker trunk at the foot of it, the same weathered bedding roll — the CO liked to have things fixed so that he could leave for anywhere in half an hour — the same military brushes on the bureau, the same bootjack under the bureau, and the same framed photograph of Joe's mother.

"Close the door, Joe," the CO said, and he sat down on the edge of the bed. "At ease. I'm mad, but I'm not mad at you, son."

Joe stood in front of him, and the CO looked at him without speaking for a while, drumming his fingers softly on his riding boot. He was looking at Joe in the very intent way he sometimes looked at a map in a war game, while he endeavored to get the contours in his memory and to discover the shortest routes of march.

"I've told you about the family," the CO said. "I hope I've taught you to be as proud of it as I am. Well, I guess this is a family matter. Do you see what I mean?"

"No, sir," Joe answered.

The CO's fingers drummed on his riding boot, rat-a-tat-tat, rat-a-tat-tat. "You're young," he said, "but still you've got to see. It's pretty close to a question of honor, but it isn't your fault, son. There was no reason for you to know what those people are. I guess we've got to talk to each other as man to man. I want to ask you a question, and I want the truth. Are you ready?"

"Yes, sir," Joe answered, and he cleared his throat.

"Joe, how far have you gone with that girl?"

"How far have I gone, sir?" Joe repeated.

"You know what I mean," the CO answered. "I don't have to make it any clearer, do I? I'm your father, and I want the truth. How far have you gone with that girl?"

Even when Joe knew what the CO meant, he was still too young to see why the CO was justified in asking. He was so young that he could see only the brutality of the question. There was an insult in the implication, a lack of wisdom, a lack of perceptiveness. His knees began to shake, but he had to answer.

"I like her, sir, that's all," he said.

"Don't be afraid, son," the CO said gently. "I'm here to help you. You can tell your father. The family sticks together, just remember that. Remember you're going to the Point, son. Remember you're going to be an army officer and a gentleman. Don't be afraid."

"I'm not afraid," Joe answered.

"Then what are you shaking for?" the CO said. "Joe, are you telling me the truth?"

"I like her, sir, that's all," Joe said again. His voice was thick, and he cleared his throat again. "I wouldn't — " He stopped because he did not want to say anything further.

"You don't like her," the CO said. "You think you love her. You don't know what love is. You can't. But you think you do."

"I wish you wouldn't, please, talk about her that way, sir," Joe said. "I wouldn't — She isn't that kind of girl."

The lines about the CO's mouth relaxed. "Son," he said, "you wouldn't know, but it's all right now, it's all right. You don't know about people like that. Why should you? But it's all right. You've been on the way to getting the family and yourself into a damn tight box, but it's all right."

Joe did not answer, and the CO drummed on his boot again.

"You don't know what I mean, do you, son?"

"No, sir," Joe answered.

The CO was silent for a moment. He crossed his legs and put his hands carefully on his knees. "I guess I've got to tell you, son," he said, "in simple language. That's the only way to clear this up. You see, son, you're like a puppy dog going around wagging your tail and thinking everyone in the world is nice. You didn't know about these people. They just seemed kind to you, didn't they?"

"Yes, sir," Joe said.

The lines about the CO's mouth relaxed again. He nodded and smiled. "You didn't know what they were planning, did you, son? I'd better tell you about Postley. I got a line on him today. You see, Joe, this is pretty nearly the tropics, and all the bad pieces of candy in the box end up on the tropics sometime. Postley was a bank teller in Saint Louis. There was some sort of trouble, and now he's here. Just a beach-comber, that's all, Joe."

Joe stood there listening as the CO's voice went on telling about life in simple terms.

"I know his game from A to Zed," the CO said. "I've seen it tried before. You see, they were waiting to fix it so you'd have to marry that girl, Joe."

"Marry her?" Joe repeated, and his voice was thick.

"Marry her or buy them off," the CO said, "and I wouldn't have had the money, Joe. Now wait a minute. Think about it, think of ending up in a box like that. You see, you're going to the Point. I'm going to be proud of you some day."

"They wouldn't do that, sir," Joe said. "That isn't so. They wouldn't do a thing like that."

The CO stood up and pulled his belt straight. "Don't be a puppy dog, son," he said. "Don't keep wagging your tail. I just want your word as a gentleman not to see that girl again, and I'll tell you something that'll surprise you. In three months you'll forget you've ever known her. I want your word, that's all."

"Sir," Joe said, "they're not like that. You haven't any right — " His words choked in his throat, and his knees shook. "They've been kinder to me than anybody's ever been at home."

"Kinder to you than I've been?" the CO said. "Is that what you're saying, Joe?"

Joe drew in his breath and tried to stiffen his knees. "Yes, sir," he said. "It's been like home there. Yes, sir."

The CO stood still for a moment, and then he clasped his hands behind him. "Son," he said, "I'm being kind to you now, and you'll know it some day. You go to your room and stay there until you give me your word not to see that girl again. Is that clear?"

"Yes, sir," Joe said.

"And if you don't give me your word by tomorrow night, I'll ship you to your Uncle Bob on the mainland. Is that clear?"

"Yes, sir," Joe said.

The CO took a step toward him. "Maybe I've been hard on you," he said, "but I want you to be a man, Joe. We were all born in the army, and it's a hard life. You're going to be an officer, and you're not going to get mixed up with a little tart until you're old enough to know better."

"Don't call her that," Joe said.

"That will do," the CO said.

"I don't want to go into the army, sir," Joe said.

"What's that?" the CO said.

"I don't want to go into the army," Joe said, and the worst of it was he was crying, sobbing like a little boy.

"Joe," the CO said, "go to your room. You're leaving on the next boat. Is that clear?"

"Yes, sir," Joe said.

No one ever slept soundly on the street where the Postleys lived, particularly on moonlit nights. The Hawaiian boys who fished with spears and torches on the reef kept coming home at all hours, and besides there was usually a party somewhere on the street or a phonograph was going. The street was wide-awake when Joe reached it at two in the morning. Two houses away from the Postleys' someone was playing a ukulele and singing the "Song of the Islands," and a handful of children played tag in the street in the moonlight. Joe had his raincoat and fifteen dollars with him. That was all. He was so young that he simply obeyed an impulse; but even if he had wanted to he knew he could not have conquered that impulse. Already he was a long way from everything he had known, and he was glad of it, very glad.

He stood in the moonlight in the shadow of the Postleys' house and called to Ruthy very softly. She could not have been asleep because he heard the soft sound of her bare feet on the living-room floor.

"Is that you, Joe?" she whispered, just as if she had expected him. "Wait a minute." But it did not seem like a minute before she was beside him in the shadows.

"Joe," she asked, "what did he do to you?"

"It's all right," Joe said. "I've got to run away."

She never asked him why. She must have felt, as he did, that it was the only thing to do. She simply took his hand and led him into the house. "Pa," she called, "Joe's here."

He heard the bedsprings creak in the other room, and Mr. Postley was with them right away. No one ever slept soundly on that street. "Turn on a light, Ruthy," Mr. Postley said.

"It's better not to have a light, Pa," Ruth said. "Joe wants to run away."

"Oh, you want to run away, do you?" Mr. Postley said, and the idea seemed perfectly natural to him. "Where do you want to run to? This is an island, boy."

"Maybe I could hide somewhere," Joe said.

"The police would get you if you hid," Mr. Postley said. "They'd turn the army out."

"Maybe there's a ship," Joe said. "I don't care where I go."

When Joe mentioned a ship, Mr. Postley must have thought of something. "God," Mr. Postley said, "that would pay him back. Ruthy, you and Joe wait here."

"Where are you going, Pa?" Ruthy asked.

"Ruthy, you wait here," Mr. Postley said.

He and Ruthy stood alone in the shadows, holding each other tight, and Joe was certain then that he was leaving. There were ways of doing such things, and they did them very fast and smoothly on that street.

"Joe," Ruthy said, "you'll come back to get me, won't you?"

And of course he said he would. It all seemed simple then.

"Promise," she said, "just promise. I don't care how long it takes."

Of course it was the sort of thing that anyone would say.

VII

Somehow, in the telling of that story more was conveyed than ever was spoken. There must have been some common ground between Henry Ide and his friend that revealed much of what was not said. When he himself had been in the Islands, Henry Ide had passed hurriedly through streets like the one of which Joe had spoken. He had seen that strange mixture of races, all living amicably together. He had seen Fort Shafter and the Schofield Barracks. He had heard the band play when the ships came in. Now he seemed to be on the Islands again, smelling the sweet salt of the waters of the mid-Pacific, which was always mixed with the scent of flowers. He could feel that insistent motion of the trade winds. The story and all the people in it had been so vivid to Henry Ide that it was as if a curtain had dropped before a stage when his friend stopped speaking. There was the same sort of effort to become himself again. They were sitting at a table in a place off Broadway, drinking beer; but they had been away together — years and thousands of miles away. It was surprising now to see that Joe was not a boy, but middle-aged and thin and tired.

"I told you that," Joe said, "to take your mind off your own troubles."

"Thanks, it was very kind of you," Henry responded.

"You see," Joe said, "people like that stick together. They wanted to get me out of there. They weren't doing it for me, of course. They were doing it for spite." He stopped and smiled, and his face looked younger. "But they weren't bad, you know. People like that anywhere are nice people. Of course, the CO was right." He stopped again, but Henry Ide did not speak. "Why shouldn't they have wanted her to marry an officer's son if she found one on the beach? People act the same way always, any kind of people. They want the same things."

"What do they want?" Henry asked.

"They don't want much," Joe answered, "they want to be allowed to live. There wouldn't be any wars, or any trouble, if you and me and people on a street like that were just allowed to live."

It was hard to tell whether that remark was superficial or profound. Joe had stopped again. He looked kindly, tolerant, and weary.

"Where did you go?" Henry asked. "What happened to you then?"

Joe pushed back his chair. "It doesn't matter," he said, "what happened then. You think it over, and you'll see the beginning is all that matters. The middle and the end are always mixed up in the beginning. All the rest is time, just time."

"But aren't you going to tell me," Henry Ide asked, "what happened next?"

"Just time," Joe said, and he stood up. "Maybe I'll tell you some more, if I get time, but I won't be around here tomorrow. I'm going away for a while."

"Where?" Henry asked, but it was not a tactful question.

"It doesn't matter," Joe said. "Just away for a week, maybe two weeks. Look in at the arcade in two weeks, and maybe I'll be back."

Henry Ide never had heard the end of it. That's the way things happen in a city like New York. You get to know someone, and then there is a gap of time and other things happen and you are diverted. Time moves too quickly in New York. For a month Henry Ide had been meaning to go back to the arcade, but he never had. His own life had been moving faster in those weeks. He had made new friends, and already he was forgetting about Joe. He might never have seen him again if he had not gone to that cocktail party, and if he had not met Colonel Blair.

It was dark when Henry Ide and Colonel Blair drove toward Broadway. In the taxicab neither of them spoke for a while, and Henry Ide's thoughts kept moving beyond the limits of the taxicab among the vague shadows between darkened windows and dimmed-out street lights. He was thinking of all the accidents through which one lives— most of them half perceived, none of them ever properly evaluated. He was struggling with the guilty sensation that comes of interfering with the lives of people who are no concern of yours. It was peculiar because inadvertently he had learned so much and had guessed so much. They were strangers, and yet he knew more of them — he believed he understood them better — than any of the people he called his friends.

The colonel sitting next to him with the posture of an army officer used to regular and rigorous exercise might almost have been the CO of whom Joe had spoken, and this was natural because he was his father's son. Yet at the same time he was not formidable and never could be, because he was only Johnny Blair, a little boy studying his French verbs in Honolulu, the last of the CO's sons.

"Where did you say this place was?" the colonel asked.

"The penny arcade?" Henry answered. "Somewhere near the Fifties."

"Just what is a penny arcade?"

It occurred to Henry Ide that there was no reason why Colonel Johnny Blair should ever have seen a penny arcade. "It's an amusement place," Henry said.

"You mean tables and drinks and hostesses?"

Henry knew exactly the picture that was forming in the colonel's mind. Johnny Blair was thinking of a place like the Florida in Colon and of places like it all around the world from which the MP detail customarily dragged intoxicated soldiers.

"No," Henry answered, "it isn't like that. It's just a place where you put a penny in the slot of some machine or play a game."

"Oh," the colonel said, "slot machines."

Henry could tell exactly where the colonel's mind was moving. He was thinking of the slot machines in the officers' clubs all around the world, where you put in nickels and dimes and quarters and pushed the lever — a drink in one hand, your money in the other.

"No," Henry said, "not slot machines."

It was difficult to give a sensible idea of the shooting gallery, the miniature ball games, the wheels of fortune, the toy bombing planes.

"What makes people go there?" Johnny Blair asked.

"I don't know," Henry answered. "I guess to get away from something else."

The colonel did not answer, and Henry Ide knew the reason. Johnny Blair never had needed or wished to get away from anything.

"It's funny meeting you," Johnny Blair said.

"Yes," Henry answered. "I suppose those things happen sometimes."

"Yes," Johnny Blair said, "you never can tell what's going to happen, can you?"

"No," Henry said, "you can't."

"Now, Joe," Johnny Blair said, "you'd never have thought anything like this would have happened to Joe. I used to think a lot of Joe."

Henry Ide did not answer. He could put himself in the colonel's place. He was keenly aware that he was a stranger who knew more than a stranger should.

"Well, what did happen to him?" the colonel asked.

"He never told me," Henry answered. "He only said he'd run away."

"Of course," the colonel said, "he'd be ashamed to tell."

"As soon as we get there, I'll leave you," Henry told him.

"No," Johnny Blair said, "don't do that. It will be easier if you stay." And then he was silent for a second. "What's Joe like?" he asked.

There never is a quick and definite way of telling what anyone is like. "He's kind," Henry said. "He's very kind."

"Kind?" Johnny Blair repeated. "What's he kind about?"

"Well," Henry answered, "it's hard to say. About everything, I guess. There's another thing, he's happy."

"Happy?" Johnny Blair repeated. "He isn't crazy, is he?"

"I don't know," Henry answered. "Why, no, I wouldn't say he was."

"We always thought he was crazy," Johnny said. "But you know, I always liked him."

Neither of them spoke for a while. The cab had stopped in the cross-town traffic, and Johnny Blair moved uneasily.

"God," he said, "I wish I didn't have to see him."

"I don't suppose I should have told you," Henry said. "I'll go as soon as you meet him."

"No," Johnny Blair answered, "don't do that. It wouldn't make it any better."

Henry Ide began wishing deeply that he had not come. It would be like the ending of a grim sort of tale when those brothers finally met. It was clear that Johnny Blair felt awkward, now that he was stepping out of his own world. Already on Sixth Avenue, as they saw the early-evening crowd, Johnny Blair's stubbornly bewildered expression made Henry Ide realize how far a West Point officer is removed from the superficial vulgarities and the weaknesses most civilians accept. Nothing in his life ever had touched the joke shop on the corner, where funny buttons and sleight-of-hand tricks were displayed for sale, or the stand next to the joke shop, where orange drinks were sold. It was so early in the evening that the penny arcade was half empty; but the rifles at the shooting gallery were going, and music was blaring, and the whole place was ablaze with light.

Johnny Blair gazed about him with blank incuriosity, as though he hoped the sights and sounds would not convey anything. "Is this the place?" he asked.

"Yes," Henry answered, "this is it. The chess games are downstairs."

Downstairs they could hear the wooden crash of the balls in the

bowling alleys. It was so early that no crowd had gathered around the
railing near the chess players. It was so early that Henry Ide thought it
might end in anticlimax, that it might be too early for the house players, but then he saw that he was wrong. First he saw Joe Blair's hat
and overcoat, and then he saw Joe Blair. He was sitting at his table in
front of an empty chessboard, with his elbows resting on the table and
his shoulders slouched forward. He was looking straight ahead of him,
lost in his own thoughts; but his thoughts did not appear to disturb
him.

"There he is," Henry said, "sitting by the empty table," and he saw
Johnny Blair's head move slowly in the direction he indicated.

"Wait a minute," Johnny Blair said, and he stood quietly for a few
moments quite a distance away. "Yes," he said, "that's Joe, all right,"
and he began walking slowly toward the railing that enclosed the chess
and checker tables. Joe Blair was still staring straight in front of him,
unconscious of faces and voices, so that he did not see the officer's uniform until Johnny Blair rested his hands on the railing.

"Hello, Joe," Johnny Blair said.

Henry saw Joe peering forward and saw his shoulders straighten.

"It's Johnny, Joe," Colonel Blair said.

There was only the suspicion of a pause before the other replied.
"Yes, I know," Joe said. "How are you, Johnny? I haven't seen you
for quite a while."

When Henry saw those two facing each other, the chessboards reminded him of the remark Joe once had made about the middle game's
not making much difference. He was seeing the end game of two lives.
The resemblance that had disturbed him at the cocktail party was
much more striking now that he saw them both together. The facial
expressions, the molding of the cheekbones, and even little mannerisms
that were impossible to specify were very much the same. In fact, it
was possible to think that but for some strength or weakness of character, Joe might have been the colonel and Johnny the chess player.
The final combination of those lives assumed a frank sort of simplicity
beyond apology, and, Henry was thinking, Johnny Blair held all the
best pieces. They both held their kings, of course — in chess the game
is over before you can lose your king — but you could think of Johnny
Blair's king as being protected by the castles of a well-directed life,
and Joe Blair must have lost his rooks long ago.

Joe had risen. Henry saw his gaze move slowly from his brother's face to the ribbons on the uniform — the pre-Pearl Harbor ribbon, the ribbons for the American and European theaters — a most impressive array. There was a puzzled look on Joe's face, but nothing else showed that the meeting was not natural.

"Who told you I was here?" he asked. His voice was quiet when he asked the question — just the tone he should have used speaking to his younger brother — and then he saw Henry Ide, and his face cleared because he knew the answer.

"I'm sorry," Henry said. "I shouldn't have brought him here."

"No," Joe answered, "don't be sorry. I was going to see him anyway." He reached for his hat and frayed overcoat. "Let's get out of here," he added. "Let's go around the corner and have a glass of beer."

"I'd better run on," Henry said, and they both turned to look at him.

"No," Joe said, "you stay. Give me a hand with this coat, please, Johnny. My shoulder's a little stiff. That's right. Thank you very much."

They were out in the street walking toward the restaurant where he and Joe Blair used to sit, before Henry realized that the meeting had contained none of the elements one might have anticipated, no embarrassments, no surprise. There had not been even a trace of awkwardness, and Henry Ide could grasp the reason. It lay in that tolerant ability Joe Blair had of being beyond surprise. It consisted in a power to accept facts patiently no matter what they were. But Johnny Blair looked puzzled. So much had happened that it seemed impossible to make any beginning, impossible for anyone to bridge the gap of time; but the difficulty did not bother Joe. Somehow he alone had bridged it, because he had seen so much.

When they arrived at a booth in the little restaurant, he sat down and smiled. "You're looking well," he said.

"Yes," Johnny Blair began, and stopped. He must have stopped because his brother did not look well; but he went on when Joe did not speak, and Henry was very glad he did, because words, any words, were better than the silence. "Joe," Johnny Blair asked, "where have you been?"

"Here and there," Joe answered. "In the East, in China mostly. Johnny, you look like the CO."

Johnny Blair's eyes were watchful like his brother's as he looked at him across the table. "The CO's still alive, you know," he said. "I think you ought to see him."

"I'd like to," Joe answered, "but I don't think he'd be happy if he saw me."

"Now, listen," Johnny Blair said, and you could see that he was making an effort to be natural. "You know how the old man is about the family. Nothing that's happened can be helped. Of course he'd like to see you."

Joe shook his head slowly. "He'd look the way you look now, kid," he said. "He wouldn't realize that nothing that's happened can be helped. You don't realize it, either."

There was a shadow of annoyance in Johnny's voice. He was still trying to solve some sort of problem, and there was nothing in his background to help him with it. "That's not fair," he said. "How do you know he wouldn't?"

"He wouldn't," Joe said, but he said it gently. "You see, I've had a pretty good time. He wouldn't understand that any more than you. For instance, take one thing — do you remember Ruthy Postley?"

"Yes," Johnny said. "Yes, of course I remember. You were too young to know any better. The CO's often said so."

It was easier now that they were talking. Though the shreds of the past were mingling with the present, there was not so much time to worry when they were talking, and Joe Blair smiled.

"I went back and married her," he said. "I often wondered if you'd heard of it, but there's no reason why you should have."

"You married her?" Johnny repeated. "What became of her, Joe?"

Joe rested his elbows on the table and smiled again. "Nothing much. We're married still," he said. "We have a place uptown. We're living. That's all anybody wants — a chance to live."

Johnny Blair raised his beer glass and set it down again. "Would you mind telling me what you're living on?"

"Yes, I should," Joe answered. "On this and that, kid, and it doesn't matter. You tell the boys, if you want to, that I can get along." And he smiled at Johnny Blair across the table. "And you can tell them, if you want to, that I'd do it all over again tomorrow. I haven't disgraced the family."

"Now wait a minute," Johnny Blair said. "I didn't say you had."

"I know," Joe answered. "You always were a nice boy, and you

wouldn't want to hurt my feelings, would you, kid? You can tell them
— I suppose they'll find it out — tell them we're an army family and
I'm an army man. Tell them I'm retired, but I outrank the whole lot
of you. Tell them I'm a general, kid. How do you like that?" He
paused, but Johnny Blair did not have time to answer. "There's always
an army somewhere," Joe said, "and you're going to report to me next
week."

It was plain that Johnny Blair did not believe him. "Joe," he said,
"you can get me through the War Department any time if there's
anything I can do for you. Just remember, the family sticks together.
If you're hard up, or not well — "

"Thanks, Johnny," Joe answered, "I'm all right." And Henry saw
his face light up as it did sometimes when he played chess and a combination was working to a definite conclusion. "Maybe I'm wrong,"
Joe went on. "Maybe they've changed their minds down there; but
they told me you were going out to China, to report to General Wu
— a liaison job. That's what they told me."

"Who told you?" Johnny Blair asked sharply. "Where did you hear
that?"

Joe pushed himself from the table and sat up straighter, as he did
sometimes when a game was ending. "The combined staff," Joe said
softly. "They told me, kid — the combined staff in the place with all
the guards. They heard I was here, and they called me down to Washington. I just heard tonight they're calling me down there permanently. I'm on the active list again — a general in the Chinese Republican Army, kid, assigned to duty in Washington. You remember Uncle
Bob said I'd be on the staff some day?"

Joe's expression had changed. It had a new assurance, a new suave
sort of authority. If you are born in the army, you are always in it.
Suddenly, as he went on speaking, you could see that he had been used
to giving orders — somewhere, some time.

"That's why I heard," he said, "that you were going over to General Wu. I used to be his chief of staff, kid, before I got shot up. You're
to report to me next week before you go to China. I can tell you
quite a lot about General Wu."

Iwo Jima before H-Hour
(1945)

LIFE on a battleship is largely conducted against a background of disregarded words. For example, upon leaving Saipan, the radio loudspeaker on the open bridge produced a continuous program somewhat along the following lines:

"This is Peter Rabbit calling Audacity One — Peter Rabbit calling Audacity One — over . . . Audacity One calling Peter Rabbit . . . Come in, Peter Rabbit — over . . . Peter Rabbit to Audacity One — Shackle. Charley. Abel. Oboe. Noel Coward. Unshackle — over . . . Audacity One to Peter Rabbit — continue as directed. Over . . . Peter Rabbit to Audacity One — Roger. Over . . ."

Sometimes these guarded code conversations, all conducted with flawless diction in clear unemotional tones, would reach a degree of subtlety that bordered on the obvious.

"Tiger Two is now in a position to give the stepchildren a drink. Will Audacity One please notify the step children? . . . Bulldog calling Turtle. A pilot is in the water, southeast of Hot Rock. Pick him up. I repeat: in the water, southeast of Hot Rock. Pick him up . . ."

There was never any way of telling whether or not the stepchildren received the drinks which Tiger was kind enough to offer, or whether or not the pilot was rescued from the slightly chilly waters off that unpleasant island of Iwo. Moreover, no one seemed particularly to care. The admiral and the captain sat upon the bridge in comfortable high-chairs, not unlike those used by patrons in a billiard parlor. Their staff officers stood near them, and behind the staff officers stood the men with earphones and mouthpieces tethered by long insulated cords, and next came the marine orderlies with their .45 automatics. Occasionally a Filipino mess boy would appear from the small kitchenette below — doubtless called a galley — with sandwiches and coffee for the admiral and the captain. He would carry these on a tray, sparkling with bright silver, china, and napery, up two dark companion ladders to the open bridge. Once when the main battery of 14-inch guns was firing, some freak of concussion lifted him a good six inches off the deck. But guns or not, no one appeared to listen to the voices on that radio.

However, as hours merged into days during those vigils on the bridge, that constant flow of words could not help but appeal to the imagination of anyone whose experience on battleships and with naval affairs had been previously limited almost exclusively to an acquaintance with *Pinafore* and *Madame Butterfly*. Charley and Abel and Peter Rabbit, who kept shackling and unshackling themselves, gradually became old friends. You began to wonder what was happening now to Audacity and Oboe. It would not have been tactful to ask, since each was a special ship, a unit of the task force, but once one of those characters revealed its identity. This was when Little Abner had words with Audacity off the beach of Iwo Jima on D day minus two.

"Little Abner calling Audacity," Little Abner said. "We've got three holes and so we're going back to the line."

"What line do you mean?" Audacity asked.

"What the hell line do you think?" Little Abner answered. "The firing line."

Little Abner was an LCI — Landing Craft Infantry, in case you do not understand naval initials. She was one of the LCI's equipped with rockets, assigned to strafe the beach, and the Jap batteries had taken her under fire at eight hundred yards.

In addition to the radio on the bridge, there was also entertainment down below. When the great ship withdrew from the area, and when General Quarters had changed to Condition Two, some unknown hands would place recordings of radio programs from home upon a loudspeaker that reached the crew's mess, the warrant officers' mess, and the wardroom. Thus, above the shufflings on the deck, the clatter of mess tins and dishes, would come blasts of music, roars of laughter and blatant comedy. There was no way of escaping it if you wanted to eat. Though you were seven-hundred-odd miles from Tokyo, you were back home again.

"And now Dr. Fisher's tablets for intestinal sluggishness present Willie Jones, and all the little Jones boys, and the Jones boys' orchestra." (Whistles, laughter, and applause from an unknown audience.)

"But first a brief, friendly word from our sponsor. Folks, do you feel headachy and pepless in the morning? Just take one with a glass of warm water. But here he is, Willie Jones himself." (Whistles, applause, and cheers from that unknown audience.) "How are you tonight, Willie?" — "Well, frankly, Frank, I'm feeling kind of dumb." "You mean you're just your old self, then?" (Shrieks, whistles, and applause from the unknown audience.)

There was no way of turning the thing off, but no one seemed to mind. Perhaps after having been at sea almost continuously for thirty months, as had many members of that crew, these sounds gave a sort of reassurance that a past to which everyone was clinging still waited back at home. At the ship's service, days before the ship was cleared for action, you could buy all sorts of reminders of that past. The shaving creams and toothpastes were like old acquaintances. There was even Williams' Aqua Velva, though this line was finally discontinued when it was found that certain members of the crew were taking it internally. There was a selection of homely literature, such as *The Corpse in the Coppice* and *Murder Walks at Midnight* and *The Book of Riddles*, and there were fragile volumes of comics and nationally known brands of gum and candy. When men went to battle stations nearly all of them took a few of these things along. When the ship was closed into hermetically sealed compartments and the ventilating system was cut off you could see them reading by the ammunition hoist. You could see the damage-control groups, with their gas masks, their tools and telephones, reclining on the decks slowly devouring those pages and chewing gum. They may not have enjoyed this literature for itself but it must have given them about the only illusion of privacy that there was in a life at sea, where privacy does not exist.

"If you write this thing just the way you see it," an officer said, "maybe it might mean something to people back home. They might see what we're going through. They might understand — they never understand back home."

That was what nearly everyone aboard said. They all had a pathetic desire for people at home to know. Of course, if they had thought about it, they would have realized that this was impossible. There was too great a gap between civilian and naval life. There were too few common values. The life aboard a ship in enemy waters was even more complex and difficult of explanation than the life of troops ashore.

There was a combination of small personal comforts and of impending danger verging on calamity that was ugly and incongruous. The living quarters of the crew were overcrowded, but they had hot water and soap, hot showers, and all sorts of things you would never get ashore. There were clean clothes, and all the coffee you wanted day and night, and red meat and other hot food, and butter and ice cream. Yet, at the same time, the sense of danger was more intense. You could not run away from it as you could on land. It might come at any minute of the day and night from torpedoes, from the air, from a surface engagement. Almost any sort of blow meant casualties and damage. Even a light shell on the superstructure might cause complications incomparable to the results of a similar blow on land.

II

There had been some hope that the task force of battleships, cruisers, and destroyers that was scheduled to bombard Iwo Jima for three days before the transports and the amphibious craft appeared might arrive there undetected, but the force was spotted by an enemy plane on the evening of February 15th. No one aboard saw that speck in the dark sky.

In the junior officers' wardroom there was a complete collection of all the intelligence which had been gathered regarding the island of Iwo. Nothing was a secret any longer. It was possible to scan the latest airplane photographs, which had been taken early in the month. There were maps showing the target areas assigned every unit, with batteries, pillboxes, and antiaircraft installations marked in red. There were reports on the soil of the island. The beach would be coal-black lava sand, and the land rose up from it quite sharply in terraces. Each terrace had been a former beach, since in the past few years the island had been rising from the sea. As one moved in from the water's edge the soil was a soft sand of volcanic ash, almost barren of vegetation and exceedingly difficult for any sort of vehicle to negotiate. Higher on the island were the cliffs of brown volcanic stone, suitable for construction of underground galleries. There were patches of coarse grass full of the mites that cause scrub typhus. There were hot springs, and there was the sulfur mine from which Iwo draws its name (Sulfur Island), and a small sugar plantation to the north near a single town called Motoyama. There were believed to be fifteen thousand troops on the island. The defensive installations were all underground or carefully camouflaged. There was only one practical beach on which to land and there was no chance for tactical subtlety.

The most interesting unit of this informational material was a large relief map made out of soft, pliable rubber, that gave a bird's-eye view of the island we were approaching. Every contour of it was there in scale — the cliffs to the northward, the vegetation, the roads, the airstrips (two finished and one nearing completion), and Mount Suribachi, the low, brown volcanic cone on the southern tip.

There have already been a good many ingenious descriptions of the shape of Iwo Jima, including comparisons to a mutton chop and a gourd. The whole thing was about five miles long. Mount Suribachi, to the south, was a walled-in crater. Its northern slope was known to be studded with pillboxes and with artillery. Bushes and boulders on this slope ran down to the lowest and narrowest stretch on the island, which had beaches on the east and west. (The west beach, however, would not permit landing operations on account of the prevailing winds.) From here the land gradually rose upward, and the island broadened until it finally reached a width of two and one-half miles. The airstrips were on its central spine. The northern shores came down to the sea in cliffs. There were only eight square miles of this bleak, unpromising, and porous dry land.

Anyone could tell that the plans for the seizure of Iwo Jima must have been the main occupation of a large group of specialists for a long, long time. Heaps of secret orders showed the disposition at any given moment of every one of the hundreds of craft that would take part in the invasion. The thousands of pages made a scenario for an operation which might take place in an hour or a minute. Veterans of other invasions were not impressed by the infinite detail. They spoke of the plans for Normandy and the South of France, or they discussed the arrangements for Guam and Saipan.

"If you've seen one of them," they said, "you've seen them all."

No one spoke much on the bridge. It was chilly and rain was falling before daylight. We were a silent, blacked-out ship, moving slowly, and as far as one could tell, alone — except for voices on the bridge radio.

"Battleaxe One," the radio was saying, "Area Zebra. Shackle. Charley. Oswald. Henry. Abel. Unshackle."

"We'll start firing at about ten thousand yards," someone said.

Then the first daylight began to stir across the water and we were among the shadows of other heavy ships, moving very slowly.

"Look," someone said, "there's the mountain."

There was a faint, pinkish glow on the rain clouds above the horizon and the first faint rays of an abortive sunrise struggling against the rain fell on a rocky mass some five miles dead ahead. It was the cone of Suribachi emerging from a misty haze of cloud, and cloud vapor covered the dark mass of the rest of Iwo Jima. After one glance at its first vague outlines, it would have been hard to have mistaken it for anything but a Japanese island, for it had the faint delicate colors of a painting on a scroll of silk.

Our spotting plane was warming up on the catapult aft and you could hear the roar of the motor clearly over the silent ship. Then there was a flat explosion as the plane shot over the water. When it circled for altitude and headed for the island, there was already light enough to see the faces on the bridge.

The captain dropped his binoculars and lighted a cigarette. The clouds were gradually lifting above the island. It was unexpectedly tedious waiting and wondering when we would begin to fire. The island lay there mute and watchful. A bell was ringing. "Stand by," someone said, and seconds later one of our 14-inch projectiles was on its way to Iwo Jima. The noise was not as bad as the concussion, for your chest seemed to be pushed by invisible hands when the big guns went off. There was a cloud of yellow smoke, not unlike the color of Mount Suribachi. Then everyone crowded forward to gaze at the island. It seemed a very long while before a cloud of smoke and gray sand rose up almost like water from land. Then another ship fired. The bombardment of Iwo Jima had begun and the island lay there in the dingy, choppy sea, taking its punishment stoically without a sound.

Even at a distance of five miles, which somehow does not seem as far at sea as it does on land, one had the inescapable impression that Iwo Jima was ready for it and accustomed to taking a beating. This was not strange, as we had bombed it from the air for successive dozens of days, and fleet units had already shelled it twice. Nevertheless, this lack of reaction was something that you did not expect, even though common sense told you that there would not possibly be any land fire until we closed the range.

Another aspect of that three-day bombardment before D day was even more unexpected, especially when one retained memories of the heavy and continuous fire by land batteries upon prepared positions in the last world war. The bombardment turned out to be a slow, careful probing for almost invisible targets, with long dull intervals between the firing. Occasionally one could see a cloud of drab smoke arise from another ship, and a long while afterward the sound of the explosion would come almost languidly across the water, and then there would be another plume of dust and rubble on another target area of Iwo Jima. Sometimes, when the breeze was light, the smoke from the big guns of another ship would rise in the air in a huge perfect ring. Of course common sense again gave the reason for this deliberate firing. The fleet had come too long a distance to waste its limited ammunition, and consequently the effect of every shot had to undergo careful professional analysis.

In the lulls between the firing there was always an atmosphere of unremitting watchfulness. While the crews of the antiaircraft batteries below us sat by their guns, smoking and talking, hundreds of eyes were examining the sky and land. There was air cover far above us. In the distance were underwater listeners on the destroyers and DE's that were screening us. Our own air watch, besides, was covering every sector of the sky — and you also knew that the enemy looked back at us from his hidden observation posts. That consciousness of eyestrain and listening never entirely vanished in those days at Iwo Jima, and because of it, not a moment on the bridge was restful.

The slow approach on Iwo Jima was somewhat like the weaving and feinting of a fighter watching for an opening early in the first round. To put it another way, our task force was like a group of big-game hunters surrounding a slightly wounded but dangerous animal. They were approaching him slowly and respectfully, endeavoring to gauge his strength and at the same time trying to tempt him into action. We moved all through the day, nearer and nearer to Iwo Jima. Planes from the carrier force came from beyond the horizon, peeling off through the clouds and diving toward the airstrip; but except for an occasional burst of automatic fire and a few black dots of flak, the enemy was very listless. Our minesweeps, small, chunky vessels, began operating very close to the island. There were a few splashes near them, but that was all. The Japanese commander was too good a soldier to show his hand.

As the day wore on, we crowded close and objects loomed very large ashore. You could see the coal-black strip of beach where our assault waves would land, and the sea broke on the rusting hulls of a few old wrecks. Above the beach were the gray terraces we had read about, mounting in gradual, uneven steps to the airstrip. Beside the airstrip there was a tangle of planes, smashed by our bombings and pushed carelessly aside, like rubbish on a city dump. To the north were the quarries which had been mentioned by the intelligence. You could see caves to the south on Mount Suribachi. We were very close for a battleship and we knew the enemy had 8-inch coast-defense guns.

We continued firing at pillboxes and at antiaircraft emplacements, but there was no return fire and no trace of life upon the island. We stayed there until the light grew dim, and then we turned to leave the area until next morning. Twelve hours of standing on the bridge and the concussion of the guns left everyone very tired. We must have done some damage but not enough to hurt.

III

It was different the next morning — D day minus two. When we returned to the dull work the island was waiting with the dawn. Today the sky was clearer and the sea was smoother, and the ships closed more confidently with the shore. The schedule showed that there was to be a diversion toward the middle of the morning, and the force was obviously moving into position.

"We're going to reconnoiter the beach with small craft," an officer explained. "And the LCI's will strafe the terraces with rockets."

It was hard to guess where the LCI's had come from, for they had not been with us yesterday — but there they were just behind us, on time and on order, like everything else in amphibious war. The sun had broken through the cloud ceiling and for once the sea was almost blue. The heavy ships had formed a line, firing methodically. Two destroyers edged their way past us and took positions nearer shore.

"Here come the LCI's," someone said. "You can see the small craft with them," and he gave the initials by which the small boats were identified. They were small open launches, manned by crews with kapok life jackets. They were twisting and turning nervously as they came to join the LCI's.

"Where are they going in those things?" I asked.

"They are going to see what there is along the beach," my friend answered. "Someone has to see." He spoke reprovingly, as though I should have known the routine that had been followed again and again in the Pacific.

Eight or ten LCI's — it was difficult to count them — were passing among the battleships, with their crews at their battle stations. They were small vessels that had never been designed for heavy combat. They had been built only to carry infantry ashore, but in the Pacific they were being put to all sorts of other uses — as messenger ships to do odd jobs for the fleet, as gunboats, and as rocket ships. Each had a round tower amidships where the commanding officer stood. Each had open platforms with light automatic guns, and now they were also fitted with brackets for the rockets. They were high and narrow, about a hundred feet over-all, dabbed with orange and green paint in jungle camouflage. They were a long way from jungle shores, however, as they moved toward the beach of Iwo Jima.

Suddenly the scene took concrete shape. They would approach within a quarter of a mile of shore under the cover of our guns. Without any further protection their crews stood motionless at their stations.

Afterward a gunner from one of the LCI's spoke about it.

"If we looked so still," he said, "it was because we were scared to death. But then everyone had told us there was nothing to be scared of. They told us the Japs never bothered to fire at LCI's."

They were wrong this time, probably because the small craft that followed gave the maneuver the appearance of a landing. For minutes the LCI's moved in and nothing happened. They had turned broadside to the beach, with small boats circling around them like water beetles, before the enemy tipped his hand and opened up his batteries. Then it became clear that nothing we had done so far had contributed materially to softening Iwo Jima. The LCI's were surrounded with spurts of water and spray and smoke. They twisted and backed to avoid the fire, but they could not get away. It all seemed only a few yards off, directly beneath our guns. Then splashes appeared off our own bows. The big ships themselves were under fire.

"The so-and-so has taken a hit," someone said. "There are casualties on the such-and-such." He was referring to the big ships, but at the moment it did not seem important. All you thought of were the LCI's just off the beach. We were inching into line with the destroyers.

It appeared later that when we had been ordered to withdraw we had disregarded the order, and thus all at once we were in a war of our own, slugging it out with the shore. There had been a great deal of talk about our gunnery and the training of our crews. There was no doubt that they knew their business when they began firing with everything that could bear. The 14-inch guns and the 5-inch batteries were firing as fast as they could load. The breeze from the shore blew the smoke up to the bridge in bilious clouds. The shore line of Iwo Jima became cloaked in white smoke as we threw in phosphorous. Even our 40-millimeters began to fire. It was hard to judge the lapse of time, but the LCI's must have let off their rockets according to the schedule while the Japanese were blinded by the smoke and counterfire. When the LCI's began to withdraw, we also moved off slowly. It was the first mistake the enemy had made, if it was a mistake — revealing those batteries, for the next day was mainly occupied in knocking them out.

The LCI's were limping back. One of them was listing and small boats were taking off her crew. Another was asking permission to come alongside. When she reached us the sun was beating on the shambles of her decks. There was blood on the main deck, making widening pools as she rolled on the sluggish sea. A dead man on a gun platform was covered by a blanket. The decks were littered with wounded. They were being strapped on wire stretchers and passed up to us over the side, since nothing as small as an LCI had facilities for wounded. The men who were unhurt were lighting cigarettes and talking quietly, but no one was smiling. The commanding officer was tall, bareheaded, and blond, and he looked very young. Occasionally he gave an order and then he, also, lighted a cigarette. When they began to hose off the blood on the deck, the crew must have asked for fresh water, because our men, gathered by the rail, began tossing down canteens. Then there was a call from our bridge.

"Can you proceed under your own power?"

The blond CO looked up. He evidently had not heard, because the question was repeated.

"Can you proceed under your own power?"

"We can't proceed anywhere for three days," the CO said.

They had passed up the wounded — seventeen of them — and then they passed up five stretchers with the dead — twenty-two out of a crew of about sixty.

"That officer ought to get a medal," I said to someone on the bridge.

"They don't give medals for things like that in the Navy," I was told.

It may be so, but I still hope he gets the medal.

That evening the Japanese reported that they had beaten off two landings on Iwo Jima and that they had sunk numerous craft, including a battleship and a destroyer. There was a certain basis of fact in this, since what had happened must have looked like a landing. One LCI was sinking, waiting for a demolition charge, as disregarded as a floating can.

After the reconnaissance of the beach had been accomplished, the pounding of Iwo Jima continued through the afternoon and through the whole next day. Planes drove in with bomb loads, while the ring of ships kept up their steady fire. At night the "cans," as the destroyers were called, continued a harassing fire. Incendiary bombs were dumped on the slopes of Suribachi. Rockets were thrown at it from the air. Fourteen-inch shells pounded into its batteries. The ship to starboard of us attacked the battery to the north on the lip of the quarry. The earth was blown away, exposing the naked concrete gun emplacements, but now that the novelty had worn off it was all a repetition of previous hours. The scene grew dull and very fatiguing, but the voices on the radio loudspeaker continued tirelessly.

"Dauntless reports a contact. . . . Bulldog is ready to give a drink to any of our pigeons that may need it. Audacity One to Tiger — I repeat: Did you get our message? Over . . . "

The island lay still, taking it. No visible life appeared until the last day, when an installation was blown up and a few men staggered out from it. Some of us on the bridge saw them and some did not. One Japanese ran a few steps and seemed to stop and stoop to pick up something. Then he was gone. We had probably seen him dying.

The Japanese commander was playing his cards close to his chest, revealing no more targets by opening fire. It was clear that he also had his plan, less complicated than ours, but rational. He might damage our heavy ships, but he could not sink them, or conceivably prevent the inevitable landing. He had clearly concluded to wait and take his punishment, to keep his men and weapons under cover, until our assault waves were on the beach. Then he would do his best to drive them off, and everyone at Iwo knows it was not such a bad plan, either. He did not come so far from doing it when he opened up his crossfire on the beach. Some pessimists even admit that he might have succeeded if it had not been for that coarse, light sand, which embedded the mortar shells as they struck, so that they only killed what was very near them.

IV

At the end of D day minus one our task force was still there, without many new additions, but it was different the next morning. At dawn on D day the waters of Iwo looked like New York harbor on a busy morning. The transports were there with three divisions of marines — a semicircle of gray shipping seven miles out. Inside that gray arc the sea, turned choppy by the unsettled weather, was dotted by an alphabet soup of ships.

There were fleets of LST's filled with amphibious tanks and alligators; there were LSM's; there were the smaller LCT's, and packs of LCI's gathering about the kill. The ring of warships was drawing tighter. Small boats were moving out bearing flags to mark the rallying points from which the landing waves would leave. It looked like a Hollywood production, except that it was a three-billion-, not a three-million-dollar extravaganza. There must have been as many as eight hundred ships clustered off Iwo Jima, not counting the small boats being lowered. The officers and crew faced it without surprise. Instead they pointed out small incidents and made critical remarks.

"See the LCVP's," someone said. He was pointing out the tiny dots around the transports where the landing craft were loading. "They'll be moving into position. Here come the planes." It was all working without a hitch, with H hour not so far away. At nine o'clock exactly the first assault wave was due to hit the beach, but before that Iwo Jima was due to receive its final polishing. Its eight square miles were waiting to take everything we could pour into them, and they must have already received a heavier weight of fire than any navy in the world has previously concentrated upon so small an area.

Anyone who has been there can shut his eyes and see the place again. It never looked more aesthetically ugly than on D-day morning, or more completely Japanese. Its silhouette was like a sea monster, with the little dead volcano for the head, and the beach area for the neck, and all the rest of it with its scrubby, brown cliffs for the body. It also had the minute, fussy compactness of those miniature Japanese gardens. Its stones and rocks were like those contorted, wind-scoured, water-worn boulders which the Japanesse love to collect as landscape decorations. "I hope to God," a wounded marine said later, "that we don't get to go on any more of those screwy islands."

An hour before H hour it shook and winced as it took what was being dished out to it. In fact, the whole surface of the island was in motion as its soil was churned by our shells and by the bombs from the carrier planes that were swooping down across its back. Every ship was firing with a rising tempo, salvo after salvo, with no more waiting for the shellburst to subside. Finally Iwo Jima was concealing itself in its own debris and dust. The haze of battle had become palpable, and the island was temporarily lost in a gray fog.

"The LST's are letting down their ramps," someone said.

There could not have been a better place to observe the whole spectacle than from the air-lookout station above the bridge, but there was too much to see. Only an observer familiar with the art and theory of amphibious warfare could possibly have unraveled all the threads, and an ordinary witness could only give as inaccurate an account as the innocent bystander gives to circumstances surrounding a killing on the street. There was no time any longer to ask questions or to digest kindly professional explanations. All the facts that one had learned from the secret documents were confused by the reality.

The LST's had let down their ramps and the amphibious vehicles which they had carried were splashing through the water, like machines from a production line. Watching them, I found myself speaking to a chief petty officer who was standing next to me.

"It's like all the cats in the world having kittens," I said, and the idea appeared to interest him.

The amphibious vehicles, churning up the sea into foaming circles, organized themselves in lines, each line following its leader. Then the leaders moved out to the floating flags, around which they gathered in circling groups, waiting for their signal to move ashore. The gray landing craft with the marines had left the transports some time before for their own fixed areas, and they also were circling, like runners testing their muscles before the race. The barrage which had been working over the beach area had lifted, and the beach, with the smoldering terraces above it, was visible again. It was time for the first wave to be starting.

It was hard to pick the first wave out in that sea of milling craft, but suddenly a group of the barges broke loose from its circle, following its leader in a dash toward shore. Close to land the leader turned parallel to the beach, and kept on until the whole line was parallel. Then the boats turned individually and made a dash for it. The Navy had landed the first wave on Iwo Jima — at nine o'clock on the dot — or, at least, not more than a few seconds after nine.

Minutes of the Mulligatawny Club

These two stories, as I mentioned in the foreword to this book, I consider in many respects to be the end result of many rather groping experiments in short fiction. They move easily within the frame that limits them. Their characters are comprehensible, I hope, to any reader, even possibly to a student of the comics. Their endings are neither happy or unhappy, nor, do I think, contrived.

If these stories are successful, it is because for considerable intervals in my life I have lived in the environment of my characters and am familiar with the types that derive from this environment. I have, in short, written about a galerie *of which I know, and I wish that all writers young and old would do the same. Tolstoy said that if you have seen a street fight you should be able to describe a battle. Possibly, given genius, he may be right, but at least the street fight is the first essential, and one not to be derived from the imagination.*

There is nothing as serious as a street fight in these stories. When I wrote them, though, I considered them amusing, and completely harmless. Like other writers who have dealt lightly with manners and folk customs I was deceived. I have even been reproved by some of my acquaintances, who have told me that these stories are malicious and that I have Gone Back On My Class. The Left Wing also has given me no sympathy, not that it ever has. Instead of saying I had, at long last, developed a social conscience it ended by calling me that worst name in its lexicon — an aristocrat. In other words, like many of my literary betters, I have fallen between at least two stools. I once thought when I wrote these stories that at last, after thirty and more years of endeavor, I had solved the problem of writing a story that the readers of a popular magazine might enjoy and yet a story that a few critics might take seriously. I was wrong. These last efforts of mine in the field of short fiction were greeted by editors with restrained enthusiasm. If I must continue to buy shoes for the baby and if I want to keep a few friends, I must make an effort to find a happier vein.

Sun, Sea, and Sand

(1950)

I REALLY cannot help feeling, after viewing every side of the problem, that the Board of Governors of the Mulligatawny Club did exactly the right thing about Epsom Felch. Say what you want, they had the best interests of our whole little group at heart, and the very basis of the Club has always been one of good informal fellowship. Of course there may occasionally be a little more drinking on the premises than is necessary, especially on dance nights — and sometimes I must admit Mary has spoken to me about my behavior on these occasions — but then, the whole club has ever been supported by the keystone of good fellowship. And besides, good old Zaccheus, who has been attending to the drinks for the last eighteen years, knows everyone's capacity. You can always trust old Zac. There are a few people of course, especially among what I may call the anti-Beachcomber crowd, who have never quite approved of Epsom, and have never seemed to understand how much he has contributed to everybody's fun every winter for years and years with his singing and his jokes — but then there are always people everywhere who have no sense of humor and can never lapse into what is called on Broadway, a Good Belly Laugh.

The Mulligatawny Club would not be the Mulligatawny Club at all without Epsom. It would simply be another British West Indian cottage community with a few coconut palms and a bathing beach — and no one who criticizes Epsom should ever forget for a moment that he was the one who raised the funds for the Chowder Room and the Sun Deck. Of course there are some people who say that Epsom is what is known as a "pincher," and perhaps he is now and then, particularly at the end of a late evening. But everybody who knows and loves the Mulligatawny Club and our cottage colony around it knows that Epsom is a harmless pincher, and he has never exhibited any of the serious hand trouble observable in some members I might mention, who have never contributed an iota to the general fun that makes the Mulligatawny Club what it is. Besides, Epsom is not entirely a joke. Epsom may be a little heavy and sometimes perhaps he is unduly noisy, but anyone who has seen him put on a monkey jacket, pretend to be a drunken waiter and end by singing "Are you aware that the cats they have no tails on the Isle of Man?" understands that noise means friendliness. That is why "Are you aware that the cats they have no tails on the Isle of Man?" is practically the theme song of the Mulligatawny Club. Besides, almost any morning, no matter how long he might have entertained us the night before, Epsom can be counted on to beat par on the Coral Knoll course — which is more than a lot of young fellows I know can do, who come down from New York or Chicago for a few weeks' rest, and then criticize Epsom simply because he is friendly. Epsom may be middle-aged, but what with the sun and sea and sand he has kept himself very fit. Nearly everyone must remember how Epsom bit young Willie Wingate's ear at Governor's Night in the Chowder Room last season before they were separated; but everyone who was there understands it was just a friendly roughhouse with no hard feeling on either side. Epsom is very fit, as I sometimes remind Mary when she occasionally calls him a "lush," but Mary usually says it in a kindly way. I don't agree with Mary at all when she sometimes says that Epsom has done nothing with his life. Epsom has done a great deal by giving a lot of pleasure to a lot of people. Even if he just limited himself to his drunken-waiter act at cocktail parties, this would be justification enough for Epsom's whole existence.

As a matter of fact I have not done much with my life either since I left the floor of the Stock Exchange when Mary's father died. There has been no reason for violent or consistent effort since then, and a lot of other cottagers I might mention around the Mulligatawny Club have no reason to overwork themselves either. Our community here, as I have often told Mary, was never organized for the deserving poor, although we did a great deal to make life happy during the war for Navy boys who dropped anchor in the harbor and for flyers who came to this little Gulf Stream island for their training before going to the Great Adventure. The Mulligatawny Club, as I have told Mary, is not intended to help people to do something with their lives. It is neither a Chautauqua nor a Bach festival. On the contrary, it is a haven for people who are a little tired of doing something with their lives, especially since Truman's re-election, and who want to get away for a little while and forget, and do nothing with their lives. This may be why we, in what I like to call the old Mulligatawny Beachcombing set, believe that Epsom Felch epitomizes the spirit of this place. This is exactly what I said at my last after-dinner speech on Chowder Night. Even though there was some good-natured joshing at my use of such a long word, I still think "epitome" exactly describes Epsom.

I wish that Wallace and Claire Shirley could have understood Epsom as well as I do. I can only say that I honestly tried to make them both an active part of the community from the moment they got off the boat at Central Cay, even though Wallace was no more than Mary's half-first-cousin's child. I even suggested to Wallace that he call me by my old Yale nickname, Spike, but still he invariably insisted on calling me Cousin Dwight, which perhaps may give you some idea of Wallace. I do not like to be critical, because I always like young men, but he never did get the Mulligatawny Spirit. I am sorry for it, because this was his loss — not mine.

Frankly, I could not remember ever having heard of Wallace Shirley until Mary received his letter, written on the stationery of Matthew, Caldwell, Luke, Shed and Jones, the New York law firm that handles two of Mary's minor trusts and also some securities in her own name which she refers to as her "things." We had been breakfasting on our terrace overlooking the harbor, and it was, I remember, about an hour before it would be necessary to think of making our way to the Club beach. It is amazing how busy one can always be at the Mulligatawny Club. In fact I have heard many members say that they have never been so busy in their lives. Thus that hour between breakfast and beach is one of the few hiatuses in an active day, and one does need a few quiet morning moments to collect oneself and read the mail. The letters were already on the table beside the morning flower arrangement of red hibiscus, and Magdalena, our new maid, whom Lady Thwaite had found for us after Elija, the houseboy, had discovered the key to the liquor closet, had just brought in the coffee.

"I wish Magdalena would wear a turban," Mary said. "Then she would look like an old West Indies print."

"Magdalena would not want to wear a turban," I said.

"I could ask her," Mary said, "if I were only Lady Thwaite."

"Magdalena wouldn't wear a turban," I said, "but you can ask her even if you aren't Lady Thwaite."

"Dwight," Mary said, "I wish you wouldn't be so consistently anti-British."

"It's not being anti-British," I told Mary, "to say that you're not Lady Thwaite. I am very glad you're not and I am equally glad I am not Sir Oswald."

Mary did not answer, and I hoped she was glad I was not Sir Oswald, not that I intended in the least to be anti-British. Actually we have some very good friends among the British and we are always invited twice a year to functions at Government House. For some reason very few British ever do come to the Mulligatawny Club except for a few functions during Race Week. They have their own club, and perhaps this is just as well, and as far as they are concerned they can have it, although Mary and I do go there for occasional functions.

"Actually I like the British very much," I said. "I've always liked the British."

"You don't," Mary said, picking up a letter, "because they give you an inferiority complex, and you know it. You and Epsom Felch are always taking digs at the British, but let's not discuss it. Why, here's something from Matthew, Caldwell, Luke, Shed and Jones."

Mary opened the letter with the silver paper cutter that Magdalena always brought in with the mail. Mary had assumed a certain executive business expression that she had begun to wear quite frequently since she had inherited her late father's estate after taxes. It was the remote and somewhat grim look of one who bore a heavy burden, and it often made me slightly uneasy because it may have implied that I was the burden. On such occasions Mary was prone to forget that there was no reason for me to do any work any longer because now there was enough for everything without further contributory effort. I looked across the harbor at the native sailboats tied by the local market and wondered if any of them had brought in a green turtle. It had been a long while since there had been a good turtle pie at the Club. Mary's voice interrupted my train of thought.

"Why, this isn't about my things at all," Mary said. "It's a personal letter from Wallace Shirley about plans for his vacation."

The name conveyed nothing to me, but then one meets so many people, and so I asked who Wallace Shirley was.

"Don't you remember?" Mary asked. "Try to think. I don't know why it is that you never even try to put your mind on anyone in my family after all the things I have to keep doing for yours."

"I am trying to think," I said, "and I can't remember anyone named Shirley. It sounds like a girl's name. I did meet a girl once named Shirley. I met her at a Yale prom."

"That must have been before you got into that society there," Mary said. "I don't suppose you spoke to anyone after that."

It was a long while ago, and I could see no good reason for Mary's bringing up my college years as material for criticism.

"Don't you remember," Mary said, "my cousin Elsie? She was one of my bridesmaids? She married Rodman Shirley, and they live in Greenwich, Connecticut, and Wallace is their son, of course. I wish we didn't come down here every winter. It gets us out of touch with things, and it isn't good for you either."

It always made me very nervous whenever Mary said she wished we didn't come down here every winter.

"Well, well," I said, "what about Wallace Shirley?"

"Don't you remember?" Mary said. "He's the one who married a Powers model. I gave them a silver tea tray, and I see him sometimes when I go to that office to see about my things."

"Well, well," I said, "a Powers model."

"There's no reason to say it in that tone either," Mary said. "Lots of very nice girls model now if they can, and you know it."

"Well, well," I said, "they didn't when you were a girl."

"At least I recognize that I'm not a girl," Mary said, "and I wish that you and Epsom Felch and a lot of the rest of you wouldn't keep trying to pretend that you are still boys. Wallace and Claire want to come down here for a two weeks' rest. Claire is getting over an attack of flu. They are coming down next week. I want you to get them cards for the Club and see if you can't get them the Bougainvillaea Cottage."

"Yes, dear," I said, "yes, of course."

"That's a good boy," Mary said, and she patted my hand. "And now, I suppose, we had better think about getting to the beach, and the backgammon tournament starts this afternoon, doesn't it?"

Mary and I have always been happily married because we have so many things in common, and backgammon is one of them. Mary and I are two of the best backgammon players on the cay, if I do say so myself.

I was perfectly certain, although Mary immediately disagreed with me, as she frequently does when I am certain, that we had never so much as entertained these young people, even at a mop-up dinner in New York, and certainly not at Bar Harbor. Her sudden interest in them now she only explained by saying that blood was thicker than water. It never occurred to me for a moment that she would have disrupted the final round of the backgammon tournament by insisting that I go myself to Central Cay to meet the young people at the boat instead of letting the captain of the Club launch, the *Mulley*, collect their baggage and see them through the customs. I had a game scheduled that afternoon with Eustace Sayles, president of the Sayles Bottle and Tubing Company, one of the Club's most determined and dangerous backgammon players, but Mary actually insisted that I ask a postponement, and as matters finally turned out I also had to skip my usual after-lunch siesta. It did no good to tell Mary that I had no idea what the young people would look like. She said I would recognize them because Wallace was distinguished looking and Claire was very beautiful. I had to cross the harbor in the *Mulley* myself and wait in the confusion of the customs shed, watching the harbor boys diving for small change before the passengers disembarked.

Newcomers may feel a certain fascination in arriving at the old Bahamian town of Fort William on Central Cay and stepping ashore into a territory called quite aptly by the travel folders The Isles of June. I have no doubt whatsoever that the native police in their pith helmets and their white tunics and the vendors of straw baskets and shell jewelry and the off-island boats and the antiquated victorias combine to give an Old World atmosphere. To an old inhabitant like myself, however, and especially to one who has lived for many seasons in a self-contained community like the Mulligatawny Club, the bustle of boat day is only a disturbing interruption of normal pursuits. Though I was careful to be dressed in a Jamaican print shirt and to wear a coconut hat especially woven for me at the Cay Shoppe — not one of the ordinary coconut hats sold by hawkers along the docks — there was always the danger that cab drivers or hotel porters might mistake me for an American tourist. Besides, meeting strangers is a repetitious and fatiguing process because one always has to answer the same questions. What are those quaint stucco houses along the water front with their balconies? Where can you go to get a good Planter's Punch, and will there be a chance of getting one immediately, and where do you go to buy English doeskin trousers, and is it true that perfumes are cheaper here than in New York? Also I have never understood why all visitors invariably wish to know the names of trees.

In this respect the young Shirley couple were no different from other cruise passengers. I recognized them immediately on the theory that they would be the most attractive couple disembarking. Wallace Shirley had the same athletic build as his fellow passenger, an American tennis professional who had arrived to play an exhibition match at the Royal West India Hotel on Sunday, but Wallace was dressed, not advertising tropical tweeds. Claire, hatless, in dove gray, carrying a motion-picture camera, was just as pretty as Mary said she would be. She seemed almost to be modeling her traveling ensemble when I first set eyes on her standing by Wallace, but then, modeling is fashionable nowadays with the younger set. She had an interesting face with a few amusing irregularities of feature that would lend a piquant individuality to a professional photograph. In spite of her conventional blond hair and carefully applied lipstick, brown eyes and delicately penciled eyebrows, I would almost say she had character, and I knew immediately that she would look well in a bathing suit and that it would be a pleasure to introduce her on the beach.

"Don't tell me," I said to them, "that you two aren't the young Shirleys, because I don't think I could bear it." But of course they were the Shirleys.

"It is awfully kind of you to have come to meet us, sir," Wallace said.

"Your Cousin Mary would hear of nothing less," I told him. "And neither would I, of course. Did you have a good trip, my dear?" It was very pleasant to call Claire my dear. "Now don't worry about anything. Here's Captain Tom, who will take us across the harbor, and Captain Tom will see about the baggage. I know the customs man. We'll be out of here in a minute."

"Didn't you row on the Yale crew, sir?" Wallace asked.

"Why, yes," I said, "number five, but that was quite a while ago."

It was quite a while ago, and it pleased me all the more to have some young man remember it. It made me feel that we were all getting off on the right foot.

"There are an amazing lot of old football and crew men at the Mulligatawny Club," I told Wallace. "We have really a club of our own within a club. We call ourselves the Beachcombers, and we really have a lot of fun considering our age."

"You certainly look as though you do," Wallace said.

"And Wallace must get one of those wonderful shirts like yours so he can be a Beachcomber too," Claire said. "Where can you buy one of those shirts, Mr. Billings?"

"Don't call me Mr. Billings, my dear," I said. "He can get one at the Cay Shoppe, and he must have a coconut hat, but we can do all that tomorrow. We must get back now so that you can see the Club. There will be sun on the afternoon beach and a chance for a swim before cocktails."

I was, of course, most anxious to start back across the harbor. Also I wanted to explain to them the spirit of the Club so that they would get off on the right foot, but it was hard to start them moving because Claire kept wanting to buy jewelry and to take colored pictures.

"I have never been so far south before," she kept saying. "Now Wallace, you and Cousin Dwight stand over there with those little shoeshine boys and talk to each other. That's it — and don't look so restless, Cousin Dwight. What is the name of that huge, gray-looking tree? Wallace, throw something in the water for that little boy."

We were now completely surrounded by hack drivers, shoeshine boys, boat boys and shell and basket vendors.

"Get out," I told them. "Get along with you. Don't bother us. That large tree is a silk cottonwood, my dear. The palms are coconuts. That coral they are trying to sell you is called brain coral. There will be lots of time to buy everything later, lots of time, my dear. We must get in the Club launch now or we will miss our afternoon swim."

"I don't want to miss a single second of it," Claire said. "Throw the boys some more money, Wallace dear."

That is one of the troubles with youth. No one their age could see that you often gain more by missing a few things than by trying not to miss anything. There was no use telling them that everything at Fort William could be easily missed. We were alone on the *Mulley* going across the harbor, and Claire had used up nearly all her film so it was possible to explain a little to both of them about the Mulligatawny Club.

"I know," I said, "I know, my dear, that all this water-front color is intriguing for a little while, but you will want to get away from it eventually, even away from the British, though some of my best friends are British. You will want to be with congenial people who talk your idiom. That's why the Mulligatawny Club was founded in 1906. You can get away from everything there and simply be yourself. I know you are going to like it."

I was glad to discover they were becoming curious at last about their destination. The Club on the little island across the harbor, I told them, now had two motor boats, the *Mulley*, on which we were traveling, and the *Gatawny*. I had thought of their names myself, I told them, and had proposed them at the second Chowder Room dinner last year, when I, or rather Mary, had made a gift of the two boats. There was a real routine at the Mulligatawny Club, I explained, the morning for golf or tennis, followed by the morning swim and informal cocktails and the buffet lunch on the morning-beach terrace, a siesta, then perhaps another spot of golf and a little boating, then the afternoon swim and either the home or the Club cocktail hour. We would have our own cocktails quietly this afternoon and then dinner at the Chowder Room.

"And Epsom Felch will probably do some juggling for us," I said. "Epsom will think of something."

"Who's Epsom Felch?" Wallace Shirley asked.

There was not time to tell him in detail. Our boat was approaching the Mulligatawny dock, and there was Mary in her orange slacks to meet us, with our yard boy to take care of the baggage.

"By tomorrow morning," I told Wallace, "you will be surprised that you asked me who Epsom Felch is. He is our club's most lovable character. There's your cousin Mary, and you are going to be in the Bougainvillaea Cottage."

We were safe back and much earlier than I had expected.

"Mary," I called, "isn't there time for me to play off that backgammon game? If I don't, the whole tournament will be delayed."

"No, of course there isn't, you silly boy," Mary called back, and then she waved to Claire and Wallace.

If I have learned nothing else from living, at least I know that people with similar backgrounds are congenial. Some ludicrous fault in early upbringing begins immediately to cause innumerable small frictions, beginning with the raising of an eyebrow and ending, I am sure I don't know where. Fortunately for the success of the Mulligatawny Club, its most useful members have been brought up in the right way, have attended the right schools and so exhibit the right reactions under all circumstances. Nothing, as I have often told Mary, makes me more suspicious than incorrect background, but I can hardly blame myself for taking the young Shirleys' background for granted at first, since they were my wife's relatives, and Mary's background, with a few slight flaws, is something to which I have succeeded in adjusting myself successfully.

Consequently I cheerfully began by accepting the young Shirleys as nice young people who would fit automatically into our congenial little group. Yet, as I told Mary that very night, I have not been on the Admissions Committee of the Mulligatawny Club for nothing. Even that afternoon when I introduced Mary's relatives to the Club, because Mary was doing her household accounts and never liked to be disturbed at such a time, I was vaguely disturbed by certain lapses. I would not define these as arising from lack of appreciation but rather a general intellectual blankness which I attributed to insecurity in a strange environment. I do not mean that they did not like the Club. They really enjoyed the decorations in the Chowder Room, especially the signs above the bar, such as "No ladies admitted here except with escorts," and when I showed them the "Men at Work" sign, which Epsom Felch had filched from a New York street, I knew they were amused, especially by the caption under it: "This one was felched by Epsom Filch and carried by him to this desert island December 1948."

"Oh," Claire said, "that's the Mr. Felch we were talking about, isn't it? He has quite a sense of humor, hasn't he!"

It was still too early for the cocktail hour and so the bar, a delicious, cool, breezy room, aromatic with rum and orange peel, was deserted, with only good old Zaccheus there polishing glasses.

"Did you hear that, Zaccheus?" I asked him, because of course I introduced old Zac to the young people. "Mrs. Shirley thinks Mr. Felch may have a sense of humor. Do you think he has a sense of humor, Zac?"

"Oh yes, sir," Zaccheus said, "he's got a sense of humor."

Zaccheus is a Jamaican Negro, and his broad English accent is always a delight.

"Do you remember when Mr. Felch set off that cannon cracker behind you, Zac, on New Year's Eve?"

"Oh yes, sir," Zaccheus said. "Yes, sir, I remember."

"And there's another piece of Felchiana here," I said. "Let me see, where's that other sign, the one that Skid Butterfield had put up after the Race Week dance? Oh, here it is."

The sign read, "Fellow members, hide your wives; here comes Julius Caesar Felch."

"It's from the Latin quotation," I said, "but you must remember all about Caesar, don't you, Wallace?"

"Not all," Wallace said, "but I do remember that the evil that men do lives after them. Anthony said that, didn't he, in Shakespeare's play entitled *Julius Caesar?*"

Something about this remark of Wallace's did not entirely fit in with the fellowship of the place. I could not quite decide whether he was being unconsciously obvious or whether he was being satirical, and satire always makes me uncomfortable.

"You mustn't think for a minute that there is anything evil about Epsom," I said. "Epsom is just Epsom. Isn't Mr. Felch just Mr. Felch, Zaccheus?"

"Oh yes, sir," Zaccheus said. "There's only one Mr. Felch, sir."

Even my own remark sounded a little different from what I had intended. It sounded like an unnecessary defense of criticism when there had been no criticism.

"I was just quoting Shakespeare," Wallace said. "I can see Mr. Felch must be quite a card, and I'll remember to hide Claire."

"Oh, Wallace, don't," Claire said. "We're not Romans."

I don't mean to imply for a moment that Wallace Shirley did not have good manners. When we got to the afternoon beach, I took him to the men's Sun Deck and introduced him to Bud Hollis and Corky Collins and the rest of the regular crowd who like the afternoon sun. If anything, he might have been a trifle too formal, but I was confident that this would wear off in time. It was only when we were on the beach together drinking coconut milk brought to us by one of the beach attendants that he said something else which disturbed me.

"Isn't it a little hard," he asked, "for so many people to sit around here all winter and not get into mischief?"

"My God, Wallace," I said, "we're all too busy here to get into mischief, and besides, we all have the same backgrounds, and besides, there's the Club Board of Governors. Don't worry about mischief, Wallace."

These were only indications of a state of mind, hardly worth mentioning. Many newcomers at the Club have exhibited similar constraint. In fact some of our best members have taken over a year to become adjusted to the Mulligatawny life. It was only when Epsom Felch arrived uninvited at our cottage for cocktails that I began to doubt whether the Shirleys were quite what I had every reason to hope they would be.

Once in New York I remember hearing someone refer to the Mulligatawny Club and Cottages as "one of those escapist colonies filled with rich people who have nothing to do except to try to forget what they are." The author of this remark, who was someone I had never seen before, and obviously have never seen since, was clearly influenced by the left-wing liberalism that is doing so much to make the city uncomfortable for those who once loved it. I have always prided myself on the reply I made. I simply said this might be correct, but that anyone fortunate enough to be admitted to membership never needed to think of escaping further. No one in his senses would wish to avoid our loggia with its marine aquariums or the Chowder Room or the Sun Deck and the Beach Bar and the beach.

Yet since one cannot stay in such places all the time, there are also the members' cottages, all with Club service, each cottage designed and furnished by individual subscribers according to their own tastes. Our own cottage, the Flora Dora, a name I gave it because it is furnished with amusing Victorian odds and ends acquired from Mary's father's Bar Harbor home after his death, is, I think, one of the most enjoyable and unique. It has an other-worldly atmosphere that is frankly welcoming after a hard day on the beach or on the golf links, and one must relax occasionally. I love our cool living room with its General Grant sofa and its glass-covered wax flowers on their marble-top stands. I especially love our terrace at the cocktail hour, with its cochina-rock flagstones, its fine bush of sea grape and its view of the sunset and of the surf beating on the reef. No one who has ever seen our terrace has ever wanted to leave it, except when the sandflies appear, but these arrive only at rare intervals. As Epsom Felch has said, they are the only living things that can't be kept permanently out of the Mulligatawny Club.

Mary and the young Shirleys were there already when I made my entrance in my burgundy-silk cocktail coat. Mary wore the interesting new cocktail gown she had purchased from one of New York's most creative couturières. It was of hand-painted silk with a brilliant motif of violet and red mixed drinks in long-stemmed glasses. Wallace, I was glad to see, had a white-linen dinner coat and Claire, in a reclining chair, wore a pastel sea-green dinner dress, which made her look perfectly beautiful, distinguished almost. It warmed my heart to see them. We were a group, I thought, that did honor to the terrace and justice to the view. Out at sea the few clouds were already tinted rose and gold, and the ocean at the horizon's edge was a deep amethyst.

"Well, well," I said, quoting Kipling, " 'looking lazy at the sea'?"

"Oh, Cousin Dwight," Claire began, but I stopped her. I never knew that anyone could be as completely lovely as Claire. It made me feel young to see her, and very, very gay.

"Why be so formal, my dear?" I said. "From now on you're a member of the Beachcombers and you can call me Spike."

"Oh," Claire said, "I couldn't call you that."

"Of course, she couldn't," Mary said. "We have to stop somewhere, Dwight."

"But at least you can call me Uncle Dwight, my dear, as all the other young people here do," I said, "sorry though I am to be old enough to be your uncle."

"Then see you act like one," Mary said, and she laughed in an edgy way that made me nervous, but then, we were only looking lazy at the sea, and Mary has never had any reason to complain of my conduct with old girls or young ones — at least not for a long, long time.

"Oh, Wallace," Claire said, "I wish I had the camera, but I suppose it is too dark for a picture. Look at the color of the waves breaking on the sandbar out there."

"Not a sandbar, my dear," I said, "it's a coral reef."

"Oh," she said, "a reef? that makes it all like something in a magazine story."

"Any time you want to be cast away with me, my dear," I said, "just let me know, but be sure you wear sea-green."

"I don't know why you compare this to a magazine," Wallace said, "but if you do, say it's like something in a quality-group magazine."

He was smiling at the sea and it was difficult to judge whether or not his remark was uncalled for.

"*Fortune* magazine, at least," I said.

"Dwight," Mary said, "I wish you wouldn't always bring the subject around to money."

"I just said fortune, dear," I said, "just fortune. Isn't it about time for a cocktail? Hasn't the bar boy come down yet from the Club?"

"When I was a girl," Mary said, "and thank goodness I am not a girl any longer, fortune and money were synonymous."

"It's my good fortune that they are, dear," I said. "I wonder where that bar boy is. Where's Magdalena?"

It had been our custom for some years to have drinks mixed by Zaccheus, brought down from the Club for the cocktail hour. No one could mix drinks like old Zac, and it saved messing up the kitchenette. Just as I spoke I heard a peal of laughter from the kitchenette, coming obviously from our maid, Magdalena, since it was uninhibited laughter peculiar to the colored race.

"That means the bar boy is there," I said, because he was one of Magdalena's friends, and I raised my voice, "Magdalena, is that the bar boy?"

The door to the kitchen wing opened and there was a second peal of noisy merriment.

"Oh yes, sir," Magdalena called, "the bar boy's here. He's a new bar boy."

I did not like it. Servants should not be too familiar in a Crown Colony, even under a socialistic government.

"Well, there's nothing to laugh at, Magdalena," I called. "Bring out the appetizers and have the boy wheel out the bar."

"Yes, sir, we're coming, sir," Magdalena called, but she still was giggling.

Magdalena came first with the tray of appetizers, and behind her I could hear the trundling sound of our new portable bar, and the always-welcome tinkle of the glassware.

It was growing dusk, that sudden brief dusk of the tropics. If there had been more light, I have often told Epsom Felch, I would have seen through the practical comedy at once. As it was, I could perceive immediately that the bar boy was new and not a suitable employee for the Mulligatawny Club.

"Yes, sah," the bar boy called. "Ah'm acomin'. Old black Joe's acomin' and his head is bendin' low."

"That's enough of that nonsense," I said. "Take the orders for the drinks. What would you like, Claire my dear, a rum swizzle?"

I was obliged to tell myself that nowadays there is servant trouble everywhere, even among the young male population of Fort William, which up to now has adequately answered our winter colony's demand for chauffeurs, houseboys and temporary waiters. The bar boy from the Club had obviously been sampling liquor. I would make the necessary complaint tomorrow, but now it seemed wise to put up with a half-tolerable situation in case an even worse bar boy might appear.

"Magdalena," said Mary, "stop that tittering."

If there is one thing that I can take justifiable pride in, it is my ability to handle and get on with native servants. I am successful in this because one only needs to remember that they are essentially children.

"That's enough of this damn nonsense," I said. "Boy, pour those swizzles on ice and stir them. Not that way, the way Zaccheus taught you. Damnation! What's the matter, boy?"

I was startled because the bar boy was making a series of retching sounds. I could not see him clearly through the dusk behind his bar on wheels, but I could observe his wide mouth opening and closing.

"Excuse me, sah," he said. "Ah've got something in mah gullet. Ah never did have a good gullet. Mah mammy always said so."

"I think you had better run along back to the Club, son," I said, "and straighten yourself out. It's all right, son. I'll mix the cocktails myself."

"Oh, no, sah," the bar boy said. "Ah'll tend them."

Before I could consider what to say next, the boy had lurched against the wheel-bar. The contraption plunged forward suddenly, striking Magdalena in the rear, causing her to stagger just as she was passing the appetizers to Mary.

"Oh, Magdalena," Mary gasped. "The anchovies, on my new dress."

It was true. A small shower of anchovies had fallen on Mary's hand-painted cocktail gown. My next move was purely instinctive. It was necessary to push the bar boy away from the ice and glasses before he did further damage. I did push him, but to my surprise he pushed me back so violently that I lurched against the ice bucket.

"Dwight," Mary called, "do something! Aren't you going to do something?"

At this point I realized that the whole scene was preposterous, even with the world in its present state. The boy's accent was too theatrical and, though well built, he was too fat, and Zaccheus never employed fat bar boys.

"Magdalena," I called, "switch on the lights."

We had recently installed in the sea grape a floodlight, artfully concealed, to be used for moonless evening parties. Of course, the instant this was on, the whole mystery was solved.

"Here," Wallace said, "I'll help you with him, Uncle Dwight," but now there was something wrong with my own gullet. I could not answer Wallace because I was laughing. I don't remember when I ever laughed so hard, except at the New Year's dinner in the Chowder Room.

"Oh," Mary said, "so this is what I get a new dress ruined for, is it?"

Of course it was Epsom Felch. No one but Epsom could have carried such a thing through so successfully. There was Epsom in one of Zaccheus's white monkey jackets, with stove blacking on his face and hands. Of course, I should have suspected him from the beginning, but up to now Epsom had always played the part of a white, never a colored, waiter, and this explains, in a measure, my obtuseness. It shows you the sort of person Epsom is, that he should go to such thought and trouble just to entertain Mary and me and the Shirleys. There is nothing like a Good Belly Laugh, as they say on Broadway. No one in his senses could possibly have been annoyed at Epsom, especially when he sang a snatch of our theme song, "Are you aware that the cats they have no tails on the Isle of Man?" It seemed as though I could never stop laughing.

"Go inside and wash yourself, you damn fool," Mary said, "and don't get black all over the powder room," but even Mary had to laugh.

"Yes, sah, boss," Epsom said. "Thank you, boss lady."

"Oh, stop," Mary said, "don't go on with it, Epsom," but even Mary could not stay mad long at old Ep.

"You see what I mean?" I said, and I slapped Wallace hard between the shoulder blades because I wanted Wallace and Claire to be in on the fun. "There's never a dull moment at the old Mulligatawny. Wally, this is Epsom Felch."

"Pleased to meet you, son," Epsom said. "Dwight, why do you make me humiliate myself like this in front of you and in front of Mary?"

"I didn't," I told him. "You made yourself humiliate yourself in front of yourself." The charm of Epsom Felch was that you found yourself growing funny simply because he was funny.

I didn't know what Epsom was building up to, but I knew it would certainly be something good. I was sorry to see from Wallace's face that he did not seem quite to appreciate the beauty of our repartee.

"I mean, you only said a nice young couple were staying here," Epsom said. "You never told me you were entertaining the most beautiful girl in America, and you make me humiliate myself even to get a glimpse of her."

"Oh," I asked him, and I suppose I am, as Mary says, occasionally a little slow on the uptake, "you mean Claire, do you? Romans, hide your wives; here comes Julius Caesar Felch."

It was a simple joke but no one could help enjoying it after taking a look at Epsom. He was too stout for Julius Caesar and he was still covered with stove blacking. This made it all the more delightful when he clicked his heels together like a Frenchman and bent over Claire's delicate white hand.

"Honey chile," he said, "Ah done been waiting for this all these years. Cain't you and me be alone for a little while, honey chile, and leave all these nawsty people?"

I will say for Claire that she got into the spirit of it all a good deal better than Wallace.

"Oh, Mr. Felch," Claire said, "Ah'd just love to and the moon's coming up, but don't you think it would be a little obvious?"

"Don't let that worry you, darling," Mary said. "Epsom and his desires are always a little obvious."

I think Mary was trying to be gay but occasionally her sense of humor cuts two ways without her intending it. Consequently I was relieved that Claire still maintained the spirit of the moment.

"I never heard that song of yours before, Mr. Felch," Claire said, "that one about cats having no tails."

"You couldn't be referring to our genial hostess, honey chile, could you?" Epsom asked.

Of course, he shouldn't have said it, but no one, not even Mary, should try to cross swords with Epsom Felch.

"Your genial hostess," Mary said, "suggests that you go in and wash your face and stop being the end man at a minstrel show."

There comes a time when it is just as well not to go too far with Mary.

"All right, Duchess," Epsom said, "right away, Duchess."

"And you can have my other cocktail coat, Ep," I told him.

"I brought my own," Ep said. "It's in the kitchen. I know how to behave in nice houses. Don't drink it all before I get back, kiddies. 'Are you aware that the cats they have no tails on the Isle of Man?'"

It is hardly possible to maintain a mood indefinitely. Epsom's whole prank had been perfectly delightful, but I think we all felt a certain letdown directly after he had left us. I heard Claire sigh and I saw Wallace look uneasily at the portable bar.

"Does he do this sort of thing often?" Wallace asked.

"Often?" I said, pouring the rum swizzles, and it was obviously high time to do so. "Why, Epsom does this sort of thing every minute."

"Day in and day out?" Wallace asked.

"That's exactly it," I said, "day in and day out. Wait until you see him at the Chowder Room after dinner. I don't know how he does it. He never seems to get tired."

"Well, I see what you mean," Wallace said, "when you say there isn't a dull moment here."

"Now you mustn't get Ep wrong, Wally," I said. "The main thing is that Epsom loves people. He loves everybody."

"Well," Wallace said, "I'm glad he loves everyone and not just Claire."

"Wally, dear," Claire said, "come here," and she took his hand. "I'm not like Mr. Felch. I don't love everybody."

"Mary, darling," I said, "don't worry. I'll buy you another cocktail dress."

"Oh," Mary said, and she raised her eyebrows. "*You'll* buy me one, will you?"

"Technically, dear," I said, "just technically. You know what I mean."

When Mary is in a certain mood, particularly since her father died and she inherited the estate, she can make everyone uncomfortable, and there is nothing whatsoever that one can do about it. In fact, you might even get the impression sometimes that she didn't love Epsom Felch.

It is impossible not to feel responsible for guests at our little colony, but despite my anxieties it would not be fair to say that the young Shirleys made a bad general impression. I only wish that they might have made more of an effort to make any impression. Instead of water skiing or sitting on the diving float with the younger set, they invariably withdrew under a beach umbrella as far as possible from everyone, reading aloud to each other, of all things, a new translation of the *Odyssey*, or else they went on long lonely walks or took more of their interminable colored photographs. Solely because of Mary and me they were showered with numerous informal invitations to join in the general fun, nearly all of which they refused, including several offered by Epsom Felch.

"I hope those kiddies of yours are having a good time," Epsom said. "I like to see everybody happy. Are they happy here, Spike?"

"I think they are in their own way," I told him. "I suppose there are different ways of being happy."

"The hell there are!" Epsom said. "There's only one way to be happy and that's to loosen up. You don't understand women the way I do."

"Oh," I said, "don't I?"

"No, you don't," Epsom said. "Basically, all women like to have a good time and their men won't let them. That's all there is to human relationships. Every woman is at heart a rake."

We were conversing on the Sun Deck, each reclining on a wooden table, rubbing ourselves with coconut oil and sipping from cool glasses of gin and tonic supplied by old Zac.

"Who said that," I asked, "that every woman is at heart a rake? Is it a quotation?"

"Oh, you and your quotations," Epsom said. "I can use it, can't I? Every woman is at heart a rake, signed Epsom Felch."

We were reclining there, surrounded by other Beachcombers, and naturally everyone was listening because something always happens when Epsom begins to talk.

"You tell him, Ep," Corky Collins called. "It's a true quotation and I can back you right up from personal experience."

Everyone else also was very anxious to illustrate from his past to back up Ep after Corky Collins started. Curiously enough, we each had been through some similar personal experience, which intrigued each of us so much personally that we each began shouting, in order to put across our individual contributions. It began to be noisy on the Sun Deck but very, very interesting and revealing until Gregory Maypole joined us. There isn't a nicer fellow basically at the Mulligatawny than old Greg Maypole, but perhaps he had begun to take himself too seriously since he had been elected Chairman of the Board of Governors.

"Oh, oh," Epsom said, and he jumped off his table and squatted down behind it. "Here comes the house detective."

"We were just talking about women, Greg," I said.

"I know you were," Greg said. "I don't like to be sent up here to tell you to keep your voices down. Don't make a problem for me, boys."

Of course Gregory smiled when he said it, but if you can't have fun on the Sun Deck, where can you have it? I wanted to ask him that question, but I didn't. Instead I was still wondering whether or not Epsom was right and I wished that I had been exposed to that quotation when I was younger.

It was Mary, and not I, who insisted that the Shirleys should attend the Pirate Night dance at the Chowder Room instead of excusing themselves as they suggested. I recall very clearly, though Mary consistently says it is not so, that Mary, and not I, told Wallace and Claire that they would have to show themselves at at least one party, and not go creeping off together reading Homer all the time. They were her relatives, she said, and Pirate Night was an annual affair which everyone attended. All you needed was a red bandanna and some earrings, and Gregory Maypole was going to be Captain Kidd because the Chairman of the Board of Governors was traditionally Captain

Kidd and of course Epsom Felch was going in his usual original costume as Captain Kidder.

It made me a little sad when I observed Wallace's reaction. It made
me think of how much more fun I once had when I was Wallace's
age. Wallace only said he wished they could be excused. He said he
was never good at costume parties. He said he made enough of a fool
of himself anyway without having to do it consciously. It hurt me
because it was not the proper spirit and I was glad to see that even
Claire was critical, making it seem very possible that he was not letting her have the good time she wanted and deserved.

"Oh, Wally," she said. "Of course we'll go if Cousin Mary wants us
to, and it'll only take a few hours. You go to the dentist, don't you,
darling, when you don't want to?"

She was so sweet and eager when she said it that I immediately as-
sured them both there would be no pain. The Chowder Room would
be made over into a pirate's den, I explained, with pirates serving noggins of rum punch out of kegs, and neither of them would want to
miss seeing Epsom Felch as Captain Kidder emerge from the Dead
Man's Chest after fifteen Beachcombers had been sitting on it singing
the Pirate Night theme song.

"All right," Wallace said, "all right. Yo ho ho and a bottle of rum."

At least it did seem as though Wallace might make an honest effort
to enter into the spirit of things that night. Fortunately, for years we
had collected pirate costumes for these occasions, so that there were
plenty of things to lend to Wallace and Claire. I loaned Wallace my
Billy Bones costume, though I had planned to wear it myself, and he
looked well in it, thin and almost menacing. Mary and I disguised ourselves as we had the year before last, as Mr. and Mrs. Ben Gunn from
Treasure Island by R. L. Stevenson. Claire was a pirate girl, wearing
cut-off dungarees and one of my frayed white shirts that I had been
saving for Zaccheus and my best red-silk bandanna, a simple enough
costume but its simplicity was highly effective. So few girls look well
in trousers, even with a girdle, and I know that Claire was not wearing a girdle, because I gave her a hug and a kiss myself when Mary and
I called at the Bougainvillaea Cottage for them on our way to the
Chowder Room. After all, it was Pirate Night. I wish the Shirleys
could have understood that things are somewhat more informal on

Pirate Night than on other evenings. If they only had, a great deal of subsequent embarrassment for everyone could have been avoided. The Shirleys should have understood that Pirate Night comes only once a year.

They say that practice makes perfect and this dictum perhaps explains why, after so many years, this Pirate Night was better than any I can remember during my entire sojourn at the Mulligatawny colony. Everyone knew exactly what was coming next. All the backdrops and furnishings that made the Chowder Room look like the deck of a ship were set beautifully in place. The barrels that served as water butts from which one dipped out the noggins of punch did not leak, and this year there were three real parrots that set up a steady screaming; and when the fifteen men sat on the Dead Man's Chest, it did not break down, as previously, on Epsom Felch. My own speech at the dinner too went off better than I had ever remembered it, particularly the final sentence: "Now, fellow pirates, I feel that I have kidded you long enough and so I shall let Captain Kidder kid Captain Kidd."

I happened to see Wallace Shirley just as I had finished. He was bent double over his plate and I did think at last he was in the spirit of it.

"Dwight, I want you to see that they are having a good time," Mary shouted to me several times, because no one could speak in a low voice on Pirate Night, but there was no reason for her to worry. Some young pirate girls on their vacation from Vassar had surrounded Wallace and all the Beachcombers were dancing with Claire, who had somehow lost a curtain ring from one ear, but who looked perfectly adorable when disheveled.

"She wants to have a good time, and her man won't let her," Epsom said, "and she isn't wearing a girdle."

"Who?" I asked, but I knew who. I even thought that Epsom was going too far, except that it was Pirate Night. "Just remember that Greg Maypole and all the Board of Governors are around and take things a little easy, won't you, Ep?"

"Oh, oh," Epsom said, "here comes the house detective."

The secret of Pirate Night, as is true with similar functions, lies both in generous moderation and in never allowing spirits to flag. No sooner did the fun begin to wane a trifle than old Zac and his bar boys would roll out another barrel, but most of the pirates behaved very well and those who didn't, Greg Maypole made walk the plank into the boys' room. In fact there was scarcely an untoward incident to mar the entire evening until half past one in the morning. I was dancing with Mrs. Corky Collins, whom the old crowd calls Corkin, and with whom one always dances out of loyalty to Corky, and I was just thinking that I had never known Pirate Night to run so smoothly, when I saw Mary beckoning to me.

"Dwight," Mary said, "have you seen Claire lately?"

"Why, no," I said, "what of it, Mrs. Gunn?"

"Well, Wallace is looking for her."

"Well, let him look," I said.

"I think you'd better look, too," Mary said. "I'm a little worried, Dwight. She was dancing with Epsom Felch."

"And why not?" I said. "I wish you wouldn't always cast aspersions on poor old Ep."

"Don't be a damn fool," Mary said. "Go out and find them. You know Wallace doesn't like him."

"Wallace doesn't like him?" I repeated.

"Don't argue, get started looking for them," Mary said. "That's a good boy."

No one whom I have ever tried to find on a dance night has ever thanked me, but I had to go when Mary insisted. There were a number of couples wandering affectionately about the Club grounds, as there always are on dance nights, and some of them called to me jokingly but none of them had seen Ep lately. I tried the terrace, the tennis courts and the beach without seeing a sign of Claire and Epsom, and finally I went down the Bougainvillaea Walk, a pretty *allée* of vines recently planted by the house committee along the path which leads toward the cottages. The walk was lighted this evening by a few party lanterns, but many of the spaces were dark, and thus I heard Claire's voice before I saw anything.

"Will you please stop?" I heard Claire say, rather sharply.

"Listen, darling," I heard Epsom answer, "you know old Captain Kidder never stops."

I coughed but they did not hear me, and perhaps I should have coughed louder. It immediately occurred to me that this was not exactly the place for a third person and that I would be well advised to turn away and leave the field to Claire and Epsom Felch, because I have learned that most young girls of Claire's age are quite able to look after themselves in such a situation and prefer to handle matters without outside meddling. There was the sound of scuffling, not unusual under the circumstances, and I should certainly have retreated tactfully if I had not been startled by what Claire said next.

"Let go of me," I heard Claire say. "Let go of me, or I'll call my husband."

I cannot blame myself for being surprised. In all those inevitable little contretemps which have occurred at the Mulligatawny Club I have never heard of any young matron calling her husband to take part in such a controversy.

"Listen, darling," Epsom said, "you know you wouldn't do that, darling, not to old Ep."

"I will," she said, "this instant. I'm not fooling, Mr. Felch."

"You wouldn't," Epsom said, "because he would ask you how you got here," and then there was the sound of a slap. "Ouch," Epsom said. "That hurts, darling!"

It seemed to me that Claire was handling the whole thing rather clumsily and that perhaps I should break it up, and I am positive I should have if I had been allowed the opportunity.

"Wallace," I heard Claire call, "Wallace, *Wallace!*"

Immediate action was necessary, if real trouble were to be avoided.

"Now, Claire," I said, "just a minute, Claire, my dear." Then I saw them in the shadow of a friendly hibiscus and I saw that Epsom was as nonplussed as I was.

"Now, Claire, my dear," I said, "here's Uncle Dwight. Everything is all right, Claire."

"Then tell this drunken fool to leave me alone," Claire said. "Tell him — "

I have always been sure that everything would have adjusted itself if it had not been for Wallace. I had no idea that Wallace was anywhere around until he suddenly appeared and shouldered me aside quite rudely.

"What's the trouble here?" Wallace asked. "What is it, Claire?"

"Oh, Wally," Claire began, "he — "

"All right, all right," Epsom said, "the show's over. Let him take you home, sweetness, and to hell with it, as long as you don't know how to behave."

The situation was tense, but if Epsom had not displayed this understandable pique, I am certain everything would have ironed itself out. As it was, what occurred was entirely Wallace's fault, not Epsom's.

"Oh, Wally," Claire called to him, "Wally, don't!"

I was faced by one of those unbelievable moments when one can merely stand helplessly transfixed. Before I could move, or fully comprehend what I was witnessing, Wallace Shirley, Mary's and my guest, with a card to the Mulligatawny Club, had struck Epsom Felch a clean right-handed blow. It was obviously intended for the jaw, but the light was poor and the swing landed high. Even so, Epsom lost his footing and sat down hard on the gravel path. Wallace, standing over him, looked like an illustration of Billy Bones at the Admiral Benbow Inn, from the book of R. L. Stevenson, but costumes could not change reality to romance.

"I have been wanting to do that for quite a while," Wallace said. "Come on, Claire."

"Get out," I said. "Both of you get away from here, Wallace." But my advice came too late.

I have said that Epsom always kept himself very fit. Now he was on his feet and before I could say another word he had made a rush at Wallace.

"Now, boys," I said, "wait a minute, boys." But it was all too late.

I don't know why it is that people seem to appear from nowhere when they are least needed. A moment before, no place could have been more deserted than this lonely little trysting place, and now the spot seemed filled with people, springing apparently from the ground. I had a glimpse of Corky Collins with a false beard and some of the younger members with a few of the Vassar girls, none of whom exhibited the responsibility which one might have expected.

"Fight," they began chanting, "fight, fight, fight. Go it, Bones; sock him, Kidder."

The crowd increased. Suddenly I saw that Gregory Maypole was there, and even worse, Eustace Sayles, President of the Sayles Bottle and Tubing Company, and several of his British guests. Eustace Sayles was not only a good backgammon player but he was also a member of the Board of Governors and a leader of that clique that we Beachcombers have always called the anti-Beachcomber crowd. Before I could think of some way to handle him Mrs. Gunn arrived and began pulling at my arm.

"Dwight," she screamed at me. "Aren't you going to do something?"

"What's the matter with you, Maypole?" Eustace Sayles shouted. I have always thought he had a very arrogant manner. "Can't you break this thing up?"

"Of course I can, Eustace," Gregory Maypole answered. After all, Eustace Sayles had paid the Club deficit for the last two years. "Get those people separated. Come on, fellows, help me stop this damn roughhouse."

But by that time anyone could see it was more than a roughhouse. It was a public scandal by then, and members hastily wedged themselves between Epsom and Wallace.

"So it's Felch, is it?" said Eustace Sayles, when they were separated. "I have told you, Gregory, that I have had enough of this clowning, and we'll get to the bottom of this one. Will you kindly call a meeting of the Board of Governors at ten o'clock tomorrow morning?"

"Now, Eustace," Gregory Maypole said. "It would be a great deal better to keep this quiet."

"I'm sick of being tactful," Eustace Sayles said, "and I have guests who are not used to this. You heard me, Maypole. Call that meeting at ten tomorrow morning, and see you're there to explain yourself, Felch."

"Ay, ay, sir," Epsom said. "I'll be there, Captain."

No matter what was going on, you could always depend on old Ep.

"Mary," I said, "I think we had better go home now. Come, Wallace, come Claire," and we walked off toward the cottages.

"Oh, dear," Mary said, "oh, dear. I do think you might have done something, Dwight." She only expressed disbelief when I told her I had done all I could.

"Wallace," I said, "this is very, very serious."

"Is it?" Wallace answered, "I wouldn't know."

"You shouldn't have struck him, Wallace," I said. "It wasn't in the least called for."

"I don't know what else was called for," Wallace said, "and I wish they had let us alone for three more minutes."

I did not answer. Wallace was not showing the proper spirit. He might at least have been apologetic and a little bit ashamed. He did not understand the implications of a meeting of the Board of Governors. He could not have realized that entirely due to his hysteria Epsom Felch might very well be asked to resign from the Mulligatawny Club, where he had spent his most rewarding and happy years following his third divorce.

Of course I understood Wallace's position and basically it was un-assailable. Basically his wife had been subjected to unwelcome advances and Wallace had only taken what are conventionally considered necessary steps — but there are so many shades to basic facts. Wallace's action may have been correct in the abstract, but at the same time it was not adult. It was too much like the behavior of King Arthur and his Knights of the Round Table, and even these knights, if I remember my Mallory correctly, often acted with restraint under greater provocation. Wallace's action was not broad-minded. It reflected no consideration for time or place.

I tried to explain this to Mary when we had arrived home after leaving Wallace and Claire at the Bougainvillaea Cottage and after telling them not to worry about anything. I still could not understand Wallace's attitude.

"There is nothing for me to worry about," he said. "The rest of you ought to worry if you want self-respecting people in this place."

"Now, Wallace," I began, "this is essentially a gentlemen's club."

"Maybe it is," he said, "but from what I've seen of it, I wouldn't know."

Wallace continued to remain utterly aloof. They could do what they wanted, he said. It wasn't up to him and if anyone else made a pass at Claire, he would do it all over again. I can only repeat that his position, though correct, was neither broad-minded nor adult.

Mary's position was not broad-minded either. I have never seen Mary more upset, perhaps because her emotions were confused by blood relationship. She kept saying that I must do something. Claire, dear Claire, had been insulted, she said, and I must take a definite position.

"If you don't do something," Mary said, "the first thing in the morning, I'll move and we'll never stay here again."

It did no good to tell her that the Board of Governors were going to do something the first thing in the morning.

"You can go over and help them," Mary said. "You can ask them personally to get rid of Epsom Felch. He insulted our house guest, Dwight."

"Mary," I said, "you're overtired. Let's go to sleep."

She had suddenly adopted the propaganda of the whole anti-Beachcomber crowd. She said that all the decent element in the Club were sick and tired of Epsom Felch. They were bored with his perpetual clowning and now he had gone too far — but there is such a thing as loyalty. I am glad that I was able to stand my ground.

"Mary," I said, "I won't go back on old Ep."

I wanted to add that Epsom was a symbol. I wanted to tell again of all the happy hours that Epsom had given all of us, but there was no use arguing with Mary when she was in such a mood.

The morning after Pirate Night is invariably very difficult, and this particular morning was worse than any I have ever experienced, for there was the inevitable aftereffect of fun, combined now with emotional upset. There should have been clouds and rain to fit in with my mood, but instead the morning was discordantly bright and beautiful. My hand trembled as I drank a single cup of black coffee. What was the meaning of life, I was thinking? What was life if human relations were not based on good fellowship? I wanted to struggle with these thoughts in solitude but Mary had said I had to do something.

Traditionally the Board of Governors held their meetings in the privacy of the Backgammon Room. The door being closed, I could only sit in the adjoining Card Room waiting and listening to their voices rise and fall — but I could not distinguish words. There is nothing more ominous in the Club than a meeting of the Board of Governors, especially when they have some member on the carpet, and I knew poor old Ep was on the carpet as I sat there listening. There were men in there like Eustace Sayles, who did not understand old Ep. There were also men like Gregory Maypole, who did not have much strength of character. I wished that I were on the Board of Governors.

I must have been there for about twenty minutes when Epsom Felch came out. Epsom was wearing a Hawaiian aloha shirt and his face was puffy and there was a large purple swelling below his left eye.

"Hi, Spike," he said. "You look terrible."

"So do you," I said.

"If you mean my eye," Epsom said, "he didn't do it — she did. Let's go and get a gin and tonic."

"Ep," I said, "you know the old crowd is right behind you. We'll resign if you do, Ep," but Epsom still looked terrible.

"I know," he said, "I know, Spike, but this place isn't what it used to be. Let's go and get a drink."

"I can't," I said. "Mary wants me to wait here."

"Oh," Ep said, "how is Mary taking it?"

"Oh," I said, "you know Mary. She'll quiet down in a day or two. This will all quiet down, Ep."

"I don't know," Epsom said. "People don't know what fun is any more. Well, see you later, Spike."

When he walked away, he still looked terrible, and I felt terrible. I wanted to say something more but I couldn't. When the door to the Backgammon Room finally opened again and the Board of Governors filed out, it seemed like the end of everything.

The Mulligatawny Club is nothing if it is not democratic. It is not fair to state, as some of the more radical members say privately, that the Board of Governors is a self-perpetuating body. They are elected each year at the March annual meeting. Their names are submitted by the Nominating Committee. It is not the Nominating Committee's fault that an almost-identical list is customarily offered. It is only a proof that very few members are fitted to be on the Board. I am always glad to recall that I could have been on the Board myself if Mary had permitted it, but as Mary pointed out, the main function of the Board is to make up the Club's annual deficit, and, though it seemed quite possible that I might assist after the death of Mary's father, Mary and I never saw eye to eye on this point. Nevertheless, I like to consider myself a sort of ex-officio member, and I have always been ready to offer the Board advice and encouragement.

Of course I knew them all very well. Though it seemed to me that I should have been called to give my own version of last night's affair, it is just as well not to tangle with the Board. They all greeted me politely as they filed out of the Backgammon Room. If it seemed to me that their manner was a trifle cool, this may have been due only to my morning-after nerves. Eustace Sayles, of the Sayles Bottle and Tubing Company, nodded to me almost curtly, but then I had defeated him in the backgammon tournament. R. W. Smithfield, of the Smith-field Wire and Rod Company, called me Spike and seemed a little apologetic, and so did H. A. Wickford, who had married Sis Trellis, and who now represented many of the Trellis interests in Detroit. Hubert A. Bolster, of the Bolster Packing and Curing Company of Chicago, was always affable, except at the bridge table. He also called me Spike and asked me why I was up so early in the morning, as if he did not know why. S. J. Chrome, of Chrome Outdoor Advertising, who always prided himself on his sense of humor, asked me if I had been reading any good books lately, and Myron B. Radway, of Rad-way Couplings and Bearings, went so far as to squeeze my arm play-fully. They all tried to give the impression that this was simply a routine meeting of the Board of Governors, but still there was an atmosphere of constraint. I saw that all of them were standing watch-ing me uncertainly, and Gregory Maypole, who was the last to leave the Backgammon Room, seemed more embarrassed than the rest of them.

"Well, well, if it isn't old Spike," he said. "Fellows, as long as old Spike is here, we'd better tell him the bad news, hadn't we? Let's all sit down for a minute."

We began selecting chairs around the bridge tables, and my mouth felt very dry. Eustace Sayles and S. J. Chrome were the only ones who continued standing.

"I want to say again that I am against this whole business," Eustace said.

"I know, Eustace," Gregory told him, "I know, but it was put to a vote. Now, Spike, I am afraid this is going to be a little tough on you, with your fine sense of loyalty, but we've been over this from A to Zed and we want to make this as easy as possible for you, Spike."

My mouth felt very dry. I did not like the way they were looking at me and I cleared my throat.

"I don't know why I'm singled out for this attention," I said. "I'm very sorry for what happened last night, but I'm a friend of old Ep's and always will be, and I resent anything that hurts old Ep."

"Now, that's fine," Gregory Maypole said. "We all would have ex-pected you to say that, Spike, and it makes things easier."

There was a moment's silence which was broken by Eustace Sayles.

SUN, SEA, AND SAND

"I want to say again," he began, "if I had my way — " but Gregory Maypole raised his hand.

"Now, Eustace," he said, "we all know what you and S.J. think, but you didn't have your way."

"All right," Eustace Sayles said, "but don't come around to me for making up any deficit."

Everyone moved uneasily in the bridge chairs, and Gregory Maypole looked hurt.

"Now, Eustace," he began, "you know you don't mean that."

"Let's get on with it," Myron B. Radway said. "Let's stop the argument."

"That's exactly my idea," Gregory Maypole answered, "and there really isn't any argument. Now, Spike, I know this is going to be a little hard on you." He hitched his chair nearer to mine and slapped me on the knee. "We don't like to say hard things about your relatives."

"What relatives?" I asked.

"Why, the young Shirleys, Spike."

I was frankly a little puzzled. "They're no relatives of mine," I said. "They're my wife's."

"Well, well," Gregory Maypole said, "then maybe we can be franker. We've been over this thing from A to Zed, and without wishing to appear critical, we don't think that either Mr. or Mrs. Shirley, attractive though they are — "

"I don't want to listen to you damn fools any longer," Eustace Sayles said. "I'm leaving."

"I'm leaving too," said S. J. Chrome, and I remembered that he handled the Sayles outdoor advertising.

"All right," Gregory said. "We're sorry, Eustace. Without meaning to criticize your wife's relatives, Spike, we don't feel that they quite appreciate the spirit of this place. I won't say that sometimes Epsom Felch is not a little adolescent, but then, Epsom is Epsom and what would this place be without him?"

They all hitched their chairs forward and the atmosphere seemed warmer, more genial.

"Spike sees that, don't you, Spike?" H. A. Wickford said.

I began to feel a warm glow of good fellowship for the first time in many hours.

"And frankly," Gregory Maypole went on, "any young girl who knows anything of beach life ought to know what to expect if she walks outside with old Ep. She didn't have to go. She should have been able to recognize the difference between harmless fun and something else. Besides she's a model, isn't she?" Gregory paused and looked around the room.

"Spike sees that, I'm sure he does," H. A. Wickford said.

There was no need for me to answer. They were a fine crowd. I should never have lost my faith in that fine crowd.

"And when it comes to jealous husbands and melodramatics," Gregory Maypole went on, "there is no place for jealous husbands and any of that damn foolishness at the Mulligatawny Club. I suppose young Shirley was drunk, but imagine anyone, drunk or sober, hitting old Ep! You see that, don't you, Spike?"

"Of course, I do, Greg," I said but then I thought of Mary. "You mustn't be too hard on Wallace. He sometimes swings to the emotionally unstable side, that's all."

"Now, that's just it," Greg said. "We don't want to be hard on anyone. We want to forget this whole little fracas and to get back where we were before. There's only one thing we want to ask you."

"What thing, Greg?" I asked.

Greg Maypole mopped his forehead. The sun was growing higher, not yet over the yardarm, but it was growing warm indoors.

"We just want to ask you to suggest nicely to those young people that it would be just as well if they didn't use the Club facilities for a while. There's always the British club, you know, and we can attend personally to getting them a card for the British club. Just tell them nicely and explain the whole thing to Mary. Mary can't help but see our point — eventually."

It was a difficult assignment and I could tell from sympathetic looks that everyone there knew it, but my relief and my renewed faith in the old Club Spirit was so great that I was fully ready to face it.

"Fellows," I said, "I think you have done exactly the right thing. I'll help you in every way I can."

"Atta boy," Gregory Maypole said. "We knew you wouldn't let us down, Spike. This has been a very tough morning, fellows, and the sun isn't over the yardarm yet, but let's call in old Zac and have him bring us a little something, and let's all sing the old Club theme song.

Come on now, 'Are you aware the cats they have no tails on the Isle of Man?' "

I never enjoyed that song as much as I did that morning. Even though I kept thinking of ways of explaining the situation to Mary, I enjoyed every word of it. God was in his heaven and all was right with the world.

King of the Sea
(1952)

IT still seems to me that what happened to Percival Norton last winter, while he dwelt among us in the Bahamas, has genuine elements of pathos. Furthermore I feel that one should be loyal to Percy even though he is not as colorful a member of our Club and Cottage colony as some individuals I might mention. After all, as I have often told Mary, a community is a community, and the Mulligatawny Club and Cottage, with its well-selected, congenial membership, has its own strong traditions. I told Mary, when she told me that Percy and the Meredith girl were becoming interested in each other, that it did not seem to me that Janey Meredith had such a high intelligence quotient either, even though she was a sophomore at Vassar College. Furthermore, as I told her, the Meredith girl's legs were too large for her, and they had always struck me as being muscle-bound.

I have never been able to understand why this remark should have annoyed Mary or why she should have asked me if I could not think of something better to do than examine young girls' figures. It made her weary, she said, seeing a group of persons every morning on the beach, myself among them, acting like judges in a bathing-beauty contest. Speaking of figures, she could say something about the figures of middle-aged men in our community, who ought to be ashamed to expose themselves. She wished we were back in the days of our youth, when men wore tops on bathing suits. There were reasons for these conventions.

"There is nothing wrong with my figure," I told her, "or my posture either."

"You're growing corpulent," Mary said, "now that you never do anything. I don't know about your posture but there's something wrong with your attitude. We really ought to stay north in the winter. A few good old-fashioned head colds might deplete you."

It was unkind of Mary to say I did nothing, simply because I had ceased working on the floor of the New York Stock Exchange after Mary's father had died and his will had been probated. There was no necessity for such efforts on my part any longer, as Mary very well knew herself. Actually I had never been so busy as I had since Mary's father's death, even though a winter resort tends to discourage routine activity. I pointed out to Mary that I did setting-up exercises every morning, including thirty-five push-ups. Furthermore I was always on the beach at least two hours before the buffet luncheon and I constantly played eighteen holes of golf each afternoon, and I had improved my playing until I was now in the low eighties. Besides, there were the Club activities and long social evenings and bridge tournaments, all of which required concentration, and I was specializing in backgammon. None of these activities was a joke, no matter what Mary might say about them.

"Oh, stop it, Dwight," Mary said. "Please don't labor over every point, and don't start telling me that you rowed on the Yale crew in 1914, because I remember it."

"And don't forget, Mary," I told her, "that we met at the Hotel Griswold in New London."

"I haven't forgotten," Mary said. "Father always said it was a mistake that we took the yacht down that year."

"Your father was interested in rowing, Mary," I said.

"You needn't remind me," Mary said. "I remember the details distinctly, Dwight."

I was relieved to see that Mary's mood had softened and that memories had drawn us closer.

"Besides, Mary," I said, "I was not discussing the Meredith girl's figure. I was only saying that her legs were overdeveloped, and besides she wears glasses."

"Janey Meredith is a very sweet girl," Mary said, "and don't forget that I wore glasses at New London."

"Now, Mary," I said, "you of all people should know that I'm partial to girls with glasses."

"If they're on a yacht," Mary said.

"You weren't on a yacht, Mary," I said. "You were on the veranda of the Hotel Griswold."

This was absolutely true and Mary knew it. I was glad to see that her mood was milder.

"Mother and Father began worrying right away," Mary said. "They always knew I was impressionable."

"Your father mentioned that several times," I told her. "And I remember what your mother said."

"What did Mother say?" Mary asked.

"She said in a very sweet way," I told her, "that once you got the bit in your teeth nothing could ever stop you."

"Oh, she said that, did she?" Mary asked.

"Yes," I said, "in that sweet way of hers, but you know your father began to understand me in the end."

"Well, let's not go over it now," Mary said. "I was very selfish, and I know now what Mother and Father must have gone through, and I know what the poor Merediths are facing."

"Why 'the poor Merediths'?" I asked. "What are they going through?"

Mary sighed and put on her glasses.

"Their problem with Janey," Mary said. "Poor Hortense Meredith. She said only yesterday that she wished that Janey had spent her vacation in Poughkeepsie. Oh my God, Dwight," and she took off her ordinary glasses and put on her sunglasses, because the morning glare was beginning to come on our terrace, "their problem with Janey and Percy Norton," and she repeated it in a louder tone, as though she were speaking to a foreigner.

"What about them?" I asked.

"Oh, Dwight," Mary said, and she spoke more slowly. "Janey Meredith is infatuated with Percy Norton."

"Is she?" I said. "Why is she?"

Mary's expression reminded me very much of her late father.

"Why does any poor girl get infatuated?" she asked. "Because she doesn't know any better. Propinquity and loneliness, I suppose. I know just how the poor Merediths must be feeling."

"But what's the matter with Percy Norton?" I asked.

"How would you feel," Mary asked, "if we had a daughter and she fell in love with Percy Norton?"

We did not have a daughter, but there was such a thing as loyalty, and a community is a community. "Mary," I said, "Percy has been a member of the Club for several years. You mustn't say anything against old Percy."

"Why is it," Mary asked, "that you think everybody in this Club is perfect?"

"Now, Mary," I said, "everyone here has been passed upon by the Committee on Admissions. Percy has never made trouble for anyone and he gave the aquariums for the wall in the Chowder Room, and furthermore he keeps the aquariums stocked with interesting fishes."

"Really," Mary said, "I wish you wouldn't labor every point, Dwight."

"Just because Percy never says anything," I began, "doesn't mean he doesn't have his good points."

"Be quiet, Dwight," Mary said. "Here they come now, Percy Norton and Janey Meredith, and, oh my God, they're going fishing."

But I did say one thing more, and I said it very loudly.

"Don't forget, Mary," I said, "that Percy did very well in the war. He was one of those people who blew up coral reefs. He has very steady nerves and he's a very powerful swimmer."

"Then why doesn't he grow scales and marry a mermaid?" Mary said.

Then she assumed a more gracious look, because the Meredith girl and Percy Norton were moving up the path that ran between our terrace and the sea, and it was obvious that we would have to speak to them.

I cannot help it if I have a fellow feeling for any young man who has done his "bit" in World War II, since I myself participated in World War I. It may be true, as Mary invariably points out when I endeavor to reminisce on that earlier conflict, that I had seen no action. Yet if one has once worn the uniform, one cannot help but entertain a warm and kindred feeling for everyone else who has worn it; and it was only natural that I should have thrown a playful salute to Percival Norton as he was walking with Janey Meredith past our terrace.

"Please stop doing that, Dwight," Mary whispered.

There was no reason in the world why I should not have done it, and if Percival did not respond, I am sure he understood the spirit of the gesture, because he stopped and looked up at us.

"Good morning," he said. "Good morning, Mrs. Billings."

Then he scraped his heavy bare toes self-consciously on the rough concrete of the beach walk, making a sound like sandpaper.

"Well, well, Percy," I said, "are you off for a little underwater dynamiting?"

As a matter of fact he looked very much as he must have somewhere in the Pacific, except that during the last few seasons his yellow hair had thinned noticeably and I now observed that the top of his skull was sunburned to a deep, angry red that made me wonder why he never wore a hat. Actually he was wearing nothing but an abbreviated pair of swimming shorts, and his stomach bulged slightly above them. It was not corpulence, however, but muscle. There is seldom much of the Greek god about really good swimmers. Though Percival was over six feet, the thickness of his torso and the slight bow of his legs and the length of his arms made him look shorter. His freckled skin was red and peeling but there were pale circles around his eyes, due to his wearing diving goggles. He was holding a dingy canvas bag and a fishing spear in one hand and a pair of rubber gloves and rubber swimming fins in the other, and he scraped his toes for a second time on the concrete walk.

"Please don't make that noise," Mary said. "It sends shivers up my spine."

Percival gazed at his feet, and then Janey Meredith, who was walking just behind him, laughed nervously.

"Percy can walk on anything barefoot," she said. "You ought to see him."

"It comes from being on the reef at low tide," Percival said. "It toughens up your feet out there on the reef."

"You ought to see Percy on the reef," Janey said. "He killed a green eel yesterday. It bit his glove and Percy cut its head right off."

Percival shook his head slowly.

"Not a green eel," he said. "A green moray. You've got to watch yourself when you mix it up with a green moray."

"Why should you want to mix it up with one?" Mary said.

"You don't always see those jokers," Percival said.

"That's right," I said. The conversation was growing stilted, and I hastened to get things on a more genial basis. "Like the octopus in Victor Hugo. You know — in *Toilers of the Sea*."

"What?" Percival asked.

"Don't be so literary, Dwight," Mary said. "Percival isn't a toiler."

"You wouldn't say that if you saw him underwater," Janey Meredith said. "He really is like someone in Hugo."

Percy turned to look at her. It was amazing how far he could turn his head without moving his shoulders.

"It's only I like spear fishing," he said. "I'm nuts about spear fishing. If you like it, you like it."

"You ought to see him in the water," Janey said. "He was looking for lobsters when the eel caught hold of his glove."

"Not lobsters," Percival said. "Crawfish."

"All right, crawfish," Janey said. "It's just like another world when you look at the sea through goggles — all sorts of little fishes and things, all colors, and sea fans and caves. You can swim right down among them and you're just like a fish yourself."

"That's right," Percival said. "You are kind of like a fish, but you've got to have the right gear and watch yourself. I hit a fifteen-pound grouper out there yesterday, but I got him too near the tail."

"You should have seen Percy," Janey said. "I wish I knew the names of fish the way Percy does. I'm going to take a fish course when I get back to Vassar. What do they call the study of fishes? Ichthyology, isn't it?"

"Gosh," Percy said, "I wouldn't know, Janey. I spear something and Artemus tells me what it is. He always has the word."

"Who's Artemus?" Mary asked.

"Why, Mary," I said. "Artemus is Percival's boat boy."

It was very dull of Mary. She should have known that Artemus was one of the best boat boys in the harbor, but then she always hated boats.

"Artemus says Percy's the best white man he's ever seen underwater," Janey said. "Artemus is married and has six children and two by another wife."

But I was not as interested in the private life of Percival's boat boy as I was in the loquacity of Janey Meredith. Her bathing suit was unbecoming and so were her spectacles. Her face and shoulders shone uninvitingly with coconut oil, and she, too, was freckled, but she had almost made me believe that there was another world out there on the reef.

"Oh," she said, "here's Artemus looking for us now."

Sure enough, Artemus had appeared around the bend of the path, an emaciated middle-aged Negro, barefoot, in khaki trousers, and wearing one of Percival's old sport shirts.

"Suh," Artemus said, "boat ready."

"Take this gear, will you, Artemus?" Percival said. "Come on, Janey we've got to shove."

"And we'll bring you back a lobster," Janey said.

"A crawfish," Percival told her.

"When I get back to Vassar," Janey said, "I really am going to take a course in ichthyology."

"Janey," Mary said, "will you be back in time for lunch?"

"Oh, no," Janey answered. "We'll be out on the reef all day."

As soon as the couple had left, I began to make a mental list of our own activities for the day. There would be the usual informal luncheon on the beach terrace. Then in the afternoon there would be the semi-finals of the Christmas-season bridge tournament. We were facing the usual heavy holiday schedule and I had almost forgotten about Percival Norton and Janey Meredith until Mary spoke.

"Dwight," Mary said, "please bring out the telescope." She was re-ferring to an excellent and very cumbersome instrument that had come from her late father's summer home in Bar Harbor.

"And don't bang it against anything the way you did last time," Mary said.

"But, Mary," I told her, "it's time we were going to the beach."

"Please don't argue, Dwight," Mary said. "Set it up right here. Now turn it on the reef."

Then of course I understood what was on her mind. The lens was surprisingly powerful and a slight adjustment contrived to bring the long reef, two miles offshore, almost beside us on the terrace. The tide was ebbing and I could see the gray ridge of rock and the spray of the ground swell beating against it.

"Mary," I said again, "it's time to go to the beach."

"Don't argue, Dwight," Mary said, and she seated herself behind the telescope.

There were a number of things I might have said. I might have said that I did not approve of spying.

"Mary," I said, "we were young ourselves once."

"Yes," Mary said. "You needn't remind me, Dwight. Of course it's
he Merediths' money. There is always someone thinking about a poor
girl's money. Mother always used to say so."

"Yes," I told her. "I remember."

"Don't argue, Dwight," Mary said.

"I'm not arguing," I told her, "but it isn't fair to put everything on a
financial basis, Mary. Besides, Percival doesn't need money."

"He has a mere pittance," Mary said. "After all, what do you know —
what does anyone know — about Percival Norton?"

This was not a sensible question, as Mary would have been the first
to admit, had she been in a different mood. If it is nothing else, our
small Bahama community, nestled on the end of a small island, or
'cay,' hardly more than a biscuit's toss from the delightful little
British colonial town of Fort William, is an intimate community. No
one going there to escape the rigors of a northern winter could very
well be a stranger to his fellow emigrees. The Mulligatawny Club,
named after an informal sort of fish chowder first cooked upon the
cay by the late New York financier and the Club's founder, Mr.
Charles H. Bostford, has always been set foursquare upon a firm foundation of good fellowship. Started originally just after the turn of the
century by a group of congenial New Yorkers and a few friends from
Chicago and Pittsburgh, the Mulligatawny Club, like its now-famous
chowder, has never lost its first fine flavor.

For those who enjoy congeniality and good fellowship and who have
an honest craving for cheerful relaxation, the Mulligatawny Club and
Cottages have much to offer. Such happy individuals have always
found an intense and rewarding joy in the palm-shaded private bathing
beach, in the airy, breeze-swept Club rooms, in the two really delightful bars, in the Saturday and the midweek get-together dances, and in
all the organized games and activities, so carefully and selflessly arranged by our hard-working entertainment committees. Admittedly, I
have seen persons who have said that the Mulligatawny Club was an
ingrown group of persons who have measured everything solely in
terms of comfort and money. Personally I have never been able to understand the left-wing criticism of money, the accumulation of which
I have always considered the basis of American progress. Fortunately,
from my point of view, the Mulligatawny Club is neither a debating

society nor a winter home for indigent professors, and certain persons
do exist, including myself, who tire of interesting people. The occasional artists and writers who have appeared as guests in our group, and
even some corporation lawyers, swept thither by fortuitous chance,
have almost invariably created a sense of malaise and strain. As I have
often pointed out to Mary, if one has a craving for interesting people,
why bother to search the Mulligatawny Club when there are always
a few such individuals hardly more than a biscuit's toss away in Fort
William? And this has always seemed to me and most of us at the Mulligatawny a very good place for them. There are fortunately some who
like to escape such things, choosing instead peace, mental rest, and comfort, and a fine Planter's Punch made by old Zaccheus behind the bar
in the Chowder Room.

At any rate we all know each other at the Mulligatawny Club and
we are all intensely familiar with everyone's capabilities. It was very
foolish of Mary to ask who knew anything about Percival Norton.

I remembered clearly the first time that I had ever seen him. It was
four years before, during Yacht Week, when the Club was customarily
open to yachtsmen who participated in the annual ocean race from
New York. Percy Norton had sailed down as one of the crew on
"Howdy" Bishop's trim schooner, the *Lulu*, which came in third after
very stormy weather in the Gulf Stream. Naturally, any friend of
Howdy Bishop's — a delightful sportsman and always a welcome guest
at the Mulligatawny whenever his *Lulu* dropped anchor at Fort William — was a friend of ours. I first saw Percy Norton in the Chowder
Room on the occasion of the Yacht Week dinner dance, when the room
was filled with battered mariners drying out after their arduous voyage.
His nose was peeling and he had a rope burn on his right hand.

"I met that boy in the South Pacific," Howdy said. "He was in underwater demolition and he comes from Duluth and he deserves to
have a good time. See that he has a good time, will you, Mr. Billings?"

It hurt me that Howdy Bishop did not call me "Dwight," but then
there was that gap in age.

"Well, well," I said, quoting Masefield, "he does look like a sailorman. 'And all I ask is a tall ship and a star to steer her by.'"

"What?" Howdy said.

"Just a line from Masefield," I told him. "It just whipped through
my mind."

"Well, all that aside," Howdy said, "make him feel at home and give him some rum. Percy's kind of slow on the uptake, but green water can go right over him and he doesn't even grab for the line. Now off Hatteras, you old-timers ought to have seen Percy. It was like this. . . ."

I did not listen to the rest of the anecdote. I felt somewhat out of it, being termed an "old-timer," but I was there to do my bit as a member of both the House and the Membership Committees, and hospitality to yachtsmen has always been our watchword.

"Well, well," I said jovially to the young stranger, "how about a noggin of rum, shipmate?"

I remember that Percy shook his head slightly, as though he still had water in his ears.

"How's that?" he asked.

"How about a noggin of rum?" I repeated.

"Oh," he said, "you mean a drink?"

"That's right," I said. "Something to splice the main brace, shipmate."

Percy seemed to be having a little trouble following me, but he finally did.

"Well, now," he said, "maybe I would like some of that stuff in those long glasses. I would really like to hold one in each hand, if that is permissible. It balances better."

It began to dawn on me from that moment that Percival Norton might be real Mulligatawny material. Old Zaccheus behind the bar was making the drinks very strong that night, but they had no appreciable effect on Percival Norton — which could not be said of most of his fellow yachtsmen. I could only observe that he was somewhat vague, and later I knew that his vagueness was normal.

"Say," he asked, "what is this place we're in?"

"How's that?" I asked, and then I had to laugh in spite of myself. "Why, my boy, you're safe in a snug harbor. This is the Mulligatawny."

"Oh," he said, "I was thinking maybe it was a club or something."

" 'A club or something?' " I could not help repeating after him. "Listen, son, haven't you ever heard of the Mulligatawny Club?"

He shook his head again, as though he still had water in his ears.

"Well, no," he said. "I just hit the beach with the crowd. It's a kind of a nice place, isn't it? Homey — all those stuffed fish."

"It *is* a nice place, son," I told him. I could not help calling him "son," even if he was somewhat old for it. "It's about time you learned the ropes around here, son. You are standing in what is called the Chowder Room. So you like the fish trophies, do you?"

"Yes," he said, "I always go for fish. Only there ought to be live fish in the wall."

"Wait a minute," I said. "How's that again?"

"Aquariums," he said, "set in the wall, with sea water pumped through them and lights behind, and fish."

The possibilities in what he said came over me in a flash. It was feasible. I could see the whole south wall of the Chowder Room filled with swimming fish. No one had ever thought of such a thing previously, but that is the way it is with a fine idea.

"You've got a real thought there, son," I said, and at that moment I saw "Bops" Merrill, who at that time was our Club president and who had, I always thought, a fine and broad-gauged mind. It was only a matter of an instant before I had him over and introduced him to Percy Norton.

"Bops," I said, "here's a real suggestion — the whole wall over there full of fish behind glass, swimming in salt water. What do you think of that one, Bops?"

I know nothing more warming than sharing an idea with someone who gets it, and Bops Merrill had the vision to get it right away.

"You know," he said, "we've really got something. But who would get the fish?"

"I could," Percy Norton said, "in a net."

"By God," Bops said, "it would be just like Bimini, wouldn't it?"

It was wonderful, the companionship of a shared creative thought, and you couldn't help liking Percy Norton, and we called Sandy Bowles over, who was also on the House Committee.

"We've got to hang onto this young fellow," Bops said. "Let's take him out and show him the whole layout. Let's see if he has any more ideas."

In a few minutes quite a crowd of us from the House Committee began showing Percy Norton all around the Club, and it was a fine night for sight-seeing — a full moon and colored lights in all the palm trees.

As was customary, there was dancing on the seaward terrace, and music was wafted beguilingly on the light sea breeze. The lights from the cottages surrounding the Club house twinkled companionably through the Junelike dark, and I was agreeably surprised that Percival Norton did not ask the names of the various trees and shrubs with which the Club grounds were landscaped. He merely said that they reminded him of the things you saw in New Guinea and then listened carefully when I explained to him the spirit of the Mulligatawny Club. When I was in the midst of my explanation, one of the newer bar boys came with a message that Mrs. Billings was ready to go home, but it was no time to take Mary home. Percival Norton was saying that he would like to own a little shack down here, and someone remembered that the Wilson cottage was vacant and probably for sale. We were showing him the cottage when another message reached me that Mrs. Billings was anxious to go home. It may have been that my tardiness was what always influenced Mary against Percival Norton. It might have been better if I had gone home, but there is such a thing as loyalty, and the Club right then was running at a deficit and was short of paying members.

Of course there was criticism later, as there always is regarding a new member. It was even said in some quarters that Bops Merrill should have shown more judgment and that Percy Norton was railroaded through by a small clique and that I vouched for him personally. I have never been able to understand the general conviction that I should be an apologist for Percy Norton. Actually his status was examined carefully by the Committee, and it appeared that he owned a block of common stock in the Norton Glass Company of Duluth. Although he was not active in the management, this would seem to be nothing against him, since there were many other members, including myself, not engaged in lucrative business. It was not fair to say that his personality contributed nothing to our Club life, when he did contribute a great deal by merely not being a problem. As I have said, the Mulligatawny Club is neither a debating society nor an intelligence quotient laboratory. Percival bought the Wilson Cottage and the fishing launch, the *Dolphin II*, and he was aboard her all the daylight hours and he was tired at night, and other people in the Club besides Percival Norton occasionally fell asleep early after dinner. Besides, he did contribute the aquaria in the Chowder Room, all manufactured by the Norton Glass Company. He was passed not only by me but by the entire Membership Committee.

Very few steps that one takes can be wholly right or wholly wrong, but they should always be regarded with a certain amount of broad-minded charity, as I tried to explain to Mary as she sat on our terrace in front of the telescope, focusing it upon a northern reef.

"Don't try to apologize," Mary said. "It was a mistake he came here. Everybody says so. There's that boat of his now. It's dropping anchor."

"Why shouldn't it?" I asked.

"Jane's lying face down on the forward deck," Mary said, "and she's undone her halter, right in front of that boatman."

"Where's Percival?" I asked.

Although it was not sportsmanlike, looking through the telescope, it was difficult not to be interested.

"He's fixing a spear," Mary said. "Now he's overboard in the water. Now he's underwater. Now I can't see anything of him. Now I see his head. No, it isn't his head."

"What is it?" I asked.

"It's his posterior, if you want to know," Mary said.

"Ha," I said facetiously, "bottoms up."

There was no time for Mary to reply to this sally of mine, because Virginia, our Bahamian maid, came to say that Mrs. Meredith wished to speak to Madam on the telephone. It was high time to be going to the beach, even if I had to go alone.

"Yes, dear," I heard Mary saying, "they came by here half an hour ago. His boat is anchored on the reef."

I am usually patient and anxious to adapt myself to Mary's moods, but it was time to be going to the beach. It was not like Mary to prefer to stay on the terrace, but she was still there with the telescope when I returned two hours later. I could not help but ask the news.

"Well, well," I said, "what have they been doing?"

"There must be something wrong with him," Mary said. "He's been in the water every minute, and she's been trying to get him to come aboard."

"Hasn't anything happened at all?" I asked.

"Nothing," Mary answered. "Absolutely nothing."

But this did not seem strange to me, considering Janey Meredith. I could not understand why anyone should be worried about Percival. The only thing that he ever did care about was the water.

I was not surprised that everyone in our little community soon began seriously to discuss Percival Norton and Janey Meredith. After all, friendship and interest in others are two of the watchwords of the Mulligatawny Club and Cottages. Still, I began to be somewhat embarrassed when people came to me for answers.

It was the custom of a small group of us to foregather of a Thursday evening in the seaside corner of the Chowder Room for cocktails. The life of this gathering was always Epsom Felch, who is one of the most amusing people I have ever known, and then there was Spike Willoughby, the industrialist from Pittsburgh, and Will Smythe, a newer member of our group, who recently had done very well in Texas oil and whom we playfully called "Tex," and finally Janey's father, Jason Meredith, the New York banker. Our minds were entirely concentrated on the rum drinks that good old Zaccheus, our barman, had served us, and also on the customary dice throwing. I am sure I do not know how we started on poetry unless our thoughts were lulled by the sound of the sea and the sight of Percival Norton's fish swimming behind the glass on the Chowder Room wall.

"I cain't seem to keep my eyes off those fish yonder," I recall that Tex Smythe said in that inimitable Texan drawl of his.

"Well, shut your eyes," Epsom Felch said, "and you won't see them." You could always be sure that Epsom would have a ready reply for anything.

"I don't want to shut my eyes," Tex said. "There's a new fish in there yonder since yesterday. A little sassy blue one — swimming there yonder."

"He's always been there," Jason Meredith said.

"No, suh," Tex Smythe said. "That blue one's new. Zaccheus, isn't that blue fish new?"

"Yes, sar," Zaccheus said. "Mr. Norton and Miss Meredith put him in fresh this afternoon when they come home from fishing."

There was a moment's silence, not awkward but still an appreciable silence, and then Spike Willoughby asked a literary question.

"Didn't someone once write a poem about a fish?" he asked. "No — not a fish. It was something about a merman."

"I've got it," Epsom Felch said, quick as a flash. "Ethel Merman!"

You could always count on Epsom to say something delightful at the right time. But even when the laughter subsided we were not thrown off the subject.

"No, no," Spike Willoughby said. "It was something about a boy mermaid, not a girl — a merman who kept hanging around the beach."

"Where?" Jason Meredith asked. "At some winter resort?" But I was more interested in the poem than the question, having once taken a course in poetry at Yale myself.

"It seems to me I remember it, too," I said. "It was about a merman who fell in love with a girl and then something happened around Easter time. I can't seem to remember what."

"You've got the dates wrong," Epsom Felch said. "It isn't Easter yet."

"Who wrote it?" Jason Meredith asked.

It surprised me and pleased me that Jason Meredith should have been interested, because he usually cared nothing about poetry.

"I've got it," Epsom Felch said. "It was a lyric out of a show. You can't get a merman with a gun."

It was very clever of Epsom Felch, and everyone except Jason Meredith joined in the laughter that followed.

"I don't remember who wrote it," I said. "It was about a merman and an English girl, and it had something about church bells in it."

"I've got it," Epsom Felch said. "Wedding bells. The merman married the girl. They got the merman with a bell, when they couldn't get him with a gun."

By this time everyone was in the spirit of the moment except Jason Meredith. I was very much surprised when he pushed back his chair and rose.

"Well," he said, "I'll have to leave you comedians now."

"Why?" Epsom said. "What's the matter, Jason?" But instead of answering him, Jason Meredith turned to me.

"Dwight," he said. "I'd like to see you alone, if it's possible, at your cottage at nine o'clock tonight."

We were all silent and puzzled for a moment when he left us. It was not at all like Jason Meredith, who always enjoyed our little Thursday get-togethers. There was no doubt that he was upset about something but I could not imagine what.

"Wait a minute," Epsom Felch said. "I've got it. He thought we were kidding him about Percival Norton and Janey. The merman. Get it? Percy Norton's a merman."

The strange thing was that none of us had thought of this until that moment. It had not dawned on one of us that Jason Meredith might think we were jesting about Percival Norton and his daughter. We had never thought until that moment of Percival Norton as a merman.

Though good fellowship was the watchword of our community, I had occasionally entertained the uneasy suspicion that the Merediths were not an integrated part of our group. I had never been able to quite understand what Mary saw in Hortense Meredith, and it was no fault of mine that Hortense Meredith had grown to be Mary's best friend, although I accepted the fact cheerfully and broad-mindedly. In fact, because of Mary's friendship, I had done all I could to interest Jason Meredith in our many activities. If I had found him stiff and aloof in the past and lacking in a sense of humor, I had always excused him because he was a banker. I had never realized so fully that Jason was not one of us until he came to call on me later that evening.

I was sitting beneath the colored lights on our terrace listening to the soothing monotone of the sea, dressed, as I recall, in blue slacks and sandals, and I wore one of my most engaging silk shirts, with amusing fishes on it. It is true that Mary had told me to put on something else if Jason Meredith was coming over, but I could see no reason for it, since informality was one of our watchwords. I only saw the reason for Mary's suggestion when Jason appeared in a tropical tuxedo and a stiff shirt.

"Well, well, Jason," I said facetiously, "I didn't know we were supposed to dress."

"When one reaches a certain age, I like to be that age," Jason Meredith answered. "Where did you get that shirt with fish on it? That's all there is around this place — fish, fish, fish."

"Well, well," I said lightly, "after all, we're surrounded by the sea."

"Fish, fish, fish," Jason said. "We had three kinds of fish for dinner — rockfish, red snapper, and something called a big-eye John. That's a fine name for a fish, isn't it?"

"Who caught them?" I asked.

"You know damned well who caught them," Jason said.

I could see by then that Jason Meredith, in spite of his composed features, was deeply disturbed, but all I could do was to try to make things easier.

"Jason," I said, in a gay, offhand manner, "I have that poem we were talking about over cocktails quite clearly in my mind now. Its title is 'The Forsaken Merman,' by Matthew Arnold."

"It's nice to have the record straight," Jason Meredith said, "after all the fun you had with it."

"Now, Jason," I told him, "you mustn't mind a little good-natured spoofing during the cocktail hour. A light touch is part of the charm of this place, but nothing personal or pointed was intended. It was only later that we realized that you thought that we were referring to Percy Norton and your daughter Jane, and you really shouldn't take it personally."

"Look here," Jason Meredith said, "don't try to tell me that everyone isn't talking about Jane and this man Norton."

"But what is there to talk about?" I said. "Just two young people on a holiday."

"This is no place for an impressionable young girl," Jason Meredith said. "Janey's always been enthusiastic and young for her age. We never should have had her down here for the Christmas holidays. I've told Hortense so."

"Now, Jason," I began, "why be upset about two young people on a holiday? Besides, Mary watches them through the telescope. Mary will tell you that he was in the water all the time. He likes the water."

"Sometimes, Dwight," Jason Meredith said, "I wish very much that you could try to be your age. Hortense agrees that Jane should have stayed in New York. This environment is no place for a girl like Jane; and Hortense says so too, and Mary agrees with her."

"Oh," I said, "so you've been talking to Mary, have you?"

"Of course I've been talking to Mary," Jason Meredith answered. "Look here, Dwight, who is this Percival Norton?"

It seemed to me very necessary to get the record straight. I went over very carefully the details of my first meeting with Percival Norton. I explained that the responsibility of his being a member of the Mulligatawny Club rested squarely on the shoulders of its Membership Committee.

"What is there, Jason," I said, "that you think is wrong with Percival?"

He looked at me in a pitying way and the composure of his features made me feel as though I were applying to him for a loan without collateral.

"You know as well as I do," he said, "that there must be something wrong with any young man who spends his winters doing nothing in a place like this."

All at once I began to feel very sorry for Percival.

"On the contrary," I said, "he does a great deal. He's fishing all the time."

"Why doesn't he get a job up north like anybody else his age?" Jason Meredith asked.

I had not intended to defend Percival Norton, but somehow the question annoyed me more than it should have. It was utterly characteristic of Jason Meredith to believe that working in some office was the answer to everything.

"Why should he if he doesn't have to?" I asked.

Jason flushed slightly.

"Suppose you answer this one," he said. "Would you want your daughter to marry anyone like Percival Norton?"

"How can I answer that," I said, "when I haven't got a daughter?"

Jason Meredith moved his head slowly from side to side.

"Let's put it another way," he said. "If you were Percival Norton, why would you want to marry my daughter Jane?"

Though I felt tempted, I could not very well tell Jason Meredith that I could think of no reason for marrying his daughter.

"Well, Jason," I said, "Jane is an enthusiastic, outgiving girl, and they share a common interest."

"Don't beat about the bush, Dwight," Jason said. "You know as well as I do that he wants to marry her for her money."

I felt my face redden.

"I don't know why you should assume that," I said.

Then I saw that Jason Meredith looked startled.

"I intended nothing personal, Dwight," he said. "I wasn't thinking about you at all — not about you and Mary."

But whether he intended it or not, of course it was personal. Never before had Percival Norton and I had so much in common.

"Jason," I said, "I'm beginning to feel very sorry for Percival Norton."

"I don't quite get that," Jason said. "Why should you be sorry for him?"

"Jason," I said, "there is one thing I can do for you."

"What?" he asked.

I was thinking of some of my own experiences with Mary's parents, which were very close to me at the moment.

"That poor young fellow doesn't know what he's getting into," I said, "but I know very well and I shall be very glad to tell him."

"Look here, Dwight," Jason said. "I never intended to be personal and I apologize."

"You have nothing to apologize for," I said. "Good night, Jason." There was one thing about that interview, painful though it was in part. I have never thought there was anything that I might say that could upset or embarrass Jason Meredith.

For several minutes I stood alone on the terrace after Jason Meredith had left, telling myself what is perfectly true, that no two persons who marry can be expected to possess exactly the same financial resources, but I still felt a deep emotional disturbance. It was possible to tell myself the complete truth, one which Mary frequently ignored, that Mary had married me as much as I had married Mary. She had been attracted to me because I rowed on the crew for Yale. There are invariably two sides to the problem of natural selection. It was possible to add that I had not married Mary for her money primarily, although there had been a certain glamour to the setting. The vision came back to me of Mary's father's yacht on the river Thames, but at that time I had possessed no fixed idea of Mary's father's financial resources. There certainly had been no reason for me to continue on the floor of the New York Stock Exchange after Mary's father's death, and it was Mary herself who suggested that the effort was unnecessary.

The terrace had never been so beautiful. The bright tropical starlight made a soft sheen on the sea. The terrace and its location had been largely my idea. The electric lighting and the huge sea grape in the center of the terrace were entirely mine, and what was more I had paid for the installation of the lighting out of my personal savings. Nevertheless I found it hard to get myself back to my usual state of cheerful calm.

Mary was sitting in our Victorian living room, which was cheerfully and beautifully furnished with pieces which had once been in her father's home at Bar Harbor. This room had been entirely Mary's idea, and of course she had paid for the house as well, and there was absolutely no reason why she shouldn't have. She was seated by the card table playing a complicated game of solitaire.

"What were you and Jason Meredith talking about?" she asked, taking off her glasses. "And why didn't you bring him in before he left?"

Of course she knew very well what we had been talking about, and it did not seem necessary to tell her why I had not brought him in.

"Well," she said, "what did he say about Janey and Percival Norton?"

"He said he wants to marry her for her money," I answered.

Mary smiled in a way that showed me she was in one of her more difficult moods.

"Well," she said, "what did you say, Dwight?"

I have always found it best not to argue with Mary at certain times.

"I told him I was very sorry for Percy," I said.

"Exactly why on earth should you be sorry for him?" Mary asked.

"Because he doesn't know what he's getting into," I said. "I told Jason I knew very well, and I said I was going to explain a few things to poor Percy."

It was the first time in a long while that I had spoken as freely as this to Mary — certainly never since the death of her late father. I was certainly not myself that evening.

"I wish you wouldn't keep calling him poor Percy," Mary said.

"I'm sorry," I told her. "That's the way I think of him. Neither of us may amount to much but we're very much alike."

I had not spoken to Mary in such a way for many, many years, and I felt a slight qualm when she picked up not her reading but her long-view spectacles.

"Dwight?" she said.

"Yes, Mary?" I answered.

"You look very handsome and distinguished tonight, almost the way you did at the Hotel Griswold, and you *have* managed to keep your figure."

"Thank you, Mary," I said.

She was still looking at me through her long-view glasses.

"Dwight," she said, "you were talking about a new set of matching irons and some new woods. I'm afraid I didn't pay much attention. I'd like to buy you a new set."

"Thank you, Mary," I said, "but I'm used to my old clubs."

"Dwight?" Mary said.

"Yes, Mary?" I answered.

"I'm afraid Jason Meredith hurt your feelings. He's very insensitive in many ways and he really doesn't know anything about you personally."

"That's ridiculous, Mary," I said. "How could he hurt my feelings? Well, it's been a long, hard day. I think I'll go to bed now."

"Dwight," Mary said, "wouldn't you like to get another pack of cards and play Russian Bank? We haven't played it for a long time, and, do you remember? — you taught me how on the yacht in New London."

"Yes," I said, "I remember, but I'm feeling rather tired, Mary. If you'll excuse me I think I'd better go to bed."

The truth was that, though normally a gregarious person, I wanted to be alone. I wanted to think seriously what I would say to Percy Norton.

"Well, kiss me good night, dear," Mary said.

It was one of the most unusual conversations that I had had with Mary for many, many years. In fact nothing about that conversation had sounded exactly like Mary or exactly like myself.

Percy Norton seemed surprised when I told him over the telephone next morning that I should like to drop over to his cottage for a short, informal chat. He said he hoped that I would make it quick because he was just getting his gear together and he and Janey Meredith were going fishing.

"What," I said, "again?"

"We've got to shove off quick," he said, "the way the tide's running."

Then he asked what I wanted to talk to him about. He should have known as well as I did that Miss Humphries, who has run the switchboard of the Mulligatawny Club for many years, invariably listened to all the conversations. Though she knew everything about everyone, I did not want to have Miss Humphries hear what I was going to say to Percival. It was more than mere gossip; it was personal — a part, in fact, of myself.

The Bahama Islands, among which the Mulligatawny Club is situated, have, I have heard veteran travelers say, one of the most salubrious winter climates in the world. It has always surprised me to hear some people, including Mary, say that the invariably fine weather bores them, because, to my way of thinking, one cannot get too much of a good thing. It was a beautiful morning as usual. The sea was a vast chromatic scale that changed from green to blue to purple. The fronds of the coconut palms rattled mirthfully in the soft, clear breeze. It was hard not to be happy on such a morning, particularly when one was a member of the Mulligatawny Club.

Percival Norton's cottage, which had been built by Mr. and Mrs. Jethro Wilson, who had unfortunately lost their money, was constructed of native stone that made it seem a part of the rocky promontory on which it stood. I wondered what the Wilsons, who had impeccable taste, would have thought if they could have seen their living room now that Percival was in it. Gill nets and throwing nets were cast carelessly over the chairs and sofas. Percival, in nothing but his swimming trunks, was sprawled on the floor where Artemus, his boat boy, was arranging a box of fishing gear, and they were surrounded by rods, reels, gaffs, and spears.

"I've got to get out there before the tide turns," Percival said. "What is it you wanted to see me about, Mr. Billings?"

I told him I wanted to see him alone for a few minutes.

"Artemus has got to keep working on this," Percival said. "We've got to shove."

I had to tell him again that I wanted to see him alone, but even so Percival kept right on sorting plugs and fishhooks.

"Percival," I said, "I've just come here to speak to you as an older man to a younger one. As a son, Percival, if I had a son."

"That's all right," Percival said, and he began winding a new line on a reel. "That's all right, Mr. Billings."

I could not understand what he meant and the reel made an annoying clicking sound.

"Percival," I said, "I had a talk with Mr. Meredith last night. He's worried, Percy."

"Say," Percival said, "give me a hand with this line, will you?"

"Percival," I said, and I raised my voice, "are you interested in Janey Meredith?"

"This line was advertised to take a fifty-pound strain," Percival said. "It doesn't look to me as though it can. What time is it now?"

"Percival," I said again, "are you interested in Janey Meredith?"

Percival sat back on his heels but he still continued to wind the line.

"How do you mean?" he asked. "She's all right in a boat."

"Will you please put down that reel," I said. "Percy, are you in love with Janey Meredith?"

At last I had his attention and he looked up at me.

"What's that one again?" he asked.

"Will you please give me your attention, Percival," I said. "Are you in love with Janey Meredith?"

"Gosh," Percival said, and he rubbed his hand carefully over the bald spot on top of his head, "I wouldn't know the answer to that one, Mr. Billings."

"Of course you know, Percy," I said, "one way or the other."

"Gosh," Percival said, "I never thought of it until right now."

"Oh, come," I said, "of course you've thought of it."

Percival stood up and scraped his bare toes across the floor in the way that always annoyed Mary.

"It's like this," Percival said. "When you're spear fishing you've got to keep your mind on it. You can't think of love when you're under-water."

"Well, Mr. Meredith thinks Janey's in love with you," I said.

"Gosh," Percival said, "he does? Say — why should Janey be in love with me?"

"I'm sure I don't know," I said, and I was sure I didn't when Percival began to scratch his stomach.

"Gosh," Percival said. "This is all a new idea to me, Mr. Billings."

I felt very much relieved for Percy — delighted and relieved.

"Well, well," I said. "I'm glad things haven't gone any further. You see, he thinks you're trying to marry Janey for her money."

"What?" Percy said. "Have those Merediths got any money?"

"Good gracious, Percy," I said. "Don't you know who the Merediths are?"

"Gosh," Percy said, and he scratched his stomach again. "Well, what do you know about that! Well, I'd better get going. Janey's waiting at the dock."

"Just a minute," I said. "Just as an older man to a younger one, per-haps it isn't such a good idea to marry a girl with a lot of money."

"I don't get you," Percy said. "Why isn't it?"

"Well, Percy," I began, "there are certain complications. You don't realize what they are until you get mixed up with them. It isn't what you think it's going to be. I ought to know. You see, Mrs. Billings is very rich."

"Gosh," Percy said. "That's swell, Mr. Billings."

"I'm trying to tell you, Percy," I said, "that it isn't so swell. Now look at me, Percy. I suppose you think I'm always happy. It's a serious matter, marrying a very rich girl, Percy. Now look at me. I used to row number five on the Yale crew."

"Sure," Percy said, "I know that, Mr. Billings. Gosh, I've got to think this over but I've got to be going now. Gosh, I wonder why he thinks she's in love with me. She must have said something."

"Percy," I said, "I want to explain this to you. This is very serious."

"I'll say it is," Percy said. "But I've got to be going now — honest, Mr. Billings. The tide's running."

I had not said all I intended to say to Percival Norton, but under the circumstances there was no reason why I should have. I could only feel very much relieved as I watched him hurrying toward the dock, with Artemus just behind him. There was obviously so little in what people had been saying that the sight of Percival's vanishing bare torso could only fill me with a wistful sort of envy. He was as free as I had once been when I rowed number five on the crew for Yale, as free as the fish that he was seeking to ensnare, beyond all need of good advice. I wished that I might be like him for a day or even for an hour.

When I returned, Mary was on the terrace beneath the beach umbrella reading the morning mail. I was sorry to see that there were a number of bills and that she was working with a pad and pencil.

"It's high time we were starting for the beach," I said. "Don't you think so, Mary?"

"Never mind the beach," Mary said. "What did you say to that Norton?"

"Oh, nothing in particular," I said. "He was in too much of a hurry."

"Oh," Mary said, "so you didn't warn him against your hard lot then?"

"Now, Mary," I said, "what makes you think I was going to warn anyone about my hard lot? I was only going to tell him a few general truths but he was in a hurry."

"In a hurry for what?" Mary asked.

"He's going fishing with Janey."

"Dwight," Mary said, "please bring out the telescope and set it up."

"He told me there was nothing in it," I said. "It's what I tell you and tell you. He's only interested in fishing."

"Don't argue, Dwight," Mary said. "Get the telescope."

She was still looking through the telescope when I returned from the beach.

"Well, well," I said, "what's going on?"

"Nothing," Mary answered. "He's still in the water."

I had to laugh, even though Mary seldom enjoyed laughter at her own expense.

"Well, well," I told her, "none of us can be right all the time. I told you there was nothing in it, Mary. He's only a poor simple merman," and I laughed again. Occasionally it is very pleasant to know that one is right.

It was a very busy day. In fact it was the day of the Tombstone Tournament, and if I may say so, my swing had been absolutely free and my approach shots beautiful. It was a pleasure to return to our terrace for a well-earned gin and tonic and to start describing the game to Mary, hole by hole. I had got as far as the thirteenth, a very tricky dogleg, before she stopped me, but on the whole she had been very patient.

"Well, well," I said, "is the boat back?"

"Yes," Mary said, "it left the reef half an hour ago."

I had to laugh again. It is very pleasant occasionally to be right.

"Well, well," I said facetiously, "the poor Merediths."

"Oh, stop it, Dwight," Mary said, and of course I did stop it, but I could not refrain from telling her one thing more.

"He didn't even know that Janey was a rich girl," I told her.

"And I suppose you told him that she was," Mary said. "That would be just like you, Dwight."

I had to laugh again.

"He didn't even listen," I said. "He was in a hurry to catch the tide."

I was about to change the subject. I wanted to think of my golf game hole by hole and to sit in peace watching the setting sun. I was about to say this to Mary when we were interrupted by a patter of running feet. It was Janey Meredith, and frankly, she was not a pleasant apparition on our terrace. She was still in her bathing suit. Her hair was stringy from immersion in sea water, and, as I have said before, her legs were too large and her eyes too round without her glasses.

"Oh, Aunt Mary and Uncle Dwight," she said, "I'm so glad you're here. I haven't seen Mother or Father yet, and I want you to be the first to know."

There was a hollow sensation in the pit of my stomach and I spilled some gin and tonic upon my linen trousers.

"Percival and I are engaged," Janey said.

I had never been so completely surprised and I could think of nothing to say, but there was no chance to say anything, because Janey was still speaking.

"And it wouldn't have happened except for you, Uncle Dwight. Percival said so. He said you were so sweet and understanding this morning, Uncle Dwight. He said he wouldn't have thought about loving me if you hadn't mentioned it. Isn't it just like Percy? And now I'm going to kiss you."

She was still dripping wet with sea water and there was no time to say anything, because she was still speaking.

"I've never been so happy. It's just like being in a new world all made over, isn't it — being engaged. Do you know what Percival and I are going to do? We are going to start a marine museum and I'm going to drop math and take up biology. There's the funniest little man in Poughkeepsie who gives the course. His name is Pettigrew — all skin and bone and glasses. The girls call him 'Petty.' I'm going to do the scientific side while Percival does the collecting. I've never been so happy."

Her voice had a new quality of vibrant strength that already made me feel exhausted, because though her father had spoken of the violence of Janey's enthusiasms, I had never felt their full impact. The physical force of her elation left me confused and tongue-tied, and a glance at Mary showed me exactly what she was thinking — that the whole thing had been my fault.

"My dear," Mary said, examining Janey through her long-view glasses, "I am afraid you will find there is more to marriage than aquatic life."

There was a familiarly sharp edge to her voice that showed she was approaching one of her worst moods.

"Now, Mary," I said, "young people have to get married sometime," and I laughed pleasantly, "or else there wouldn't be a world."

"If two people love the same things," Janey said, "they are just bound to keep on loving each other. Haven't you and Aunt Mary found it that way, Uncle Dwight?"

"Yes, yes," I said, "of course, my dear."

"It's going to be so wonderful," Janey said, "like a beautiful dream — as soon as I get Percival's fishing on a scientific basis. It will give his life an object, and that's what he's always needed, hasn't he?"

"Yes," Mary said. "I'm sure it will be delightful for him as you describe it, Janey, and now I suggest you put on some dry clothes before you tell anyone else your news."

"Oh, I nearly forgot," Janey said. "Percival sent you this with his love," and she pulled a large fish out of a straw basket. "It's a grouper, and Percival proposed to me just after he speared him."

"Dwight," Mary said, "take it out and give it to someone in the kitchen."

I have never enjoyed handling the limp forms of fish, but I welcomed the opportunity to escape for a few moments and to prepare myself for what Mary would obviously say when we were alone; and, as I expected, Mary was waiting for me, in the exact center of the living room.

"Don't say you didn't tell him she had money," Mary said. "Don't go back on that statement, Dwight."

"It's entirely my fault, my dear," I said.

"We won't discuss it now, Dwight," Mary said. "Go upstairs and take off that shirt with fish on it."

"Yes, my dear," I said.

"I never want to see it again. Give it away to someone, first thing tomorrow morning."

"Yes, my dear," I said.

"And put on a dinner jacket. From now on I expect you to dress for dinner."

"Yes, Mary," I said. "Is there anything else?"

"I'll think of something else by the time you are dressed, Dwight," Mary said.

I was very sure she would. Mary had a very active mind.

On the whole, as Mary put it, the poor Merediths did everything they could about poor Janey. They only told the news to their closer friends, saying that it was more of an understanding than an engagement. There was no need, Mr. Meredith said, to talk over plans and prospects with Percival until much later. There was only one detail which relieved the situation. The Christmas recess at Vassar College was drawing to a close, and Janey left us one day later. Percival was allowed to take her to the airport, and personally it was a relief to see her go. I never so appreciated the old dictum, "Out of sight, out of mind." When Percival returned from the airport, I could almost believe that nothing whatever had happened.

"Well, well," I said to him, "you must be feeling lonely, Percy."

"That's right," Percy said. "It's going to be quiet on the boat tomorrow."

"Well, well," I said, "she'll be back by Easter. Easter will be along in no time."

"I hope it comes up quick," Percival said. "Do you know what she wants me to do? She wants me to write her a long letter every day. I never was good at letters. What can you say to anyone every day?"

"Say the same thing in different ways," I said.

"Gosh, Mr. Billings," Percy answered, "there's only one way to say most things."

I have never been able to see why I should have been considered an authority on Percival Norton, but I could understand even less why Percival Norton should have considered me an authority on Janey Meredith. True, I have always taken a friendly interest in pretty young girls in our winter community, but this interest only vaguely included Janey, who never did have the sprightliness of some of the others. Very soon I began wishing that I had never had a personal talk with Percival Norton. I was not a Cyrano de Bergerac, and I wished that he would not keep consulting me about his correspondence with Janey Meredith.

Three days after Janey had left us he actually sought me out on the Club sun deck, where I was reclining on a couch after a hard morning on the beach.

"Say, Mr. Billings," he said, "is this all right?" and he handed me a piece of note paper. "It's the best I can do but I want to know if it's all right."

"Dear Janey," I read. The writing was bold and legible. "The wind was fresh northeast yesterday. We anchored off that place that old Art calls 'The Lizzard.' I got three of those blue-colored fish you like, the ones Art calls 'Pumkin Seeds,' that he says are good for rheumatism. Then I got three slippery Dicks and six big-eye Johns and three crawfish that I gave to your father. I also mixed it up with a small turtle out there, but he got away. He must have weighed about sixty pounds, but I never got a fair grip on him. Old Art says I'm no good with turtles.

"I hope you are having a fine time back at college. Well, that's about all the news the way it looks from here today. Art and I are working on that net tonight. With love, Percy."

It was not up to me to write his letters and I was glad he did not show me the letters Janey wrote.

"She writes mighty long letters, Mr. Billings," Percival told me once. "She has a lot of Latin names in them and she has a lot of new ideas. They're hard to read sometimes, Mr. Billings."

I was glad that I did not have to see her letters, and I wished that her father did not speak to me about the letters that he received from Janey.

"If she could only get her mind on something else," Jason Meredith told me, "instead of fish, fish, fish. Do you know what I think?"

I did not know what he thought. I only wished that he would not select me for his confidences because they were almost beginning to spoil my winter.

"I think she's more infatuated with fish," Jason Meredith said, "than she is with this young Norton. Do you know what she wants me to do now?"

"No," I answered, "I'm sure I don't, Jason."

"She wants me to build her a laboratory," he said, "She's bringing a professor down for Easter to show me how to build it."

"What professor?" I asked.

"That's exactly what I want to know," Jason said. "He teaches biology up there. She says he's the cutest little man — all skin and bone and glasses. His name is Pettigrew — Leon G. Pettigrew — and he knows all about fishes, too. Did you ever hear of anyone named Pettigrew?"

"Why, no," I answered, "I don't think so, Jason."

It seemed to me that Jason looked unusually drawn and tired.

"I try to cling to the thought," he said, "that maybe it's just fish. Janey was never interested in men before. You know, this Pettigrew sounds even worse to me than Norton."

There is an old dictum that hindsight is easier than foresight. I should have known that there were straws in the wind. I should have pieced odds and ends together. I surely should have known that certain clouds were gathering, but the Four Ball Tournament was starting and this demanded my closest attention. Thus I can only put it all together now in retrospect, but I should have known that something out of the ordinary was happening when Percival asked me to come to his cottage for a talk.

It was another beautiful day and he was alone in his disorderly living room.

"Well, well," I said, "mending a fish net, are you?"

It was obvious he was mending a fish net because the entire floor was covered with mesh.

"I've got to do something," he said, "to keep my mind off other things. Say, I want to ask you a personal question, Mr. Billings. You were saying sometimes marriage isn't easy."

"Well, well," I said, "at the same time it's a lovely institution."

He did not answer for a moment, but it was interesting to see him working at the fish net. He was very good at tying knots.

"Say," he said, "does Mrs. Billings ever try to boss you around, Mr. Billings?"

His question was both embarrassing and disturbing, since it probed too deeply into my personal life to make it agreeable.

"Why, yes," I said, "perhaps occasionally, Percival. Women like to make men over, occasionally."

"Maybe that's a part of marriage," Percival said.

"Why, yes," I told him, "I think perhaps it is."

"That's the way it is with Janey," he said. "Sometimes I think things aren't going to be the same as they were before when we get married."

"They very seldom are," I said, "but there are certain compensations, Percy."

"Do you know what Janey wants?" he asked.

I did not answer because I had no idea what Janey wanted.

"She wants me to make my letters more personal and she wants me to call fish by Latin names. She's given me a list to learn."

"Well, well," I said, "perhaps it would be as well as learn the list."

Percival stopped knotting his fish net. His fingers looked clumsy when he stopped, but at the same time I became aware that he had an admirable quality, something that one might call integrity.

"Listen," he said, "I get the fishes' names from Artemus. Old Art knows everything about fish, and I don't like Latin, Mr. Billings. There won't be any Latin from now on out. I wrote that to her yesterday."

"Well, well," I said, "it might have been wiser not to, Percy."

It might have been wiser, but I could not help admiring the stand he took.

"You've got to stop somewhere," Percival said. "And one thing more. Did you ever hear of a professor or somebody named — " he paused and scratched the back of his head — " named something like Pettigrew? She keeps writing about him all the time. I don't think he has a good influence on Janey."

A breath of sea air laden with the indescribable scent of tropical salt water was wafted into the living room.

"Well, I've got to get going on this net," Percival said. "Thanks for talking to me, Mr. Billings."

Though I could hardly say that I had talked to him, I did feel closer to Percival Norton than I ever had before, and I could not help but wonder what would have happened in my own life if I had possessed more of his sterling qualities.

It was beginning to come over me that I was reliving parts of my own past in terms of Percival Norton. Of course there were wide differences. Certainly as a young man I was more presentable, both in manners and in appearance, and my interests were not centered in fishing. Instead I had rowed number five in the Yale crew, but all the world had been my oyster, as they say, before I met Mary at the Hotel Griswold in New London. I could not help wondering what would have happened to me if I had been a little more like Percival. I had to admit that I had not been. I would have learned Latin, Greek, or Sanskrit if Mary had asked me then.

Without meaning to be critical I had often observed that Mary had a nervous temperament. Small things frequently disturbed her and she was always difficult when life was not on an even keel. My main effort for many years had been keeping things on an even keel. I realized that evening that something was disturbing the fixed pattern of our life.

"Dwight," she asked me, "is anything upsetting you?"

I was startled by the way she asked me, and it was always best not to argue.

"Is it anything about that Norton and poor Janey?" she asked. "I think you'd better tell me what it is."

There was nothing to do but turn it off with a hearty laugh.

"Why, nothing worries me, my dear," I said. "I've just been thinking how happy we've always been together."

"Every time you see that Norton something happens to you," Mary said.

"Nothing happens to me, Mary," I told her. "He just keeps reminding me of when I was young."

"You didn't have to marry me, you know," she said.

I was very startled by her remark and very much upset. She must have been thinking also about the Hotel Griswold.

"Well, I wanted to marry you," I said. "I was most anxious to marry you."

"That's true," she said, "you certainly were." But the tone of her voice still made me nervous and I hastily changed the subject.

"She wants him to learn the Latin names for fish," I said.

"What under the sun has that got to do with anything?" she asked.

"He's just written her," I told her, "that he will call his fish any names he wants."

It had seemed to me a harmless remark, but there was a stony sort of silence.

"Well," she said, "I think that was very disagreeable of that Norton."

"That's just what I think too, my dear," I told her.

"You were never as disagreeable as that to me," Mary said.

"No, my dear," I said with a pleasant laugh, "I wouldn't have dared to be."

There was another unpleasant silence. The conversation did not have the jovial give and take that I had intended.

"Why didn't you dare?" she asked.

There was nothing I could do but pass the question off with another pleasant laugh. "Why, Mary," I said. "You were you and I was I."

Mary sniffed. Things were always bound to be difficult when she sniffed.

"You didn't dare," she said, "because you wanted to get on that damned yacht."

It was the truth and I had to admit it, but it would all have been much better left unsaid.

"Yes," I said, "of course I did."

"You needn't say that so emphatically, Dwight," Mary said. "Do you know what I've been thinking? You never should have resigned from the Stock Exchange. I'm afraid it was my fault, Dwight."

"Now, Mary," I said, "please. I wanted to resign."

"You ought to be up north doing something," Mary said.

"Now, Mary," I said, "please. I don't want to do anything." It was the truth — not creditable perhaps, but it was the truth. "You see, I'm not like Percy Norton."

I was not proud of what I said, but at least it was the truth, and somehow it was better now that it was in the open. I was relieved to see that the lines about Mary's mouth had relaxed, and suddenly she smiled. Suddenly she looked almost as she had at the Hotel Griswold.

"It's nice to be frank, isn't it?" she said. "To tell you the truth I never wanted you to do anything. Now don't let that Norton disturb you any more."

"Don't call him 'that Norton,' Mary," I said. "I like him even if I'm not like him."

"All right, I won't," Mary said. "Kiss me good night, Dwight."

Without being able to explain it, somehow I felt happier than I had for a long while. Something between us was settled — beautifully, completely settled. I was I and Mary was Mary and at last we both completely understood it.

There is another dictum which I have always found true in life. Crises always come upon one unexpectedly. The crisis of Percival Norton came upon us one morning a few days later, only a few minutes after Mary and I were seated at breakfast on our terrace. It was a beautiful morning. As I have said, there is nothing like our weather, and Mary had said as usual that she would like to see a gray, cold day. I had just put two saccharine tablets in my coffee, because my weight had been increasing lately, and I remember that I hoped, after Mary had commented on the weather, that she would not express a desire, as she sometimes did, to spend a winter in the North.

"Well, well," I said, to get her mind off the subject, "I see we have a fine large stack of mail this morning."

I saw immediately that this remark was unfortunate, because the mail, which was invariably placed beside Mary, was largely made up of bills, and bills always challenged her disposition.

"Is there anything there for me, Mary?" I asked, simply to start matters along a new line.

As a rule there was nothing for me, since I had left the floor of the Stock Exchange and had severed my business connections, but still my question had its desired effect.

"Look through it yourself, Dwight," Mary said. "The mail should be given to you and not to me at any rate."

"Why, my dear," I said, "it never has been."

"It will be from now on," Mary said. "It will give you something to do, Dwight," and she handed me the letters.

I remember thinking that there had been a change in Mary during the last few days, but I was very glad to have the bills at my side of the table for the moment.

"Well, well," I said, "let's see. Why, here's a letter for me in a woman's hand," and I laughed facetiously.

"It's a hand-addressed advertisement, isn't it?" Mary said. "Let me see it, Dwight."

She put on her reading glasses when I handed her the letter. At least her mind was off the bills.

"Why," she said, "the postmark is Poughkeepsie. It's from Janey Meredith. Why can she be writing you?"

"I'm sure I don't know, my dear," I told her.

"Well, open it and read it aloud," Mary said, and she handed me the silver paper knife which I had given her once for Christmas.

I can still remember the letter and its cramped penmanship, very clearly.

"Dear Uncle Dwight," I read. "I want you to be the first to know what has happened to me, even before I tell Father and Mother. There is something I want you to do for me before I tell them. I want you to tell Percy Norton my news. It would be kinder, I think, to tell him than for me to write."

I paused and looked across the table at Mary. I still did not know what was coming. I was more interested in Mary's expression. She looked worried and I could not imagine what could worry her.

"Go ahead," she said. "What news?"

"Uncle Dwight," I read, "I have been very foolish about Percival. I don't know what came over me down there. It must have been too much sun and sea, and he is wonderful in the water, but I know what Father and Mother thought of it, and they were so very right. I still love him in a way but not in the right way, but I shall always remember what dear Percy did for me and I shall always be grateful. You see, it is really Percy who has given me my great happiness.

"Well, my pen seems to be rambling on in a very hysterical manner. I don't know whether you've heard me speak or not of my biology professor, Leon G. Pettigrew. I won't describe him to you now except to say, in so many ways he is everything that Percy isn't. Well, to be brief, I'm going to marry Leon. What do you think of that? I want you to tell Percy. You'll do that for me, won't you? Tell him in your kind, sweet way, because I do feel a teensy-weensy bit guilty. I think they call it 'free guilt' in psychoanalysis, but wait till you see Leon. He . . ."

I put the letter down. There were several pages more, but I did not wish to read them. I put the letter down and listened to the sea breeze rustling through the leaves of our sea grape.

"Well, well," I said, as brightly as I could. "All's well that ends well, Mary."

No matter how I tried, it seemed to me lately that I was always saying the wrong thing. Instead of looking pleased, Mary had taken off her glasses and was staring at the sea.

"Oh," she said, "the poor Merediths."

"Look here," I told her, "that's exactly what you said before."

"I wish you wouldn't interrupt me, Dwight," she said. "Never mind what I said before, and that poor Norton boy. What a thing to do to him. Poor Percy Norton."

"Now wait, Mary," I said. "You know you never liked him."

"I wish you wouldn't contradict me, Dwight," Mary said. "Just because he was quiet and calm. Just because he had a mind of his own and wouldn't do everything she wanted. Poor Percy Norton. I want you to promise to be kind to him, Dwight. Tell him he's well out of it. Tell him so for me."

"Mary," I began, "I don't exactly understand."

"I'm not asking you to understand," she said. "It's sad and I can feel sad if I want to, can't I?"

She was still looking at the sea without her glasses.

"Out there all alone," she said, "out there on the reef. Dwight, did you ever read a poem by Matthew Arnold called 'The Forsaken Merman'?"

I started slightly. Mary had always objected to my quoting poetry.

"Why, Mary," I asked her, "whatever put that into your head?"

"Oh never mind, Dwight," she told me, "The other night I began thinking about things — the Hotel Griswold and things. Dwight, go upstairs and get me the *Oxford Book of Verse,* and bring me down a handkerchief."

"Mary," I began, "there's nothing to be upset about."

"Do you remember what you said the other night?" she answered. "I'm me and you're you. I'm not upset. Please get me the *Oxford Book of Verse.*"

She put on her glasses when I returned with the volume. Then she blew her nose and turned the pages briskly.

"Listen to this," she said. "It's so sad and so true.

> "Here came a mortal,
> But faithless was she:
> And alone dwell for ever,
> The kings of the sea."

She closed the book and blew her nose again.

"Yes, I know, my dear," I said. "We call him a merman sometimes, but I wouldn't call him a king of the sea exactly."

"Dwight," Mary said, "I wish you wouldn't argue. Go and tell him now and ask him for dinner tonight. Poor Percy Norton."

School and College

I wish I could face the stories in this section with the same enthusiasm I felt for them when I wrote them long ago for the Saturday Evening Post. Instead I find myself viewing them with a somewhat jaundiced eye. My idea, I can see, of taking the fashionable secondary school apart may once have been a good one, but in our fast-moving social scene even this idea is an also-ran in the race of progress. Secondary schools, I am sure, are better now than they were in the mid-thirties.

In any event I should advise the young writer to write only of what he knows, and here I am hoist by my own petard. Frankly I never did attend a fashionable boarding school, but instead was educated in public institutions. I never had, by a long shot, a jeunesse dorée either, and anything that may hint of this in these stories is an outrageous form of wishful thinking. These facts help explain the atmosphere of unreality that lurks in the background of these fictional examples, but for this there are other reasons. Since these stories were written, as with others in this volume, time has changed many values. Except for Texas millionaires, favored by an inequitable tax law, social security in this country is in the process of being lost, and no social-security compensation, I am afraid, will bring it back. Thus some of my characters may appear as difficult and frivolous to a modern reader as my young officers in "Good Morning, Major." They were living, you see, in what I now know was a rather happy era, the age between two wars. They were all in a barrel, without really knowing it, though a few of them may have had the premonition that they were approaching Niagara Falls. Don't blame them altogether if they seem overelaborate and fantastic, even if I admit that some of their defects may have been due to my own lack of worldly experience.

For many years, doubtless because I could not join the group, I was annoyed by the pretensions of my contemporaries who had attended Eastern boarding schools. I never came in contact with these institutions until my son attended one, and then I occasionally stepped within the cloisters to call upon him. This experience gave me several ideas, including the hysterical discovery of the obvious, that the child is the father of the man. I tried to incorporate some of these ideas into these stories. I wish that there might have been some more, but then ideas, if any, should appear in fiction only through the utmost indirection.

Fourth Down

(1932)

The self-conscious academic failure still exists in our modern world in principle, but he is quite different from his predecessor of the year 1910. In that happy era when there were no draft boards and scarcely a rumor of war it was quite possible, and fashionable, for any ambitious young man to turn himself into an elaborate problem. If he had the means, the chances were that he had the leisure in which to make the attempt. To prove this point I can cite Flandleau's "Diary of a Freshman" and Owen Wister's "Philosophy Four," both stories of a bygone Harvard, the latter such an outstanding social document that it roused the ire of the late Alexander Woollcott. In me, I fear, it aroused mainly a wish that I might crawl backward for a while through two wars and through social upheaval to the age of confidence that surrounded me when I was young — an age so serene in spite of the Progressive Party and the Lawrence, Massachusetts, textile strike that it could readily support elaborate behaviorism.

Beverley Witherspoon and the narrator of "Fourth Down" were children of that age. Once I frequently observed their habits as well as I could from a distance, and I do believe that these adolescent portraits were more accurate than they may appear today. I was only seven years out of college when this story was written, but I already could perceive the pathos of the class reunion, which has values that will never change as long as such folk customs continue. I did better with these ideas and people in a novel I wrote subsequently, but in some ways this story was not a bad beginning.

In one of those class reunions where one tried to set the clock back, only to pay for the insolence on the morning after, Beverley Witherspoon made us both unhappy by recalling a serious phase of college life. It probably made us unhappy chiefly because a lack of achievement in our respective careers gave us an antipathy for anything serious, and because the very sight of the Class of Umpteen was beginning to raise grave reflections about the basic purposes of existence.

Beyond this, however, Beverley recalled an incident in which we took no pride; not that we had much in our college careers to be proud of, but in this incident was an element of chicanery, and the meddling with a soul and destiny.

The cheerleaders were shouting again, across a gap of time.

"Now then!" they were shouting. "A long cheer for Brooks! Brooks . . . Brooks — "

Now that the class was together again, the echo of the roar came back, as disturbing as distant thunder, but the horrid irony of the whole thing was that no one remembered Brooks until Beverley raised a forefinger to pierce the veil.

"Has it ever occurred to you," Beverley was saying — and he had to raise his voice above a barrage of stimulated sound — "that these reunions are the saddest things in the world? Thank heaven I can see beyond the mask of fun, and 'fun' is a horrid word. I can see that 98 per cent of our friends gathered here tonight are failures. I'm a failure, you're a failure, and here we are, in the name of higher education, celebrating frustration and failure, watching the ghosts of what might have been come stalking past, and yet we call it fun."

"Well, you needn't spoil it for the rest of us," someone reminded him. "We've paid twenty-five dollars apiece."

"I tell you I see ghosts," Beverley repeated, "and I suppose that ghosts come high. Now, look at that classmate of ours — no, that one over there. Doesn't he mean anything to you? Well, men, he does — to me."

The scene was what made it particularly grotesque, and reminiscent of wasted years. We were seated on the porch of an "Inn and Cottages," which had been rented body and soul for the occasion, and the occasion had reached that stage when the management was exhibiting acute qualms that it had not charged enough for general breakage. This year each member of the class was dressed in a cotton costume, designed to resemble a champagne bottle, with a small hat to simulate a cork.

"No," said Beverley, "not that one — the big one trying to walk on his hands. Does he mean anything to you?"

He was indicating a powerful, exuberant but undistinguished individual, half bald, with a broad, honest face, burned into a purple shade from a day out in the sun. Though the face was slightly familiar, it meant absolutely nothing.

"You don't mean to tell me," said Beverley, "that you don't remember Binkey Brooks? Now then, give him one long one! Brooks . . . Brooks . . . Brooks! . . . Doesn't anyone remember?"

The process of memory had become an effort. No one could remember.

"If you don't, I do," Beverley said. "I suppose I should, because it's one of the lives I've ruined. Listen to him. You don't know how it hurts me. Listen!"

As a matter of fact, Brooks was speaking loud enough for anyone to hear.

"No, Ed," he was saying, "you've got that wrong. It was exactly on the fifteen-yard line — fourth down, eight to go. He was there and you were there. Their halfback was over there, and you wiped him off yourself, and Cosey Green took out Jones. I ought to know, wouldn't I? He took out Jones. . . . Clever, wasn't it? You get the point. It wasn't his assignment, but he gave me that chance. I'm not boasting about it, Ed. I'm only saying that he took out Jones."

Beverley Witherspoon sighed. There was genuine pity in his glance as he listened.

"It hurts," he said. "Such things always hurt me, and when I think that I did that — "

He paused and stiffened slightly in his chair. We all stiffened, because the veil of time was breaking, and values were breaking with it. An involuntary respect for a specialized and overemphasized form of sport had seized us.

A figure had moved toward us from the dark of the lawn outside. It was Tubby Harris — and heaven knows Tubby had always been a moron, but he was first marshal of the class and one of the best open-field runners who had ever made Camp's All-American. And he had tossed us in a blanket once at school.

"Why, Bev," he said. "Gosh, it's great to see you, Bev! Swell party, isn't it? Nothing like everybody getting together, is it? Gosh, I'm having a good time! Everybody's having a good time. Gosh, this is great! It's great seeing you. Gosh, you've always made me laugh, ever since St. Swithin's! . . . I'm going to take a swim in the pool. Come on, let's all jump in. Let's all take a swim in the pool."

"Tubby," said Beverley, "can't you act your age?"

"No," said Tubby. "Gosh, I'm having a swell time! . . . What do you bet I can't throw you in the pool?"

"Tubby," said Beverley, "do you remember Brooks?"

Tubby Harris blinked and set down his glass.

"Gosh, Bev," he said, "I'd almost forgotten that! . . . Say, what'll you bet I can't throw any two of you in the pool at once?"

But memory was growing plain at last, as the characters appeared in that crude drama.

"Now then," the cheerleaders were shouting, "a long one for Brooks! Brooks . . . Brooks —"

Brooks was standing on the veranda talking, but he was not the same. The Brooks he had been once came out of nowhere, obsessed by his desire, and Tubby Harris was not the same. We were the only ones who had not altered. We were still the useless members of society, staring cynically at fame, unable to still approve of the great ones of our day. But values were changing into other values dizzily. There was the rattle of the streetcars in the Square. The crowds were pushing toward the gates. Boys were scrambling for pennies.

"Program, mister!" someone was shouting. "Buy your winning colors!"

There was a glamour — there would always be a glamour to a crowd. It was not hard to remember the time and place where we first met Binkey Brooks. I could even remember shivering in my pajamas in the cool of an autumn morning, as Beverley was saying:

"You mean the only thing you want is two minutes in a game?"

And there was Brooks, with his plain environment behind him, younger, thinner, staring into space, opening and closing his hands.

"Yes," he said, "that's the only thing I want. It's the only thing I'll ever want."

"I can't quite follow you," Beverley was saying, "because, as far as I know, I don't want anything at all."

*   *   *

The time when we met Binkey Brooks was when five or six of us shared rooms in one of those overemphasized dormitories, now only a memory in the history of our college. Except that we were graduates of St. Swithin's School and had been told on leaving there that we were the incipient leaders of the nation, there was nothing to recommend us — absolutely nothing, either physically or scholastically.

It was one of those clear New England autumn mornings when we met Binkey Brooks, when the cool air and sunshine used to come like conscience through the window, filling us sometimes with doubts as to the use of our existence. Our living room, supposedly devoted to study, was strewn with clothing which had been discarded after a party in town the night before. There was no use recollecting the party, for life was a succession of such things then.

The clock was striking eight that morning and there was a knocking on the door. As it was a period of financial stringency, everyone was alert for trouble with that early-morning knock, and aware that it could mean no good. Beverley, in his pajamas, came out of his bedroom and listened carefully to the knock, for he was always able to judge a situation; and the rest of us also listened.

Then Beverley whispered: "It's that sheriff again. Give me half a minute before you let him in. I'm going up the fire escape."

There was no one so adroit as Beverley in times when he had no money. A crisis always made him like a razor blade, and he tiptoed to his bedroom window without an instant's hestitation and stepped upon the fire escape.

"What?" he said to me. "Are you coming too?"

"Yes," I said, "if he's after you, he's probably after me."

Beverley nodded. "We should have slept in our clothes," he said. "I told you that tailor was going to be unpleasant."

"Look here," I asked him. "What are we going to do?"

We were climbing up the fire escape and it was bitter cold.

"You and I," said Beverley, "must keep away for a few days. I've had experience. You leave this to me. I'd rather not telephone the family."

"But where are we going?" I asked him. "We can't hang on this fire escape."

"You leave this to me," said Beverley. "We're going in some open window somewhere."

It would have been a time to consider the fallacy of our mode of life and of extravagance, if the novelty of the situation had not obtruded itself upon our thoughts. Those were the days when we were without inhibitions, confident that our social importance would cause us to be received in almost any quarter with consideration. We had that difficulty common to our kind in forgetting that we were graduates of St. Swithin's School and members of a certain final club; we were the hopeless products of indulgence, or else we would not have been amused.

"What do sheriffs do?" I asked. I was as young as that, and as ignorant of the processes of law. Beverley glanced at me over his shoulder. We had been climbing with agility and were somewhat out of breath.

"He will attach our personal effects," said Beverley, "until we pay that bill."

"You mean our clothes?" I asked.

"Yes, you ass," said Beverley.

"Wouldn't he give us something to wear if we went back?" I asked. "He wouldn't let us freeze, would he?"

"You ass," repeated Beverley. He was growing fatigued and out of temper. "Do you want to be an object of charity?"

Even then his logic did not seem convincing, but in those days there was no standard of experience.

We had arrived nearly to the top of the building, when we encountered an open window. Without checking himself for an instant, Beverley stepped through it.

"Hurry up," he said. "He'll think of this fire escape in a minute."

Beverley closed the window behind us softly, and we glanced about, both repressing a desire to giggle, as we considered the beauty of our exploit. We were safe in a small bedroom. The bed was still unmade, and the place reflected the character of its owner. A banner on the wall bore the white letters ZENO ACADEMY, which was an outlandish, unknown name. A silver-framed photograph of a lantern-jawed, middle-aged couple reposed on a mission bureau beside a pair of military brushes, and a snapshot of a girl was stuck in the edge of the mirror. Beverley examined it carefully and beckoned to me to look. It was plain from the face and figure that the girl was sensible and approved by the parents on the bureau. The only other picture was a

posed group of a football team, whose players had evidently represented Zeno Academy and were as remote and undistinguished as the
name.

The whole story of a humdrum life was there. Beverley made a
gesture of distaste and opened the bedroom door.

Then he said: "Excuse me."

We were standing on the threshold of a study. There was no atmosphere or imagination about the place. The furniture was the sort
which might be in any college room not abused or broken by the hilar-
ity of careless nights — a Morris chair, a desk, a swivel chair, a leather-
covered couch. There was no tobacco. The only pictures were photographs of teams. There were no medals on the pictures.

But the thing which made us pause was the attitude of the owner of
this place. He was hunched over his desk with his head in his hands, obviously, openly weeping.

Such an exhibition of emotion filled us with distaste. Yet the sight
made it unpleasantly clear to us that we had encroached uninvited
upon privacy. I gestured to Beverley to leave, but the situation had
intrigued him already, and he only shook his head.

"Excuse me," he said again, and the person at the desk turned. He
was a stranger to us, which was only to be expected. He was a type
which meant nothing to us — absolutely nothing.

Clearly we were descending into a mediocre world, for this stranger
had none of those ineffable stamps by which we measured style. He was
so poorly schooled that he was aware of his own inferiority. His clothes
had the cut indicating points west. His figure, bulging in his imitation-
tweed suit, was as ungainly as Rodin's Thinker's. His face was healthy
and honest, and actually smeared with tears.

"How did you get in?" he asked, and he drew his shirt sleeve across
his nose.

"Off the fire escape," said Beverley. "There's a sheriff waiting for us
downstairs. We're awfully sorry to have troubled you. I hope you
don't mind." Beverley was speaking easily, with a cultivated facility
for making any moment humorous. When he wanted, simply by the
use of words he could make anything all right.

"Oh, that's all right," the stranger answered, and paused and stared
at Beverley's pajamas; "but I wouldn't have been making — a damn
fool of myself if I thought you were coming."

"No," said Beverley, "of course you wouldn't. Don't give it another thought."

"My name's Brooks," the stranger said.

"Brooks?" said Beverley. "Haven't I seen you somewhere?"

For a moment the other's face lit up happily, as though we all were friends.

"Maybe," he said, "you've seen me out at football. They put me in against Bates for five minutes to do some kicking, just the end of the last quarter. I used to be pretty good — but I never got in again."

"Oh," said Beverley. "Well, that's the right thing to go out for. I suppose you know Tubby Harris, don't you? I went to school with Tubby."

Brooks opened and closed his hands. There was no doubt he was a football player, once you saw his hands.

"Yes," he said, "I know him."

"You don't like him, do you?" said Beverley.

"I haven't got any right not to like him," said Brooks. "What difference does it make? Not a bit of difference."

"Don't mind me," said Beverley. "Get it off your chest. I know Tubby. After all, why should you like him? I don't. He used to bully the life out of me at school."

It was a part of Beverley's intuition to bring in Tubby Harris then. It was amazing, though not wholly pleasant, how easily one could see through the simplicity of Brooks. Simply through idle curiosity, Beverley was drawing Brooks along in a careless wish to learn why Brooks wept there alone.

"All right, then," Brooks was saying. "All right, then; I don't like him. If you want to know, I wish he'd break his foot or something. I know he's better than I am. I don't mind that. But he won't even look at me when I meet him on the street."

"No," said Beverley, "he wouldn't."

"Well," said Brooks, "I guess you think I'm a fool. I don't know why I'm telling this to you."

"Because you wanted to talk to somone," Beverley answered.

The thing was indecent, so far as there is always something indecent in the unburdening of a soul. There was no use recalling what was said, for under Beverley's detached capacity for sympathy, words meant nothing. The whole history of Brooks was there, poignant, almost shocking, because the simplicity of Brooks was as shocking as his honesty.

"I guess you know about me now," Brooks said, just as though we were his best friends. "The only thing I care about is to play in a big game."

When he said it the confession was grotesque. Beverley pulled himself up straight and looked at him.

"You mean," he said, "you hope this will get you somewhere. Well, you're right. It usually does."

But Brooks was absolutely frank; there was no doubt he spoke the truth, and that he was obsessed by one idea.

"No," he answered, "I only want to play in a big game. That's all I mean. It's the only thing I've ever cared about, I guess."

"You mean," asked Beverley, "that's all you want?"

"Yes," said Brooks, "that's all."

It was not amusing, because the whole thing was too serious to be amusing. We had come face to face with a tragedy in life which was the result of certain forces playing on credulity. There was a believer in that room, and there was power in the belief, heavy with a pathos transcending humor.

"Well," said Beverley, "why don't you do it, then? What's the matter, Brooks?"

Unbelievably, but actually, tears came to Brooks's eyes at the question, so that it did not seem right to look at him. He was pitying himself enough to give way to tears.

"I'm not good enough," he said. "They've as good as told me. They'll use Harris. All I'm good for is a drop kick, and what's the use with Harris?"

Beverley looked at me, and looked away, as he always did when the vagaries of life surprised him. Brooks was speaking rapidly, and the thing was like a page of juvenile fiction as far as its point went. We were listening to a belief in the game and glory where artificial values drove out sense, but Brooks's situation was easy enough to understand, from the athletic records of the time. He was trying to compete with Tubby Harris, and he could not compete with him. There was no need for a second-string drop-kicker when Tubby Harris had absolutely everything. When you thought of Harris, the capabilities of Brooks were pitiful. Anyone could remember the echo of Harris's boot.

His leg swung as unerringly as a mechanical pendulum from school days to a higher sphere, until you could imagine Tubby kicking his way to heaven, and betting he could do it. Thirty yards — fifty yards — it was all the same to Tubby.

And when one comes to think of it, Tubby kicked his way to heaven just because the world remembered. He married money with that kick of his, and a partnership in a bond house. When one comes to think of it, ten million dollars' worth of second-rate securities went into the world from Tubby's toe, but that was afterward, although it was inevitable.

Beverley was abstracted, only half listening, as Brooks went on. Clearly something was on his mind which had to do with Brooks.

"No," he said, "you're right. You can't compete with Harris. . . . Brooks, have you got any clothes? We need two suits of clothes."

"Gosh," said Brooks, "I've only got one other and the one that I've got on."

"That's all right," said Beverley. "We'll probably only need them for half an hour. You don't mind getting out of that suit for just a half an hour?"

There seemed nothing peculiar in the request as Beverley stated it, for everything came easily then. It was as though he had asked the most casual favor of an acquaintance, and the simplicity of Brooks was like a limpid spring.

"Why, not at all," said Brooks, "Why, sure. Why, not at all."

That was how we happened to step outside in the hall, leaving Brooks in his underwear. We had done it probably in much the same way that the Dutch had seized Manhattan Island.

"These clothes are terrible," said Beverley. He was right, in that the clothes were too large and of a monstrous cut.

"Yes," I said, "they're terrible. . . . Now, what are we going to do?"

Beverley was hitching at the waist of his trousers.

"I'm sorry for Brooks," he said.

"No, you're not," I told him. "You're interested. That's all."

"Just the same," Beverley said, "you and I are going to have a talk with Tubby Harris. I can sympathize with Brooks. Do you remember how Tubby used to bully us at school?"

"You know perfectly well," I told him, "that it won't do any good to talk to Tubby."

"You leave this to me," said Beverley. "It seems too bad that anyone should want anything as much as Brooks. It makes me sorry."

That was how it happened that we took the role of gods and meddled with human fate. With the fluent superficiality which was to rise and be our curse, we went to Tubby Harris's room and pulled the helm of destiny.

It was the hour in the morning when Tubby was engaged in his exercises, which he always followed conscientiously; and his physical conscientiousness was as primitive as his sense of the ridiculous. When we told him what had happened, he stood motionless in his athletic underwear in the center of his room. Though he weighed a hundred and eighty-five, he was too well-proportioned to seem large. The newspapers had already begun comparing his waist and biceps measurements with the dimensions of ancient statuary. They were right, even to his features, for these had always seemed to bear the clear dullness of the faces from the golden age of Greece, even down to the conventional curl of the hair and to the twist of the upper lip.

His face, as he listened to Beverley tell of our escape, which ended in the discovery of Brooks in tears, first betrayed a bewilderment, which altered gradually to amusement, until he suddenly bent double as though we had hit him in the stomach.

"Gosh," he said, "that's funny! Say, the only reason we stand you, Bev, is because you make things funny."

"Well," said Beverley, "if I can make you laugh, I've accomplished something, haven't I?"

But the barb of sarcasm bounced as harmlessly from Tubby as a tackler in midfield.

"So Brooks was bawling, was he?" Tubby said. "All right. We know he hasn't any guts. Now, you had 'em when I used to handle you, bareback, at school. Some day I'm going to have a talk with you. Honest, Bev, we were talking about you the other night at dinner. It's time you did something that has some sense. . . . Excuse me. Go right on talking. Don't mind me."

"May I ask," said Beverley, "what you're doing now?"

There was some reason for the question, because it was difficult to understand exactly what Tubby was doing. The room where we stood reflected him. The furniture and woodwork were entirely of heavy fumed oak. Even with Tubby barefoot in his underwear, there was the insolence of paladins as Tubby stepped noiselessly across a heavy carpet and opened a closet door. Instead of taking clothes from the closet, he paused with the edge of the door in front of him, measuring it carefully with his eye. Then, balancing himself beautifully, he directed an unrestrained kick at the edge of that door. His foot traveled in a perfect arc, which ended above his head. For an instant it seemed inevitable that Tubby's bare toes would collide with the door edge, but instead his foot just missed, seemingly by a fraction of an inch, and passed safely with the precision of a planet on its orbit.

"Sit down," said Tubby. "Don't mind me. Go ahead and talk. I've got to stick with this for half an hour. It's a kicking exercise. The Old Man makes us do it. It's a great idea. I kicked your pants at St. Swithin's once, and I bet it did you good."

Beverley moved a chair close to the open door and stretched his legs out comfortably, while we watched Tubby's foot move back and forth, admiring the idea and thinking of the past. There was no doubt it taught absolute accuracy, and you could understand, just from watching him, why the team was good that year.

"Tubby," said Beverley, "you're good. . . . Yes, I remember, Tubby."

"Yeh," said Tubby. "You bet I'm good. It takes years to go at a door like that. I bet there isn't anybody else who could go at one like that. Don't look scared. I won't hit it. Watch me graze the edge now. . . . So you're sorry for Brooks? Well, I'm not. The Old Man gives everybody an even chance."

"Swish" his foot went past the open door.

"You see," said Tubby, "you've got to have guts to get ahead. You've got to put everything you've got into everything all the time — like this."

"Swish," his foot went past the door, and just to watch him, there was no doubt that he was obsessed by a single idea, just as Brooks was.

"You're good at everything," said Beverley, "aren't you, Tubby?"

"Yeh," said Tubby, "I'm good. I know I'm good. I've got to be good."

"And Brooks," said Beverley, "isn't. Is that it?"

"Oh, Brooks," said Tubby. . . . "Don't mind me. I can go on doing this with my eyes shut — blindfolded. What do you bet I can't do it with my eyes shut? . . . Brooks is all right, but he isn't good. The

Old Man might use him if I weren't there. I'll say that for Brooks, but we're not going in for charity this year. Why use him when I'm there? Brooks hasn't got any guts."

"I wish you'd be careful," said Beverley. "You might hit that door. . . . You mean there isn't a chance for Brooks?"

"Listen," said Tubby, pausing. "Brooks might get his letter for playing half a minute when everything is over, but can you imagine Brooks going in when I'm there? Listen. The boy is just an ox."

"And you've got everything," said Beverley. "Well, you always had everything."

"Yes," said Tubby, "everything comes easy to me." He was not boasting. He was only speaking unconsciously, because his attention was concentrated on that act of kicking past the door edge. Beverley slouched farther back in his chair and half closed his eyes, thinking.

"Don't think," said Tubby, "that I'm boasting. This just comes to me. I guess I've got a gift that way. What do you bet I can't go at that door with my eyes shut, boys? Here goes. Watch and see!"

Having gazed until he memorized the distance, Tubby Harris drew his leg back and at the same time closed his eyes. Everything he did looked simple, because it was so accurate and perfect. Tubby never did anything halfway. He closed his eyes so tightly that his face went into wrinkles, and hurled his foot confidently into darkness — and crack it went against the door.

The agony must have been terrific, because Tubby had collided with all his strength against the door edge, but there was no doubt that Tubby had the attributes of which he spoke. He stood, holding his foot in both his hands, and his face was a grimace which seemed to convey more of amazement than pain, and he was gazing at the door and not at us. In fact, Beverley looked more upset than Tubby. As he supported Tubby by the elbow, he looked ill, as though he himself had run into something much harder than a door.

"Gosh," was all that Tubby said — and he neither railed nor swore — "I guess I bust my toe!"

"You must have," said Beverley hoarsely. "You hit that door full speed."

"The draft," said Tubby, "from the window must have blown that door."

He could not have taken it better. He hopped over to a chair and sat down. For the first time I had ever known him, his conceit was entirely gone from him, leaving only a primitive stamina. It was the first time that either of us saw anything in Tubby Harris either to admire or to respect.

"Gosh," said Tubby, "this will be awful for the team! . . . One of you get the Old Man on the telephone. . . . Gosh, I was a fool! . . . Don't go saying I shut my eyes. . . . But I guess I had it coming to me. . . . Call up the Old Man."

"Tubby," began Beverley, "I couldn't seem to help it." He was still white as a sheet, and clearly he had something on his mind, but Tubby would not listen.

"Shut up!" he said. "Talk to me some other time. Now call up the Old Man."

For some time afterward neither of us spoke. Probably for the first time in our lives we had found ourselves face to face with the enormity of reality, and, having met it, it was clear to see why it was best to avoid reality like a plague.

We walked down the street in silence. It was a fine autumn morning. There was honesty in the freshness of the air and in the brightness of the sun. Once Beverley looked at me, but something between us which was unspoken made me look away. Then Beverley remarked, staring into space:

"Tubby took it very well."

I knew exactly what he meant. Tubby Harris had taken it too well for anyone to derive satisfaction from the justice of retribution.

Brooks was waiting, and the whole scene was as simple as the autumn sun.

"What's the matter, fellers?" he asked, just as though we were friends of his — and we were in a way. For a little while our lives were very close together.

"Brooks," said Beverley — he tried to speak calmly, but reality had robbed him of his poise — "Tubby Harris has smashed two toes of his right foot. He was kicking at the edge of his closet door."

Brooks's mouth gaped open. His whole face was honest wonder, and you could see emotion run across it utterly unconcealed.

"You're kidding me," said Brooks. "You must be wrong."

Beverley's lips were tight together, almost white.

"I'm not," he told him. "I was there."

Then the truth and its significance were dawning like the rising of a sun, and we were watching a great moment. Who was it who said when one has seen a street fight one has seen a battle? Napoleon was there, not Brooks, bathed in the glow of Austerlitz. The impression was the same, for destiny was there, touching Brooks with a magic wand, raising him above the humdrum slough until he was transfigured in the raiment of a dream.

"If that's so," Brooks was saying, "why, the Old Man will put me in on Saturday. He'll have to put me in."

"Yes," said Beverley, "don't worry. You're going in on Saturday."

Then the truth burst upon me, so ugly and so utterly beyond suspicion that there was no time for balance in the enormity of truth.

"Beverley," I began, and then I stopped, because Beverley was a friend of mine. It had never occurred to me that his resentment would last so long, but there had been something peculiarly irritating about Tubby's complacency, and you had to remember that Tubby Harris had handled Beverley very roughly back at St. Swithin's School.

It must have been the impulse of the moment, and there was the excuse of irresistible temptation, but I knew as sure as fate, though he never said a word, that Beverley, and not the draft, had moved that door.

It was not a thing to speak of, but Beverley was speaking without words, and he was ashamed of everything. But Brooks was the element which made it worse — the innocent happiness of Brooks. He might have been Balboa, staring from the heights of Darien at the unknown waters of a Southern sea, or a fool, gazing into a paradise of fools. It did not matter which, for the result was just the same.

"Yes," Brooks was saying, "the Old Man's got to put me in."

"Will you stop saying that?" Beverley shouted at him suddenly. "How many times do you have to say it?"

But Brooks looked at him with utter simplicity, eyes unnaturally bright from some flame within him.

"I can't help saying it," he said. "It don't mean anything to you, but it means everything to me."

There was only one thing more — a moment, and that was all, but it was one of those unrelated moments which give an insight into life. All the events about it had grown hazy. It might have been any one of a dozen days when we went to a big game.

You met the girls at the train the evening before. Then there was a party and a luncheon next day, where everyone was talking, and a taxicab and flowers. The game never seemed to matter as much as the tradition, for the game was always an excuse for something else.

I brought the Fielding girl — Natalie Fielding from New York. It was pleasant to see a New York girl; it was as though a door opened and the world came in. Beverley was taking Lou Van Holden. Beverley was in love with her at the time, not painfully but enough to make it pleasant. The kites were flying above the stands; the light from the sun was growing soft; high up above the noise, the telegraph instruments were clicking; the ball was on the fifteen-yard line in the center of the field.

"What are they doing now?" asked Natalie. "They always stand around."

"There's time out," I said. "It's fourth down. We'll try to kick a goal."

"Oh," said Natalie, "aren't there any more downs after a fourth down?"

"No," I said.

"All right," said Natalie. "I wish you'd take me seriously. . . . I wish the band would play."

"There goes the band," I said. "Don't you know I wouldn't have you here, if I didn't take you seriously?"

The band was playing and her feet were tapping with the music.

"Well, then," said Natalie, "how many downs make a touchdown?"

"Natalie," I said, "the only thing that matters is you're beautiful. Let's concentrate on that."

Then Beverley leaned toward me, and I knew there was something wrong with him.

"Look," he said. "Will you please look?"

"No," I said. "I want to look at Natalie."

"No, you don't," said Beverley. "Will you look? Brooks is coming in."

Then I saw him running. There was no doubt it was Brooks. He seemed to have come out of nowhere, holding his right arm above his head, running to the center of the field. He was speaking to the referee, and the referee was nodding.

"Brooks?" said Natalie. "Who's Brooks?"

"Never mind," I said. "He's going to try a drop kick, Natalie."

"What's a drop kick?" said Natalie.

There was no use explaining.

"Natalie — " I said, but Beverley's voice broke in.

"There they go," he said, but I did not care, and Natalie did not care.

"Brooks!" shouted Beverley. "You damn fool, Brooks!"

His voice made me look at the field again, and suddenly I was there with Brooks, and Natalie was gone. In that supreme moment the very worst had happened. The ball had been snapped back and Brooks had missed the pass. It had slipped through his fingers and was bouncing at his feet, while Brooks stood looking at it like a soul in purgatory, incapable of motion. Then instinctively he picked it up and ran, because it was too late to kick. He did not even have the sense to pick the open field, but blundered into the center of the line and through it. There was no element of skill or thought. Hands were groping toward him, bodies were flung against him, but there was no natural law. For an instant Brooks transcended life or reason. For ten seconds — the whole business could not have been as long as that — there was no one in the world like Brooks.

"He's over!" Beverley shouted. "Look at him! Do you see his face?"

It happened that we were sitting near enough to see. Brooks was lying on the ball, but he got up almost at once, and stared about him dazedly, opening and closing his hands. And then comprehension came upon him. You could see the realization of what he had done break across the mud smears on his face. He turned and looked at the stands; for a second — that was all — he stood staring into a sea of sound.

"Now then," the cheerleaders were shouting, "a long one for Brooks! Brooks . . . Brooks — "

"Who's Brooks?" Lou was asking. "I don't know him, do I?"

"No," said Beverley, but his mind was on something else. He was staring at the field. "They put him in to kick, because Tubby broke his toe."

"Well," said Lou, "I think he's rather cute."

And that was all there was — that beat of time. Brooks had turned away, walking slowly with the team, and the noise was dying down. He was walking from the sphere of our consciousness, an instant on its way to oblivion. He was the past already, and the noise was dying down.

"Listen," Beverley was saying — and he looked as though he had seen a ghost. "It's all my fault. Brooks was all right, and it's all my fault."

"I don't see what you mean." I said, and Beverley took me by the arm. "As long as you apologize to Tubby, you can't do any more."

"It's Brooks," said Beverley. "His face — didn't you see his face?"

"Well," I told him, "he was happy, wasn't he?"

"That's it," said Beverley. "Don't you see? Brooks was all right, and I've ruined him."

"Ruined him?" I said. "You're crazy."

"No," he said, "I'm not. Didn't you see his face? He's not built to stand a thing like that. He won't get over it — don't you see? There won't be anything like that for him again, and he won't forget — he can't forget. Anything he might have been, he won't be, and it's all my fault. I swear I've ruined Brooks."

"Of course," I said, "you're crazy."

"No," said Beverley. "Don't you remember those pictures on his bureau? . . . Let's get away somewhere. I want to forget I hate myself. I want to forget his face!"

It was long ago that Beverley had fixed things up with Tubby Harris, but it did not seem so long, once Beverley had spoken.

Yet, though the details were clear enough, it seemed like another life. There we were on the hotel veranda, dressed like champagne bottles, for no other reason than an effort to escape the fact that time was moving, but the idea of escape was illusion, if you let yourself stop and think. That was the reason for excess breakage, because no one wanted to stop and think.

Nearly everyone on the veranda was joining in an anesthetic chorus:

> Hoop her up for Old Umpteen,
> And hoop her up again.
> I doubt if there has ever been
> A finer lot of men.

And Brooks was seated on the veranda rail, flabby and overweight, with a patina of life upon him as awkward as his costume.

"Yes," he was saying, "it was this way. The ball was on the fifteen-yard line and I was on the twenty-five. Then Joe snapped back the ball, and all I thought all the time was I had dropped it, until I found that I was running. Gosh, I don't know how! Don't think I'm boasting. It was just a combination. It just happened. It was this way — "

Beverley sighed and shut his eyes and opened them.

"There he goes again," he said, and Brooks was like a squirrel in a cage running with that ball. "Oh, Lord," said Beverley, "he sees me now!"

There was no doubt Brooks had seen him. The pleasure ran across his face naïvely, and he hitched himself off the veranda rail.

"Hello," he said, and then something in Beverley must have checked him, for he suddenly looked at Beverley doubtfully. "I guess you don't remember me."

"Yes," said Beverley. "Yes, of course I do."

"Well, I always remember you," said Brooks, "because I associate you with the best time I ever had. . . . On the fifteen-yard line . . . Don't you know? The time I made a touchdown, you know?"

Then it was plain that Brooks had had too much to drink, though under the circumstances that was not against him. The extraordinary thing was that his condition made him entirely transparent, so that all his past was written on him like letters on a board. You could see the course of Brooks, leading on to nothing much, and lighted by a single light. You could see his years, unobstructed by wishes or complicated tastes, and lighted by that single light of a moment — that one great pulse of time.

"You know, don't you?" Brooks was saying. "You remember?" And he shook hands with Beverley for the third time. "The ball was on the fifteen-yard line, fourth down — "

"Yes," said Beverley, "that's exactly where it was."

"Well," said Brooks — and he swayed slightly on his heels — "I don't know why I'm telling this to you, but that's the best time I ever had. The only absolutely good time — first-rate time — I ever had."

"Was it?" said Beverley. Suddenly his voice was kindly.

"Yes," said Brooks, "the one first-rate time I ever had, but it means more than that to me. It's the reason for my success."

"Your success?" said Beverley. "Brooks, are you a success?" and he sat up straighter, watching Brooks swaying on his heels.

"Maybe not exactly that," Brooks said, "but it's got me where I am.

No matter what happens, I just have to say to myself, 'I was there.' I took the ball, see? I only have to remember that."

Beverley drew a deep breath.

"Brooks," he said, "I wish you'd told me sooner. I never thought of that. Sit down and tell me. . . . No, I like to hear. . . . The ball was on the fifteen-yard line — "

"Yes," said Brooks. "You see it was this way: The ball was on the fifteen-yard line. It was fourth down, eight to go — "

Just Break the News
(1937)

From my observation past events, at least in the world of fiction, as-sume added depth and value if they are viewed by the persons who participated in them from the perspective of the present. Teachers of-ten call this technique of moving from the present to the past in fiction "the flashback." Whatever it may be named, personally I have found it, when properly used, a valuable means of building character and often of sustaining interest.

"Just Break the News" represents one of my fairly early experiments in this field, as does also the story that follows it, "Beginning Now." As I read them today, I believe that the flashback may be more suitable for long than for short fiction. At any rate these stories indicate that this is true; since they both might very well have been improved had they been written in chronological narrative. In the limited space of the short story time shifts are frequently confusing and the disturb-ance of sequence may easily offset any increase of artistic illusion. "Just Break the News" is too crowded. I would make it far simpler, if I were attempting to write it now. I must also apologize for another of its aspects. To my consternation I find that I was still on the subject of generals, and furthermore that part of this World War I sequence is suspiciously similar to that of "Good Morning, Major," in that here, too, we have a young lieutenant going out to carry a message through a field of fire. This serves to illustrate how readily a writer's besetting fear, that of repeating himself, may be justified. However, these two events were not altogether parallel and communications were not as good in War I as in War II. But both wars present a common truth. You are more apt to be killed while walking about than while staying in one place.

My son had been polite to me — indeed, he had been almost gracious, considering what he had to suffer. I could remember well enough the embarrassment which assails one when one's parent arrives at the school. I could recall myself standing near Jaques Hall, where parents customarily made their appearance on Saturday afternoons, and examining my schoolmates' forebears with a malicious pleasure. You could tell a good deal about a classmate when you saw his papa and mamma, and generally the news was bad. Yes, I knew what my son had suffered when he was obliged to walk beside me past the boys of his own form. I could see these little fellows regarding myself and my automobile with an interest not intended for me alone. I realized that I stared back vulgarly, that my clothes did not fit properly, that I possessed neither the dash nor the finesse, and not the self-effacement of the ideal parent.

"I can go now," my son said, "I can go anytime. I don't have to be back till five."

"But I want to see some of your teachers," I said. "I particularly want to see your Latin master."

"He's away somewhere," my son said. "He couldn't see you. He's busy this time of day."

"Well, then, I should like to see Mr. Harrison."

It was dull of me not to realize that my son would look shocked, since I had been shocked myself when my own father had wanted to see the headmaster, and mortified at his assumption that the headmaster would have the time to receive him.

"You can't see him," my son said. "He doesn't want to see parents."

And then I realized that I was speaking from another plane of existence, as every parent must who tries, in his pathetic dullness, to understand the cares of youth. Nevertheless, I continued, even when I knew better.

"But I'd like to see some of your friends," I said. "Isn't there some boy that you particularly like?"

"They've all got other things to do," my son said hastily. "It's Saturday afternoon."

I am glad that I finally had sense enough to try no longer to project myself into a life which, for me, was gone forever. Yet the vitality of youth which pervades a school made me almost forget myself. Standing there in the mellow autumn light, surrounded by sights and sounds which had undergone no appreciable alteration, one had that unfortunate illusion of perpetual youth.

The boys looked just the same as they had when I was a boy. The types had not altered and I could pick them out — the fat boy, the stupid boy, the rich boy, and the bully, and the boy who collected cocoons, and the boy who collected postage stamps, and the one who cheated. All the elements of the old social order were continuing, uneffaced by time, and the boys brought back memories, interesting probably only to myself.

I was not surprised when I saw a red-nosed, cadaverous youth come hurriedly out from one of the buildings and walk away alone. He had the furtive look of a boy who had been crying, and it seemed to me that he might have been there always, utterly unchanged since I had left the school. In the rigorous life of an athletic education there must exist a maladjusted, unhappy social type. At the time of the Norse sagas there was a weakling at whom the men threw bones in the banquet hall, and, in many ways, a boys' school possesses much of the cultural level of Beowulf.

"Who's that boy?" I asked my son. "Is he in your form?"

"Oh, him," my son said; "yes, he's in my form, but I guess he won't be long. His name is Merch. We call him 'Diapers.'"

I did not inquire the reason for the name.

"When I was here at school," I said, "there was a boy who looked just like that. His name" — I paused for a moment, trying to pull his name from the web of the past — "his name was Chadwick, Diapers Chadwick. When he was older, we used to call him 'Di.'"

But my son was not interested. He was too wrapped up in his own problems to appreciate reminiscence.

"Was there?" he said.

"Yes," I said. "He led a dog's life here. If you get a chance, be kind. It won't hurt to be kind."

"It wouldn't do any good," my son said. "Where do we go to eat?"

"Why wouldn't it do any good?" I asked.

"It wouldn't help any," my son said, "that's all — not with him."

He was probably right. At any rate, it was what we had said about Chadwick a quarter of a century ago, and I began to wish that Chadwick had not come to haunt me out of nowhere, because it didn't do any good. As my son sat at table, eating fried chicken, Chadwick haunted me. He was by my elbow, demanding my attention when I tried to give a few words of sound advice.

"Let's have a Chadwick hunt," I heard them calling. "Somebody get Chadwick. We'll give him a two-minute start."

We had lived an important part of our lives together, but Chadwick had never improved. I often wondered what induced his parents to keep him on at school. I even asked him once, in the frankly brutal way of adolescence, but he could give no satisfactory answer.

I had told my son to be kind, but as I tried to think of some examples of kindness displayed by contemporaries in my own boyhood, I was amazed that I could think of hardly any; and such of those as I could conjure up were patently done for personal gain, not for any reasons of humanistic altruism. I should have remembered that boyhood is seldom kind, that thoughtfulness for the plight of antisocial human beings is a civilized attribute which only a good deal of personal humiliation can properly develop. I should have recalled that I was once like my own son, a snob who lived up to the tenets of a rigorous code, and who could only feel contempt for one who broke certain rudimentary rules. I had been about to tell my son how I had been kind to Chadwick once at the cost of considerable bodily risk, when I realized that I had not been kind. I had been actuated merely by a desire to increase my own importance, and by a carefully weighed conclusion that I was capable of licking a fourth-former named Hughie Jenks. Certainly I had disliked Chadwick's gratitude, because it was cloying and unmanly, and because Chadwick was frank enough to be a physical coward.

It was not strange, when I considered, that I could remember all the circumstances so clearly, for episodes in an average life that reach a wholly satisfactory conclusion are rare enough to be exceptional. The deeds one attempts so seldom reconcile themselves with the rigid proprieties of drama that one is left with a feeling of doubt when everything is over. In the case of Jenks, however, there was no doubt until I reviewed the circumstances as I watched my son.

I had been noble that afternoon, as inevitably noble as Tom Brown at Rugby. Besides, it had been my good fortune, coupled with my own good judgment, to connect with all my force on the end of Jenks's nose. It had been a day like the one through which I was living in the present, a clear autumn day with the smell of burning leaves in the still air. The Blue team had been practicing for its final game against the Reds, since *esprit* and manly competition had their definite place in the school curriculum. I was coming up from the lower field to get dressed in preparation for evening study, when I saw Jenks, who had grown fast enough in the last six months, twisting Chadwick's arm.

"Please don't!" Chadwick was shrieking. "Jenks, please don't!"

And Jenks was saying: "Shut up! That doesn't hurt you much. If you can stand it for a minute without yelling, I'll let you go."

It was not a pretty picture, but the fault was obviously Chadwick's. He was making a wretched and unmanly exhibition, because Jenks was quite right — he was not hurting Chadwick much. If it had been anyone but Jenks, I must admit that I should have approved of the experiment, but our personalities had grated upon each other in little ways which are useless to recall. I know now that the indignation that I felt was entirely spurious and opportune.

"Let that kid alone, Jenks," I said. "Take somebody your size." I still can savor the perfection of that moment, because that moment was perfection. Chadwick was no more of a kid than I was, and Jenks was not my size; he was ten pounds heavier than I, and a good two inches taller. Yes, the moment was perfect, because justice, everything, was on my side.

"Mind your own business," said Jenks. And that, now that I came to think of it, was exactly what I did. I dispensed with the usual personalities and vilifications and waded into Jenks before he was adequately prepared.

I should like to recall the battle, blow by blow, because it was so eminently satisfactory. I realized that I was right and that Jenks was wrong. The publicity of it was also desirable, since, after all, there was nothing better than a fight in those days, and all forms of competitive sport paled before it. By the time Mr. Sanderson, our housemaster, came to separate us, Jenks and I were performing before a large gallery, and there was not much doubt who was getting the better of it. Jenks's nose was bleeding so freely that his face, as the sports announcers have it, was a bloody smear, and I was standing toe to toe to Jenks, exchanging blows, when Mr. Sanderson got me by the neck of my sweater.

"What's this about?" Mr. Sanderson inquired. "What's the trouble here?"

My righteousness was such that I had no necessity to explain.

"It was Jenks's fault, sir," someone else was saying.

"Hendricks," Mr. Sanderson said to me, "go up to your dormitory and wash yourself and wait until you're called."

There have been few subsequent times in life when I could feel such a pride in my own rectitude. I walked away alone, but Chadwick caught up with me.

"Did he hurt you, Hendricks?" Chadwick asked.

"No," I said. "Shut up!"

Old Dr. Murchison was in his study, but, for once in my life, I had the premonition that my meeting with Dr. Murchison would have a happy ending, because Dr. Murchison was a respecter of codes and forms.

"Hendricks," Dr. Murchison said, "I hope you recall that fighting means expulsion, unless there is a reason."

"Yes, sir," I told him, and I looked him in the eye.

"Well," said Dr. Murchison, "what is your reason?"

"I had rather not say, sir," I told him.

I was obeying the code of silence, but I knew that Dr. Murchison would understand it, and he did.

"Hendricks," he said, "while I appreciate your reticence, I must ask you to explain the circumstances, with the assurance, Hendricks, that your explanation will go no further than this room."

It was probably obvious to us both that Dr. Murchison had examined the circumstances already.

"He was twisting Chadwick's arm, sir," I said.

"Very well," said Dr. Murchison. "I abhor fighting, but there may be times, and this may be one of them — I do not say it is, but that it may be one of them — when such measures are justified. You will shake hands with Jenks, of course."

"Yes, sir," I said, "if you tell me to."

"And now," said Dr. Murchison, "there is one thing more. Between you and me, Chadwick does not seem to get on well here, he does not seem to appreciate what the school is trying to do for him. I want you to keep an eye on him, Hendricks. You will, since you have shown this interest."

"Yes, sir," I said, since it was the only thing to say. I could not very well, under the circumstances, have told Dr. Murchison that I did not approve of Chadwick and abhorred the idea of looking after Chadwick in any way.

It seems that everything one does has a definite price tag attached to it. The price that I paid for being a hero was to take care of my contemporary, Diapers Chadwick, and to struggle with his physical and mental incapacities. Had I known the full eventualities of this price, I doubt if Jenks would have been obliged to go to the infirmary with a broken nose, for in subsequent association I never did like Chadwick much. Yet if I had not been ordered to take care of him, I think he would have made me, for he clung to me after that with an assumption that I was his well-wisher, his protector and his friend. It never occurred to me that others would take this same assumption for granted.

I had no way of knowing that one's acts at school might carry far into later life. I like to think that I may have been some help to Chadwick, but I doubt it, for one does not understand much of psychology or tolerance when one is in one's teens. I had the desire of my contemporaries to conform, and the dislike of my kind for those who did not. Those I knew who were not socially cooperative in our small community had other advantages which made them acceptable, such as aptitude in games, or humor, or intelligence. One might tolerate such individuals as one tolerates the eccentricities of genius, but Chadwick truly possessed nothing except defects. It was not up to me or any of us to understand the grimmer phases of maladjustment, or the various odd forms which inhibitions take. It is possible to imagine now what Chadwick must have suffered; but in those days such charity would not have been permissible.

Yes, I like to think that I did my best for Chadwick, though all the time I knew that he was an uninviting specimen. The boy was always afraid of something, always in the grip of imaginary dread. He had the shyness and the inability of the extreme introvert to do anything well.

"Isn't there anything you can do?" I asked him once.

"No," he said, "I guess there isn't. I only want to be left alone. I wish everyone would leave me alone."

"You better get it out of your head," I told him. "You'll never be left alone."

"But I'm not hurting anyone," he said. "I'm not interfering with anybody else."

He was entirely wrong about that. His presence was a constant irritant, because he reminded one continually that something was wrong, either with him or with everybody else.

I can see him still, weedy and ungainly, never properly dressed for any occasion, always late. I can still see the look in his eye of hurt and resentment. That was the worst thing about Chadwick, a capacity for resentment which is developed by the highly sensitive, so acute that there was no such thing for him as genuine friendship.

"Forget it, Chadwick," I used to say, not realizing that the capacity for forgetting is a God-given attribute, and a gift belonging only to the more successful.

"I can't forget," he said. "I try to, but I can't." At the time, the remark seemed silly; I realized only much later that he remembered everything. He could never have possessed an efficient censor for his subconscious mind.

When I saw his mother, I might have understood Chadwick better, if I had been old enough. I remember how she took my hand, a gushing, sentimental woman.

"Henry speaks of you so often," she said. "You've been so kind to him. Promise me you'll look out for him always, always. Promise me you'll make Henry a visit this summer, a long visit."

I promised. Chadwick was a nuisance, he always was a nuisance, but there is no use in picking up little incidents in the stream of passing time.

It was not until I sat there watching my son eating his fried chicken that I realized how much a few years of school run into everything. Those years are like a drop of aniline in a bowl of water; you can see the color spread until it colors everything.

"Hey," my son said, "what are you thinking about?"

I did not tell him what I was thinking, because he would have misunderstood. I was thinking that you can't change human beings much, for personality develops too early to change, particularly when one cannot forget. I was thinking of a scene in Hoboken, New Jersey, one of the few times I have been there. Red Cross girls were passing doughnuts and coffee in the pier shed beside the reptilian, camouflaged bulk of a transport. There were all the sounds in the shed of a ship about to put to sea, the hissing rattle of the donkey engine and the voices.

"Ninth school detachment this way," someone was calling. "Officers attached to tenth brigade headquarters this way."

I was standing beside Jenks, since Jenks and I had been picked for a brigade headquarters by some inexplicable system at Platts- burgh. Neither Jenks nor I thought it was odd that we should be together, because everywhere there was always someone else from the school.

"Hey," said Jenks, "will you look who's there! There's Diapers. Did you get him here?"

"No," I said, "I don't know where he came from." No one ever knew where anyone came from in that war.

"Well," said Jenks, "you've got to look out for Diapers."

"Give him a chance," I said. "This isn't school." I did not want to look out for Chadwick. All I wished was to look out for myself; that was all that any of us wanted then. I have never seen anyone look as relieved as Chadwick did when he saw me.

"I'm on the brigade staff," he said. "Are you on the staff?"

"Yes," I said.

"Then we'll be together, won't we?"

"Yes," I said. "Your blouse is unbuttoned."

He laughed nervously, and as I remembered it, the sound of that laugh still grated on my nerves.

"It's going to be just like school, isn't it?" he said.

"You're not in school any longer," I told him. "Can't you forget about it?"

"No," he said. "Why should I? I'm always thinking about school."

I wished then, as I have wished since, that so many of us would not be so continually harking back to school days, when there was so much else to think about.

But it was a good deal like school, which sometimes makes me won- der if school and war do not go together. There was the same dis- cipline, the same obtuseness, and General Hicks might have been old Murchison.

We were kept below before we left the dock, through some idea that spies would be along the water front to count the number of troops on deck, but they let us out once we were out of New York harbor. Chadwick found me standing forward on what had been the first-class deck of that converted passenger ship, looking down at crowds of drab enlisted men standing at the bow. Our ship was a part of a formation of transports, moving forward in a wedge with a steady rate of speed which reminded one a little of ducks upon the water. At the apex of the wedge was a slate-gray cruiser billowing out black smoke. We had already been put into life vests and we had already been given the numbers of our boats. Chadwick was out of breath when he reached me.

"Hello, Di," I said.

"Please," he said, "don't call me that."

I was sorry, and I told him so.

"It's just a matter of habit," I told him. "I won't do it again."

I had never been at ease with him, and now I was less at ease than ever. There was a new nervous elation about him which did not fit the circumstances when all the rest of us were trying to behave.

"I guess you're surprised to see me here," he said.

"Oh, no," I said untruthfully, "I'm glad to see you here."

Chadwick laughed again, and I turned to look at him. I had not seen him for some time and he had changed since I had seen him.

"I guess you're surprised to think that they gave me a commission," he said. "Well, I got it in officers' training camp, just the same as you did. There wasn't any pull about it either."

Then I knew that he was changed, because for the first time in his life he had accomplished something definite.

"That's fine," I said. "I'm awfully glad."

"You know," he said, "I've been laughing ever since it happened. Sometimes I wake up at night and laugh. I fooled the crowd at school all right. I bet they won't believe it, even now."

I had an impatient impulse to tell him that no one would care, but instead I said: "Forget about the school. I know you had a rotten time there, but you've been to college since, and this is all a new deal. School doesn't last forever. You're grown up now. Your life vest isn't tied right; move around and let me fix it for you."

He moved around obediently and he did not answer, but I could tell, from the way he looked, that he was thinking about the school, considering past wrongs and past injustice. Thoughts like that would be forever boiling in his mind in an unhealthy sort of ferment.

"Don't be so sensitive," I told him. "You're grown-up now."

He did not answer me directly, but I could see those wide, restless eyes of his examining me, and his voice dropped to a confidential undertone.

"Aren't you afraid?" he said.

"No," I said, "not particularly. Don't think about yourself so much; it doesn't pay."

"But don't you realize," he said, "that we're probably all going to die?"

"Don't talk nonsense," I said. "Shut up!"

"Well, I can die just as well as you," he said. "I'll show you I'm not afraid. I'll show everybody I'm not afraid, and I'm not going to take any back talk from Jenks either. He'll respect me before I'm through. You're all going to respect me — do you understand? Just because I made a fool of myself at school — "

"Shut up," I said, "and keep your mouth shut, if you want people to respect you. It'll be all right; everything will be all right."

He did not have time to reply, because Hughie Jenks was walking toward us in a new whipcord uniform.

"Hello, Hen," said Hughie. "Ah there, Di."

"Don't call him that," I said. "We've got to stick together now."

"I'm sorry," said Jenks. "It just tripped off my tongue."

"Oh, that's all right," said Chadwick. "Well, I'll see you later."

We looked after him while he walked stiffly down the deck, pompously conscious of his military dignity.

"Whoever let him in?" said Jenks. "He's terrible."

"Yes," I said, "he's terrible."

"He's so terrible," said Jenks, "that he makes me forget that he's really sort of sad."

Generals had always been remote beings whose habits could be observed only from a distance, until I found myself on the headquarters staff of General I. A. Hicks. Even so, the general was remote enough. He was a grizzled man in his late fifties, possessing the adamantine exterior of his profession, so interesting to a democratic civilian. Through his adjutant, a West Point major, he gave the young officers on his staff rigorous treatment. It was his habit to remind us frequently that a staff job was not a sinecure and that staff officers were expendable. At the officers' mess he customarily ate in silence, but he watched us all the time. In the end I grew to like him. We were fortunate, in those days of rapid promotion, to have a lieutenant colonel, made into a general overnight, who was a first-rate officer and one who knew his job, even when we were at the front. The general was a square man, and

I sometimes think he liked me, too; although he was not the sort to allow friendship to interfere with business. He had me in to see him once when we were in quarters at the port of debarkation.

It was nearly the only time during hostilities that I ever knew him as a human being, and that was not for long. He was sitting in a room in one of those brick French army barracks and the wind was blowing puffs of dust through the open window.

"Close the door, Lieutenant," the general said. "You better close the window too. You know we're going to the front tomorrow."

"Yes, sir," I said.

The general tapped a paper on his table.

"There's an order here," said General Hicks, "detailing you as an orientation instructor. You've got a chance to stay behind. Do you want to stay?"

"No, sir," I said.

"All right," the general said. "I believe I can arrange it. In fact, I've said I wanted you already."

"Thank you, sir," I told him. "Thank you very much."

"You won't thank me two weeks from now," the general said. "You'll wonder why you were fool enough to thank me. That's all, Mr. Hendricks."

I put my toe behind me for the conventional rightabout, and then I paused.

"May I ask the general a question?" I asked.

"Very well," he said. "What is it?"

I knew that it was none of my business as soon as I had spoken, but still I went ahead.

"Would it be possible to detail Chadwick, sir?" I asked.

The general sat still; his flinty-blue eyes were motionless.

"Chadwick?" he said. "I understand you went to school with Chadwick once. Chadwick is not good enough to stay." And then the general smiled faintly. "He's been detailed as my aide. He's good enough for that. That will do, Lieutenant."

It has often amazed me to hear individuals who have been at the front speak wistfully about the war. Such talk has invariably been beyond my comprehension, even after the mellowing influence of time. The aviators may have had some excuse, and the officers in the service of supply, and officers who came too late to see more than the tail end of the big show, but I cannot conceive that there is any excuse for any-body else.

Out beyond Château-Thierry, where the brigade first went into line, the roofs were off the farmhouses and the villages were in sweltering ruins under the late-July sun. That shell-torn countryside gave one the peculiar impression that one had seen it before, from its similarity to the war photographs we had all examined, until one saw the dead. I was with Chadwick the first time I saw a dead man. We had walked into the gate of a large farmyard, half a mile off the Soissons road. The farmyard and the buildings must have been used for a machine-gun strong point in the retreat from the salient, and the gunners must have been wiped out by artillery fire, for there they sprawled about their gun where a high-explosive shell had struck, gruesomely awkward in the hot sunlight. They were Germans in that shoddy field gray, their trousers tucked into high muddy boots, their heads covered by those curious coal-hod helmets. The emotion of fear and distaste which I experienced when I saw them told me how green I was, in spite of military education. I had the impulse to turn my head and to walk away, with that instinctive desire to shut out the thought of death. Instead I tried to be nonchalant and I called Chadwick to look, too; knowing that he would have to see it sometime.

"Come in here and look," I said.

It was apparent that the sight made him sicker even than it made me. The silence in that walled enclosure was dramatic and terrible. It was worse because of the ceaseless undercurrent of artillery outside in the distance. First Chadwick went white and then color surged back to his face, but the remark he made always struck me as peculiar.

"It's just the way I thought they'd look," he said, and I suppose that he was thinking all the time of death. "I suppose you thought I'd be afraid," he added. "Well, I'm not afraid." The remark was probably characteristic of all of us. The greatest fear we had was the fear that someone might think that we were afraid.

"I guess we'll all get used to it," I said.

"I'm used to it already," Chadwick said, and I never asked him why, but perhaps his next remark explained it. "I can stand it as well as anyone else," he said. "I'm not any more of a coward than anyone else."

"Don't talk so much about yourself," I told him. "No one said you were."

That was the trouble with him; he was always talking about himself. I have said he was always afraid of something, and now he was scared of being scared. The rest of us were able to put this obsession in the back of our minds and to take an interest in the comforts and discomforts of the moment. We could be pleased with little things, such as dry socks or a tin of marmalade or a dead Frenchman's flask of wine. It did not take much to please us in those days, but it was not true of Chadwick. He made himself obnoxious in the way he talked about himself, when there was not much time for personality. Two of our battery were smashed to pieces at the Vesle River. Saint-Mihiel was a picnic, but the Argonne was worst of all.

As a matter of fact, there was not much chance to be afraid; there was too much physical discomfort; there was too much dull routine. And out of all the disorder there arose a sort of order when we learned how to move from place to place. We all became used to one another; we were all integral parts of a bad dream. If there has ever been such a thing as a brigade reunion, I have never heard of it. I should not care to see those faces again, even now, because there is too much that I do not care to remember.

Once, in the headquarters dugout, when the barrage began that started the Argonne drive, Chadwick began shouting in his sleep.

"Please don't, Jenks!" he shouted. "Please don't twist my arm!"

The dugout was in dim candlelight; the orderlies were sitting on boxes by the telephone switchboard. The bunks, three deep, made of board and wire netting, were against the wall. I rolled out of a lower bunk and seized Chadwick by the shoulder.

"Don't," he cried again. "Jenks, don't twist my arm!"

"Wake up!" I told him, and I shook him.

There was a moment, when he woke up from the depths of sleep, when he could not understand where he was, a difficulty common to all of us on occasions, and I could see that lack of comprehension in his eye.

"You're all right," I said. "No one's twisting your arm," and then I saw that the general was beside me.

He must have been awake in his cell-like cubicle off the main dugout. He was neat and hollow-cheeked in the candlelight; his gray, close-cropped hair always had the appearance of being carefully brushed; his hair and mustache were a bluish-gray, like his eyes.

"What's wrong in here?" he asked. Chadwick sat up and bumped his head while the general stood looking down at him.

"He was talking in his sleep, sir," I said, and then Chadwick knew where he was; partially at any rate.

"Excuse me, Doctor Murchison, sir," he said, "I was dreaming about the school."

"Murchison?" said the general. "Who's Murchison?"

"Excuse me, sir," said Chadwick, "I'm all right now. I was just asleep."

The general was looking at him intently, abstractedly; he was looking at Chadwick the way he looked at a battle map.

"All right," he said. "Go to sleep and don't wake us up again. We'll need our sleep."

The general walked to the blanket by the dugout door and pulled it aside.

"Are you going out, sir?" Chadwick asked.

"Yes," said the general, "but you needn't bother, Chadwick. I'll take Hendricks and I want Jenks."

It was an unbelievable sight outside, and one which, I hope, I shall never see again. As we stood in the dark, looking over the top of the trench, you could hear the shells above our heads; the air was full of shells. You could hear the strange gurgle of the gas shells, and those of heavier caliber made a sound like railroad cars upon a trestle. You could see them bursting in the darkness of the slope across the valley in ugly splashes of yellow light.

"They've pulled out across there, of course," the general said. "It will be hard to keep up communications tomorrow, very hard. Mr. Jenks, when did you twist Chadwick's arm?"

"Years ago, sir," said Jenks. "It was at school."

"At school?" the general said. "Well, that's all right," and then he cleared his throat. "We've been fortunate," he added, "that there have been no casualties on the staff. If you have any letters, gentlemen, I should give them to the adjutant, and now we'll go to sleep again. We'll need our sleep."

"So Diapers was yelling, was he?" Jenks asked me.

"Yes," I said, "but he's behaving."

"Yes," said Jenks, "why shouldn't he? And what call has he got to dream about the school?"

The general was a different man afterward, when the war was over. Later he was human, with the failings of humanity, but he had other problems then. He made use of all of us according to our abilities, and he knew our abilities, because, as I have said, he was a first-rate officer. He was not one of those brigadiers who sit at the telephone and let the colonels do it; he was always on the go with his aides behind him, turning up at odd moments and examining positions. I have never seen another military man with a better sense of terrain than he. He had the feel of the country and of the forests and of the undulations of the hills, usually possessed only by one who has traveled in the country in times of peace. The symbols on the great war maps must have made definite pictures in his mind; at any rate, he could read things on them which were not written. He could make a marvelous good guess about the state of roads and about enemy positions. I have seen him put his finger where there was nothing but a clump of woods and say: "There will be machine guns there."

"They have moved their artillery behind that crest," he said. "They should be in position to fire tonight. Colonel Jones's regiment is going to have the worst of it."

"Hey," my son said, "aren't you listening to me? We're going to have a school party on Halloween. Aren't you listening?"

"Yes," I said, "I'm listening."

It was not exactly true. I was thinking of where headquarters was established on the September night when the general had spoken of artillery. The French dugouts were flimsy affairs compared with the German excavations. We were burrowed into the side of a hill in a large room of reinforced concrete with galleries opening from it. The place was called The Crown Prince's Dugout, not for any good reason, because every place of safety had that name, but its former occupants must have had a good time there. Pictures of dancing girls were pasted on the walls; there were two cases of champagne and a piano in the corner, and a gasoline motor ran a dynamo to furnish electric light. It was comfortable enough in there, considering the rain outside. The telephone orderlies were at the switchboard and the mess orderly was opening cans of beef on a plank table while the general stood looking at his map.

"The line from Oronoco is out, sir," someone said, and then there was a crash outside. The whole place shook so that the candles spluttered. No one spoke for a moment and then there was another crash.

"They know we're here," the general said. "Major, get Colonel Jones's regiment. He may have a line to Oronoco." The noise outside was nearly continuous by then.

"Heavy shelling on the road, sir," someone said, and then I heard the orderly's voice from the switchboard.

"They can't get Oronoco, sir; both lines are out."

I was standing near Jenks at the time, and he nudged me with his elbow.

"Somebody's going out to see about those wires," Jenks whispered.

The idea had not occurred to me until he mentioned it, and then I looked about the dugout and saw that there were only three officers present, with the exception of the general and the adjutant, neither of whom counted. They were Jenks and Chadwick and myself.

The general looked up from his map, and anyone could see that something was troubling him.

"Canby 1, to speak to the general, sir," the orderly said.

The general picked up the telephone. He had to speak very loudly to make his words go through.

"The line to Oronoco is out, sir," he was saying. . . . "Yes, sir, I will get word up. . . . Yes, sir, right away." Then he set down the telephone and turned to Chadwick, who was standing just behind him.

"Give me a message blank," he said, and he leaned over the table to write.

"Do you want a runner, sir?" the major said. The general paused and listened to the noise outside.

"No, Major," he said, "I'll send an officer," and he glanced slowly around the room. "I want an officer to bring this to Colonel Jones, an officer who can explain the positions on the map. This is an important message, gentlemen. Who wants to go?"

It was strange, when I could remember small details so clearly, that the importance of that message and the real reason for it have been lost with time. They are lost like my knowledge of fire adjustment and the orders for commanding a battalion. The difficulties of the general and of Colonel Jones were lost, but perhaps they do not matter now, because the result is still clear with all its ancient stark lucidity — like a bright coin unearthed from dust. It was a bad night, and the general was looking around the room.

"Who wants to go?" he said.

Under the circumstances, the answer was completely obvious; nobody wanted to, but there was only one thing to do.

Nearly all races live by codes which must have their origin in some dark period of tribal history, and the Anglo-Saxon code, based on a shifting combination of chivalry and sportsmanship, is one of most difficult explanation.

"Who wants to go?" the general had said. The question was superfluous, because he already knew the answer and the enlisted men were already looking at us three junior officers. The logical reply, I have often thought, would have been as follows:

"Since you ask me, General, frankly, I don't want to go. The sector outside is under heavy fire and the enemy has obviously located our battery positions. The chances of a man's getting through and back until the fire slackens are very slim. If I have any choice in the matter, I certainly don't want to go."

It is hardly necessary to add that no one made such a speech, since we had been too well taught to make it. Instead I moved forward at once with that ridiculous assumption of briskness necessary for the occasion.

"I'll go, sir," I said. "I know the way." And Hughie Jenks was right behind me, taking the words out of my mouth.

"I'll go, sir," he said.

Then there was a pause, hardly long enough to be appreciable, and I heard Chadwick clear his throat.

"I'll go, sir," he said.

It must have been force of habit which made me speak again, habit rather than liking. When Chadwick spoke, I felt an inexplicable emotion, inexplicable because it certainly arose from no desire to be noble.

"Shut your trap and keep out of this," I said to Chadwick.

I had a premonition of what would happen next, and there was nothing that one could say or do about it while we stood there waiting, while the general looked us over. There was the same pause which came, years ago, when sides were being chosen for baseball. We waited while the ground shivered under the concussion of the shelling. The general's glance was impersonal. General Hicks never labored under any illusions; one could almost see his mind work with military preciseness as he arrived at his conclusion. It was not up to him to show any sympathy; it was up to him to select the one who would least be missed, if anything should happen.

"Thank you all for volunteering," the general said. "Lieutenant Chadwick will go."

"Wait," I said. "Please let me go, sir. He isn't any good at anything like that. He'll just get lost."

"Yes, sir," Jenks said, "either of us two is better."

"Won't you please" — there was a break in Chadwick's voice — "won't you please be quiet? Won't you, both of you, be quiet?"

"That will do," the general said. "Chadwick, you'd better start right now. You know the road. We were over it this morning."

"Then I'll go with him, sir," I said. I wanted to add that he needed looking after, but I knew that it would not sound right.

"No," the general said. "That's enough of this nonsense. Lieutenant Hendricks, you and Lieutenant Jenks will stay right here."

I walked with Chadwick to the dugout steps, and I could not tell why I was so deeply moved, except that I must have known that he would die.

"Pull the flap back from your gas mask," I said, and I slapped him on the shoulder. "So long, Chad; I'll see you at breakfast."

Then he turned around and faced me, and I could not understand him for a second, because his eyes were malicious and his smile was malicious.

"So long," he said. "It's too bad about you and Jenks. If I don't get back, you tell them, will you? You tell them that I was the one the general picked, not you or Jenks."

For a moment I thought he was joking, and then I saw that there was no irony in his speech. It was triumph, sheer bright triumph that he was the one who had been chosen. He did not know why he had been.

"Tell who, Chad?" I asked, and his voice is still clear enough.

"Tell them back at school," he said, "that the general picked me, not you or Jenks. Will you promise me that you'll tell them that? Tell the crowd from school!"

Beginning Now—
(1939)

There are two things above all others to be avoided in the writing of fiction, at least in my experience. Never try to deal with major characters of whom you have no personal experience or knowledge. If you do not believe this, look at Steerforth in David Copperfield. *Dickens had obviously never exchanged more than a word or two with Steerforth. Secondly, never try to say too much in too limited a space, because your readers do not know or care as much as you do what you are doing, and therefore they may not try to follow you.*

"Beginning Now" has heeded neither of these dangers. Outside the pages of Robert W. Chambers and other popular Edwardian writers, I had never encountered a Johnny Kelsey when I wrote this story. I know now that Johnny Kelseys do not exist in the form in which I endeavored to portray this one. They all have redeeming features and good reasons for their failings, which are better described in a novel than in a short story, if they are to carry the ring of conviction. My Mr. Kelsey in his abbreviated form arouses many doubts, and I am sorry, because I think he has the makings of an interesting fictional individual. There is too much in "Beginning Now" for a story of its length. Yet I believe that the idea behind it is good enough to carry it, partially. If it had been four times longer, it would have been much better, but I am not sure I would have believed this in 1939.

AFTER dinner, the parlor was filled with folding gold chairs, and the conversation of the guests, as they seated themselves, lapsed into monosyllables and whispers. It was going to be one of those musical evenings, demanding a technique in manners with which a tone-deaf person can never be familiar. The musicians filed in from a side door—

a pianist, a violinist and a cellist. There was a gentle twanging of strings. The violinist — an athletic, slightly oily-faced young man — tucked a clean handkerchief around his collar.

"It will be Brahms," our hostess said.

The announcement seemed to satisfy everyone. The silence was deepening. In a moment there would be music, and it would fill the room. Brahms meant little to me, and would mean even less when they had finished. Yet his harmonies in themselves would not be unpleasant. The only difficulty with them was that they would stir a number of repressed ripples in my mind, and turn it to subjects which I wished to forget. As soon as the first note sounded, I was thinking not of music but of my friend, John Kelsey, and of John's father and of John's wife and of their son, although I had been trying not to think of them at all. Nevertheless, I could hear their voices sounding above the music. My mind had gone with the music out the window, in a way which, I am sure, Brahms had not intended.

"I want you to go up there," John Kelsey had said just that afternoon, "and have a good long talk with Pete. Something's the matter with him — I can't make out what — just one of those jams, I suppose, and they're so important to a boy. You know the way it used to be up there at school. Just have a talk with him and help him out. I guess he'd rather see you than me. And I can't very well go myself, can I, the way things are? And someone ought to tell him about all this."

I could hear his voice as plainly as though he were sitting beside me, undisturbed, with a tinge of humor in it. Everybody always said that Johnny Kelsey never lost his sense of humor, not even when he was semiconscious for three days, the time his head had struck a stone wall in the Red Brook Run. Personally, after all those years, I was getting a little tired of Johnny's humor. There are times when one can spare that God-given sense for a quarter of an hour, times when the sporting point of view does not work as well as others, and when you might skip the stiff upper lip and the merry smile.

Nevertheless, Johnny Kelsey was correct about one thing. He could not very well go up to a boarding school to see his son. He had been out on bail for manslaughter since the night before. His car had piled up on the sidewalk against a hydrant at half past one in the morning, and he had been too drunk to drive, and the woman who had been with him, and who departed without giving her name, was not his wife. "I always have the damnedest things happening to me," Johnny Kelsey said. "The man was right under the wheels before I saw him. It would have happened if I had been living on ice water. I can handle a car when I'm tight. Maybe I was thinking about something else, but let's not worry about that side of it. The lawyers will. The point is, should anyone tell Pete about it?"

"How's he going to help hearing?" I said.

"Now, that's a silly question." Johnny Kelsey answered. "The Old Man stepped in. I got him on the telephone right away. You know how the Old Man acts. Father's a good fast worker. He knew someone at the district attorney's office, and it ought to stay out of print. Don't worry. The Old Man and the lawyers will attend to it. Of course, Jane knows something, but she's taking it all right. The only thing that troubles me is Pete's in trouble too."

"What about Pete?" I asked.

John Kelsey rubbed his hand over his short, straight hair. "Pete says he wants fifty dollars," he answered. "He says he wants it right away. There's something worrying Pete, and all the Kelseys always stick together. I wish you'd go up there and find out what it's about."

"The trouble is," I said, "you don't know what anything's about, John."

"Don't say that again," he told me. "My friends always stick by me, and that's all that anything's about."

"Someday — " I began.

"I know," Johnny answered. "I'm going to get what's coming to me someday. Don't think I don't know what a mess I've made of things. There's no use going into that, but it's going to be all right — beginning now."

If you know a person well enough, there comes a time when he cannot do much with words. You have heard them all before, if you know him well enough.

"You can't make the man you ran down all right," I said.

John Kelsey rubbed his hands together.

"Wouldn't it be simpler," he suggested, "if you weren't quite so obvious? We all take a chance, don't we, when we cross the street? We all take a chance when we drive a car. I've seen plenty of people get killed. If you go out quick, it doesn't matter. He didn't know what hit him. His family will be better off than he could ever make them. The Old Man and the insurance company will take care of it."

"That's logical," I said, "but not original. Suppose you'd run me down. Suppose I hadn't known what hit me."

His eyes met mine squarely. He always looked everyone straight in the face; and this shows nothing candid in a person's character, in spite of popular opinion.

"That remark of yours isn't bright," he said. "I should have felt sorry, because I have known you for the last twenty years, but, honestly, would you have cared?" A sharp wrinkle appeared between his sandy eyebrows and he passed his hand slowly across his forehead. "I'm worried about Pete, that's all."

"Someone has to tell him," I said.

He did not answer me directly. "Now what the devil does he want that fifty dollars for?" he asked. "He had his allowance the first of the month."

"Someone has to tell him," I repeated.

He had shied away from the idea until then; but now that he faced it, his answer was characteristic.

"Oh, yes," he said, "exactly. That's what Jane keeps saying. Jane's been an awfully good sport about it. You know how she is."

"She should have chucked you over long ago," I said.

Johnny Kelsey smiled. "Let's take one thing at a time," he said. "Will you go up there and tell Pete? Jane wants you to, and so does the Old Man. Just tell him nicely, logically. It might have happened to anyone. You'll go see him, won't you, Joe?"

There was nothing surprising in his request, because he was used to asking favors.

"I'd rather have you tell him than anyone else," he went on. "You know me. You can make him see."

"Are you afraid of what he will think of you?" I asked.

"How did you guess that?" he asked, and he seemed to be relieved that I had guessed. "I can't let him down. It's the only thing I can do for him — to let him think that I'm all right." He took three quick strides across the room and back. "I don't know what I'd do if he didn't."

"It's too bad you didn't find that out earlier," I suggested.

"Don't preach," Johnny Kelsey said. "I'll be all through if he doesn't like me. I can't sleep, thinking of it. Joe, you'll go to see him, won't you?"

"I'm going out to dinner," I said, "but I'll take the night train afterwards. But he'll find out about you sometime."

"There won't be any other time," Johnny Kelsey answered. "I've told the Old Man and I've told Jane. Just fix it up with Pete and everything will be all right, beginning now."

This peaceful phrase blended smoothly and consolingly with the music.

I was trying to think of something that had happened earlier that summer, the last time I had seen Johnny Kelsey's son. It had been so much like so many other times that it was hard to make it distinct. First the telephone had rung in the morning and Jane Kelsey was speaking.

"You haven't heard it yet, but you are elected to keep Johnny out of trouble," she said. "If you don't come out for the week end, he'll be going over to the Lees', and you know what that means."

"What?" I asked.

"You know. It's Sally Lee this summer."

"Listen, Jane," I said. "You know that doesn't mean anything."

"Everybody else doesn't," she said. "Please come out. If you meet Johnny at the office, he'll drive you down."

"Is he still working?" I asked.

"Yes," she said, "he's back again. The Old Man sent him back."

The board room at the brokerage firm where he worked was still full of stale cigar smoke, and Johnny was in a private office.

"Let's go," he said, as soon as he saw me. "Let's get out of this."

"It's pretty early," I said. "I can wait, if you're busy."

Johnny Kelsey raised his eyebrows. "It can all get on without me," he said. "Let's get out where it's cool. Pete's home. You haven't seen Pete for a long while, have you?"

I remember being surprised that John should have mentioned his son, because he generally spoke of his children collectively. Jane had always been much the same way too. There were always nurses, governesses or tutors. They came in to shake hands, and went away.

"I've always been afraid of Pete," I said. "He has your way with strangers."

"What way?" Johnny asked me.

"God would think twice," I answered, "before damning such a gentleman."

Johnny Kelsey began to laugh. "He's fifteen, but he's grown up," he said. "He's in the fifth form now. He's philanthropic too. They've made him treasurer of Spring Lake."

When I asked him what Spring Lake was, he was surprised.

"Don't you remember anything about the school?" he asked.

"Not much," I told him. "I'm grown up too."

Johnny Kelsey lighted a cigarette. "Maybe that's what's the matter with me," he said. "Just a boy at heart. Maybe I get that way because I remember things like Spring Lake. It's the camp for city kids the school runs. You know the way schools are."

After we had lunch, his car was brought around and Johnny pulled his hat over his eyes.

"Hold tight," he said. "We're going." He had always been a fast driver, but he had a good sense of speed and timing. "She handles well, doesn't she?"

"You're driving too fast," I answered. But it was only a casual remark; I never was uneasy when he drove.

"Yes," he said, "she handles well. I suppose Jane said something to you. Did she?"

"About the Lees," I said.

"Well," Johnny Kelsey answered, "every time I step off the porch, everyone begins talking. Jane knows there's absolutely nothing in it."

"There have been times," I said.

Johnny glanced at me sidewise. "Now and then," he remarked, "I don't see how I stand you, Joe. You haven't indicated approval of me for quite a while."

"I never approved of you," I said.

Johnny Kelsey looked at me again, and I wished that he would keep his eyes upon the road.

"Which one are you thinking of?" he asked. "The breach of promise and seduction? That was all a frame-up, and you know it, and the governor knows it too."

"And your governor fixed it up," I said.

"Yes," said Johnny. "It cost him fifty thousand dollars, in case you want to know"

"It's nice your father thinks you're worth it. . . . Here comes a cop," I said.

John Kelsey sighed. "It's funny they don't know me yet," he answered. But the officer did not keep us long.

"What's that you showed him?" I asked, and Johnny grinned.

"Special card," he told me. "I got it from a friend. It always works."

The shadows of the maple trees along the avenue through the Kelsey place were long in the waning golden sunlight. I could see their branches in a tunnel-like arch above the drive, as Johnny swerved his car past the gatehouse. The place was large and complicated enough for a gatekeeper, a survival of a more genial epoch, when there were no income taxes or death duties. The name Southmere, which was certainly adequately trite, was carved on the granite gateposts, and they were like the entrance to a principality. That domain had grown increasingly alien since I first visited it.

I was admitted to it now as an old friend of the family, a strange, anomalous position, which Jane and Johnny Kelsey and old Roger Kelsey, his father, took more and more for granted, until the servants themselves recognized my status and treated me with a respectful familiarity. It occurred to me that even Johnny Kelsey sometimes treated me as a dependent; at any rate, he had such an implicit belief in my loyalty that he felt it unnecessary to conceal anything. The wheels made a hissing noise on the blue-gravel drive as we moved past the garages and the stables and the paddocks, up the avenue to his father's low granite house with all its ells and additions. Down to the left I could see the white wooden house which had been built for Jane and Johnny when they were married.

"We'd better ease in and see the governor," Johnny said. "He'd like to see you."

I could remember the time when Johnny had brought me there first as a guest on a school vacation. I had never entirely lost my old shyness, and now, besides, I felt that the place, instead of being frightening through magnificence, was becoming venerable; that the trees were larger; that the lawns were beginning to look like a park in England. It occurred to me suddenly that the Kelsey house was becoming a grotesque antique, and this seemed impossible. The house had been built in 1908, and it was not right that anything built in 1908 should not seem new.

Old Mr. Kelsey had been going to town only once a week lately. His color was not good and his hair was white, but his back was straight. When I saw him I experienced a familiar sort of wonder that anyone could have made so much money, though now I had lived long enough to realize that it was better not to ask how he had made it.

"Hello, Joe," he said. "You run along home, John. I want to talk to Joe for a minute."

"The governor's been wanting someone to discuss me with," Johnny said. "See you later, Joe."

Mr. Kelsey took me to the library and slapped me on the shoulder. "How are you, Joe?" he asked.

"I could still do with a million dollars," I said, "or maybe a little less."

It was an old joke which had sprung up between us after a distant occasion when Johnny had bet me that I would not dare ask his father for a million dollars, and it had always made Mr. Kelsey laugh.

"How's John doing?" he asked.

"About the same," I said, and Mr. Kelsey nodded.

"You've never had any influence on him," Mr. Kelsey said.

"Well," I answered, "no one has."

"What about the Lee girl?" Mr. Kelsey asked.

"There's nothing in it," I said.

Mr. Kelsey clasped his hands behind his back. "I don't see how Jane stands him," Mr. Kelsey said.

"Because she's fond of him," I answered.

"I wonder," Mr. Kelsey said, "why the devil I like him. Stop in and see me again before you go."

I had seen the plans of John's house before it had been built and I had seen the terrace and the sunken garden added, and the ell for the nurses and the children. It had seemed then, and did still, as artificial as a house set up on a pole in some back yard for birds. Yet it was charming, once you forgot that sense of artificiality, just as Jane Kelsey was charming. When Johnny had married her she had been called the prettiest blonde in New York. Her hair had grown darker, so that she was hardly blond at all, but she had not lost her looks. She was standing by the French windows that opened on the terrace.

"Johnny's upstairs telephoning," she said. She rang a bell. "I hear a state cop stopped you."

"Johnny showed him a card," I said. "Everything was all right."

"Martin," she said to the houseman, "bring the Scotch and two glasses; or would you rather have iced tea?"

"Tea," I answered, "if you don't mind."

Then she smiled at me.

"I'll have tea too," she said, and then she was silent until we were each holding a glass of iced tea.

"Here's looking at you, Joe," she said. "You've been in and out of here so much, I wonder why I never fell in love with you."

"Because I'm an old friend of the family," I said.

"That's not a reason," she answered. "I suppose I might start now."

"It's pretty late," I said. "Besides, it wouldn't help."

"But then," she answered, "nothing helps. I always tell you everything. I don't bellyache to many people. He's up there, telephoning her now."

"I thought he was," I said.

"I told him that if it happens again, I'm through," she said.

"Well," I told her, "you've told him that before."

"I wonder" — and she was asking herself more than me — "whether I'd have the guts to do it."

"Everyone has disadvantages, you know," I said. But I was not sure that she heard me. She was speaking of things that must have run in her mind for years.

"It's been so easy," she said. "It makes you soft when everything is easy. It's so unattractive to be soft."

Whatever was wrong with her, she was not soft, but I did not tell her that.

"Joe," she said at last.

"What?" I asked.

"Will you talk to him, Joe, tonight?"

I'd talked to him before, but I told her that I would.

"Tell him," she began, "tell him — " And then she stopped, because the front door had slammed.

"That's Pete," she said. . . . "Hello, Pete, darling. . . . Do you remember Pete?"

Pete was new to me, because he was nearly full grown, although he was only fifteen. He looked so exactly as Johnny had when I had known him first that he was more like a memory than an individual.

"Yes," I said, "I remember. You've grown."

"How do you do, sir," he said. Then we shook hands. His voice was just like Johnny Kelsey's voice.

"I hear you're in the fifth form," I said. "Well, well."

"Yes, sir," Pete Kelsey said, and then his mother spoke.

"You remember Joe, dear," she said. "He went to school with your father."

"Yes," said Pete Kelsey. "Yes, I know. Where's dad?"

"Upstairs, dear," Jane said.

"Well, I'd better see him," Pete said. "He asked me to bring his car around."

"Why," Jane said, "it's nearly dinnertime."

"Well," Pete said, "you know dad. He's going around to the Lees', I guess. Here he's coming now. . . . Say, your car's outside. You want me to drive it for you?"

"No," said Johnny Kelsey. He had changed into a white-silk shirt. "Not right now, Pete. I'll only be gone for a minute. Just time for a drink before I go. How about a drink, Pete?"

"All right," Pete Kelsey said.

"You see," Johnny went on, "Jane and I have the right idea. It's better than his sneaking it somewhere."

Pete was looking at his father, and it was clear he thought that everything he did was right.

Johnny Kelsey stretched out his arm and slapped it over his son's shoulders.

"Well, Joe," he asked me, "what do you think of him?"

I watched them, standing side by side, almost the same height.

"He's just like you," I said.

There was a sound as though Jane had cleared her throat, and Johnny Kelsey dropped his arm from Pete's shoulders.

"Don't say that," Jane was saying. "For God's sake, don't say that."

"On your way, Pete," Johnny Kelsey said. "You're not wanted here."

The boy hesitated. There was a momentary bewilderment, as though he wanted to ask a question about something which disturbed him, but he did not.

"O.K.," he said as he started for the door. "The key's in the car."

As soon as Pete was gone, John Kelsey spoke solicitously. "What's the matter, sweet?" he asked. "Aren't you feeling well?"

"I'm sorry," Jane said. "I'm all right, Johnny; but what's the use of anything, if he's just like you?"

The artist drew his bow across the violin. There was a loud discordant scrape, which resolved itself into a softer, more melodious sound. Brahms was moving to a conclusion with the relentlessness of a final act by Euripides. Along that stream of sound Johnny Kelsey and his son were moving with me into an enigmatic silence. In another moment the music would be over; a few minutes more and I would be leaving on that errand to Johnny Kelsey's son. The music ended and there was a clapping of hands and a shifting of chairs.

"Did you hear about John Kelsey?" someone was saying. "She was in the car with him when it happened. Everyone knows that. It was going on all summer."

I was still thinking of the music which I had heard the night before when I reached Pete Kelsey's school. I had never thought before of translating a sight into a sound. The school was like a clear, high note that came from a distance over tranquil mountain air. It was a long and penetrating note, lucid and ageless. Although a school might continue for a century, it would never grow tired or old. There was no disillusion, no sordidness, no sense of futility, and no admission of defeat.

Pete Kelsey's room was in one of the new Georgian brick houses, and I was to see him in the housemaster's study. The housemaster was youngish and pale and polite.

"Kelsey will see you as soon as the hour is over," he said. "You can smoke while you're waiting, if you like."

I was a grim outsider within that room. Pete Kelsey and I would be as far away from each other as is possible in this world, each a member of a different generation. I had been trying to put myself in Pete Kelsey's place, but now that I was there I knew that I had been born a great many years too soon. The school bell was ringing, and above the bell was the sound of footsteps and of voices.

Pete Kelsey appeared, hurrying from the background of the sounds. He had on gray slacks and a tweed coat and his hair was rumpled and his breath was coming fast, showing that he had been running. He looked me straight in the eye when he shook hands, just as his father would have.

"It's awfully nice of you to look me up, sir," he began.

"You'd better sit down," I said.

He was just like Johnny Kelsey. There was the same slouch to his back when he sat down and the same expression on his face, not insolent but blank.

"Your father sent me up here," I went on. He leaned forward and his eyebrows drew together exactly like John Kelsey's.

"There isn't anything the matter with him, is there?" he asked.

"He's busy," I said.

He waited for a moment before he spoke again, and his pause gave me a sharp sense of annoyance. It seemed to indicate that he was taking it for granted that I ran errands for his father and that there was no great need for him to be polite.

"He got my letter, then, did he?" he asked. "I've been waiting for every mail."

"Yes," I said. "He got the letter. He wants to know why you want fifty dollars."

"Why is he so worried," Pete Kelsey asked, "about fifty dollars? That isn't much."

"He wants to know why you want it," I repeated.

The boy's face flushed. "If he wanted to know, he should have come up himself," he said.

I took my billfold from my pocket and drew out five ten-dollar bills. I had no desire to be kind or gentle. I did not like the way he spoke; I did not approve of anything about him.

"There's the money," I said, "but you can tell me why you want it before you get it."

Pete Kelsey moved uneasily in his chair. "I don't see why I should tell anyone," he began, "but as long as he sent you up here, I collected fifty dollars for a thing called Spring Lake Camp. I have to pay it in tomorrow and I lost it. Johnny would understand, sir. He wouldn't want you to ask me."

"That's just what he did want," I told him. "How did you lose it, Pete?"

He hesitated and I spoke again. "Now, wait a minute," I told him. "Don't think I'm interested personally. Personally, I don't care."

"You don't?" he said, and the idea appeared to surprise him.

"No," I answered, "I don't care. You'd better tell me how you lost that fifty dollars."

"On a bet," said Pete. "Johnny would understand. Johnny and I always pay our gambling debts, and I have to settle my treasurer's account tomorrow."

"All right," I said. "Here, take it."

Pete Kelsey drew a deep breath and rose and put the money in his pocket.

"Thanks," he said, "a lot. I wish you'd tell Johnny he might have been quicker about helping. I asked him to telegraph it. If he'd waited until tomorrow I'd have been fired from school."

"All right," I said. "Wait a minute. Sit down, Pete."

The boy's face had assumed his father's old blank look. "I don't see why Johnny didn't come himself," he said.

"That's just what I was going to tell you," I replied. It seemed to me, now that I had started, that the matter could be explained quite easily. "He had an accident. It might have happened to anyone. He ran over a man, Pete." Pete Kelsey stood up again, and I continued more hastily, before he could interrupt me, "Your father's all right, perfectly all right."

"Was he drunk, sir?" Pete Kelsey asked.

The complete simplicity of that question made him seem almost as old and disillusioned as myself, and there was only one answer to give, because Johnny Kelsey was a friend of mine.

"No," I said, "he wasn't." I had spoken promptly. There was no conceivable reason why he should not have believed me, but I was not sure that he did.

"Was she with him in the car?" he asked.

Again the question was simple, but I was not entirely sure what he meant.

"No," I said, "your mother wasn't with him. It was lucky, Pete."

He had that queer, inherited look, dead and expressionless, and he did not answer. His silence made me wonder for the first time if I were not speaking to a person with my own capacity for understanding, instead of to a boy. I had an intense desire to break the silence, both for his sake and for Johnny Kelsey's.

"It may all be a little hard to understand, Pete," I said, and I did not like the way I sounded when I said it. I was being patronizing, and I had hated patronage when I was young. "I'm just telling you this," I continued, "so you needn't be worried in case you hear anything about it. Nobody anticipates any real trouble."

Pete Kelsey cleared his throat. "Is grandfather helping him out?" he asked me.

I wondered later why I answered the way I did, for the last thing I had intended was to show irritation. It was not the question as much as the way he looked — that facile, take-it-for-granted family look which Johnny Kelsey had always worn. At any rate, I was no longer impersonal with him.

"Yes," I said. "He's taking care of everything, exactly the way your father is taking care of you. You both are lucky that way, Pete."

I paused, and his puzzled look reminded me that he was still hardly beyond the crossroads of childhood and adolescence.

"I don't understand you, sir."

"I only mean," I answered, "no matter what you do — whatever trouble you get into — you can count on being pulled out of it. When you take some money that doesn't belong to you, for instance, you don't have to bother."

His face reddened. "That isn't so, sir," he said. "It isn't the same thing. I used it because I knew I could get it back."

"Yes," I said, "that's exactly what I mean when I say you're lucky."

He stood there looking at me, and he did not appear precocious any longer. He was more like a boy at a blackboard, trying to work out a problem for which he was not prepared. Finally he cleared his throat.

"Well, I guess that's all I need to know. Thanks for telling me, sir," he said.

"That's all right, Pete," I began, and then I stopped. I saw that his face was working; I thought he was about to cry. "Don't take it that way, Pete," I told him. "Everything is all right."

Then I saw that he had reached into the pocket of his gray slacks and had pulled out the fifty dollars. "I guess you'd better take it back, sir," he said. "Tell Johnny I don't want it."

"What's the matter with you?" I asked. "Of course you want it."

"I don't want it," he repeated. His voice was loud and broken. "Just tell him that, sir. Tell him I'd rather take what's coming to me."

"Look here," I said. "That will hurt your father very much."

"Tell him I don't want to be helped," Pete Kelsey said.

His voice cracked. He was crying, and he did not want me to see him cry.

"Good-by, sir," he said. "Thank you very much." Then he opened the door and slammed it shut behind him.

Johnny Kelsey was in his cubicle off the board room in conference with his secretary. He evidently was not engrossed in work, because I heard him laughing just before I came in.

"Well," he said, "never mind it now, Miss Murdoch." And Miss Murdoch left us. She was a blonde. I remembered that Johnny always did like blondes.

"Not bad, is she?" Johnny said. "I won her from James, you know — the senior partner here. We put up our secretaries in the last round and I drew to a flush."

Johnny Kelsey was looking better, which was not surprising, for nothing ever kept him down for long.

"Don't look so sour," he said. "Did you see Pete?"

And I told him that I had.

"Well, don't be so sore about it," Johnny said. "How did you like him?"

"I was surprised," I said. "I liked him."

He frowned and leaned farther back in his chair. "What did he say," he asked, "when you told him?"

"He asked if you were drunk, and I said you weren't."

Johnny's eyebrows moved nearer together. "Go ahead," he said. "What else?"

"He asked if she was with you in the car."

Johnny lowered his feet carefully from the desk and gripped the arms of his chair.

"Now, what the hell made him think of that? Go ahead. What else?"

"Here's your money back," I said. "He wouldn't take it, John."

Johnny spoke softly. "Just what," he asked, "did he mean by that?"

I told him, while he sat there, about the misappropriated fund.

"He wants to look out for himself," I said. "He said he didn't want to be helped. He asked if you were getting helped. That's all."

Johnny Kelsey stood up and walked over to the window. He stood for quite a while with his back toward me before he turned around, and even when he turned he looked as though something had struck him.

"That hurts," he said.

There was so little to say and do that I wanted to leave him there, and yet it did not seem right to leave him.

"You always said I'd get what was coming to me," he went on. "Well, you're right. I've got it."

You could see him trying to control himself. He was thinking of appearance, and that studied repression made the whole thing worse.

"Suppose you look at it this way," I said: "If he knows what you're like, it's the best thing that could happen to him, John."

Johnny Kelsey squared his shoulders and straightened his coat carefully before he answered, and his voice was bland and humorous. No one could say Johnny Kelsey ever lost his God-given sense of humor.

"If that's so, everything's all right," he said. "I never thought of that."

Random Pieces

A Discussion of the Novel
(1949)

PERHAPS I should say at the outset of this lecture that I have always hesitated to embark in academic halls on the discussion of the novel, and whenever I have done so I have experienced a sense of embarrassment. This arises, I believe, from a knowledge that I am never able to discuss this subject in an approved academic manner, because my beliefs have developed more from personal experiences than from an academic background. I am a writer, not a critic, and criticism and creative writing are literary oil and vinegar.

I am not even at all sure that writing, except for a few limited techniques, can ever be taught in textbooks or lectures. Writing of fiction, at any rate, has always seemed to me a matter of self-education, and personally, most of the opinions I have formed have been derived from thirty years of professional writing — an arduous pursuit, I may say, which does not always make for sound critical judgment, much less for detached perspective. Having always been obliged to sell my wares in a highly competitive market, I have been compelled to write in a style that will be understood by a comparatively large group of readers, and this compulsion, and a few besides it, has given me some prejudices that are unattractive in an ivory tower.

Naturally I have some ideas of what a novel is, and a few on what a novel ought to be, but these may seem simple to some of you and painfully obvious to others. However, I cannot apologize for them, being a professional rather than a critic. Nevertheless I know very well that professionals, like critics, have their own areas of error.

About a year ago I became acutely aware of this, when I studied the principles of golf under a very good professional. I learned from him that in golf, as in writing, there are certain theories and limitations. I learned, incidentally, that standing at the first tee presents much the same uncertainty, the same sense of loneliness and the same insidious challenge to self-confidence, that one meets in writing. My teacher, who had started as a caddy and who now played in the open championship, had developed a devastatingly perfect swing, which he endeavored to teach me — to the tune of ten dollars an hour. He told me how to grasp the club more tightly with my left hand than the right and how, by pivoting and contorting my body, to arrive at a successful backswing, while turning up my wrists at a suitable angle so as never never to lose control of the club. He showed me how to start the club head in the arc which would connect perfectly with the ball, swinging from the inside out, shifting from the right foot to the left, always being perfectly relaxed, never taking my eye from the ball, and following through without throwing my body too much into the swing and without allowing my wrists to lead and without allowing my right hand to close the face of the club. It was a matter of balance and coordination and it looked beautiful when he did it, and I am still trying to get all the things I have to do in order to break a hundred ingrained in the proper sequence in my subconscious.

Now on one of these days while I was taking this course, I chanced to look at a nearby tee from which two individuals were about to drive, both of whom teacher told me played in the eighties. Thinking I might learn something from such an edifying spectacle, I gave my full attention to the first player who had teed his ball. To my surprise he appeared to do absolutely none of the things that my teacher said were essential. Instead of taking a firm, relaxed stance, he tensed and twisted his body in an ungainly way and grasped his club in a rude, unconventional manner. Then, instead of addressing the ball gently, he surprised me by hopping up and down. Instead of taking a slow backswing, remembering always to keep the club head in a graceful arc, he whipped back his club as though he were going to chop down a tree, and then jumped about six inches into the air. He was still off the ground when his club met the ball, and I knew, of course, that the result would be ludicrous, because he had broken with all convention. Yet believe it or not, the ball went straight for a good 280 yards, and I asked the teacher why this was and he gave me an answer which was no help at all. He said what I knew already — that the player had done everything wrong. The trouble with him was, my teacher said, that he was self-taught. He must have picked up all those bad habits when he was very young, but still he had learned to compensate. He was now able to go around the course in par, but this did not mean that he knew how to play good golf.

I respectfully submit that most of these remarks can be applied to the construction and the writing of the novel. There is, surely, no other literary form — if it is a form — which is so varied, so susceptible of compromise, and so apt to achieve a good result, even when it is full of what a self-respecting teacher of the novel would term egregious errors. The truth is, a novel can be almost anything its author desires, within the broadest limits, and it is usually filled with bad habits that the author learned when he was young. It may be filled, also, with his favorite clichés and repetitions; it may have a deplorable beginning and an inconclusive end. Parts of it may be turbid to the verge of incomprehensibility. It may defy the dramatic values and it may be lacking in thematic quality. Its plot may double back upon itself like a sluggish meandering river. Some of its characters may be wooden and others may be banal, but the end result is all that matters.

If in the end it gives to the reader an impression of reality and a somewhat lasting illusion of having lived through a phase of life in the company of fictitious personages with whose destiny one has a certain amount of concerned interest or sympathy, it may be a very good novel. It may even be an outstanding achievement, rising, in spite of its crudities, into something monumental and unforgettable. Turn, for example, to some of the works of Theodore Dreiser, who has always seemed to me, when analyzed, a prolix and careless author, although in the end he is one of the greatest novelists America has produced. It is best to forget the parts of a novel; the whole may often be much greater than the sum of all its parts. The only test of a good novel is, in the end, that it is a good novel as far as you, the individual reader, are concerned. No matter what your preceptors may tell you, and no matter what the critics may say, this is the only final test.

I am sorry to start with so many vague confusions, but then even the definition of a novel is a confusion in itself over which the orderly minds of a century of scholars have struggled without attaining any special order. The name "novel," we are told from the college rostrum, is derived from the Italian noun "novella." A novel, says the *Shorter Oxford English Dictionary*, is "A fictitious prose narrative of considerable length, in which characters and actions representative of real life are portrayed in a plot of more or less complexity." Webster is perhaps slightly more specific but I am afraid a trifle more provincial. A novel, according to *Webster's New International Dictionary*, is "A fictitious prose tale of considerable length, in which characters and actions professing to represent those of real life are portrayed in a plot. Novels usually deal with the passions, esp. love." When you think over these two definitions, obviously both of them have a sievelike quality. Dr. Lin Yutang has given one which I like better. He says that the Chinese definition of a novel is "a little talk." It might be more comprehensive had he added that the talking of a number of persons over a period of time must get you somewhere and must leave some definite impression, but at any rate a novel is actually almost any form of writing that tells of people and of the way they lived and of how they faced the problems of their lives. This last definition clearly covers a large and inconclusive field. It might help to limit it by saying what a novel is not.

A novel is not a stage drama, though it may be dramatic. A novel is not the synopsis of a motion-picture script, though some of them may sound that way. A novel is not a short story, because the evolvement of a novel is more leisurely and gives an illusion of time and breadth and dimension which a short story cannot accomplish. But exactly when a short story turns into a novel is a most debatable question which has afforded students hours of fruitless speculation. Should we call these borderline cases "long short stories" or "short novels" or should we compromise between the two and simply call them "tales"?

And what about the different sorts of novels that have been evolved? There are almost as many varieties of them as there are dogs in the Eastern Kennel Club, and strangely enough none of these forms was consciously manufactured.

The novel appears to have started as a folk tale, a poor sort of substitute for the work of a more accomplished minstrel or *chanteur*, with an innocent intention to amuse rather than edify, so that tedious hours might be whiled away in a civilization that was without the benefits of the motion picture and radio. No wonder with such plain beginnings and with such ignorant authors — and mark you, the majority of novelists from the beginning to the present are ignorant of nearly everything except a few basic facts of life — no wonder that these works were looked upon with deep suspicion by serious literary persons for many generations. Cervantes, as far as I can recall, was the first nov-

elist to reach any height of universal esteem, and he only did so, I imagine, because *Don Quixote* was not recognized by many as a novel.

Nowadays, however, every literary editor, every agent and every
book critic from the sports desk of a local newspaper, even every Hollywood flesh peddler, knows exactly what a novel is and particularly
what a good novel is. Once when I submitted a novel to a New York
literary agent, I was surprised to have him say that of course it was not
a novel. When I asked him what it was, he said he did not know but it
was not a novel because he had dealt with novels all his life. When I
asked him what a novel was, he intimated that it was almost anything
that was different from my work.

Other persons are fortunately more specific, particularly Ph.D. thesis
writers. Sound scholarship, as spearheaded by eighteenth-century Germany, loves to dissect and classify, even if there is no real purpose in
classification. So it has been with the novel. There is the picaresque
novel, as exemplified by *Gil Blas*, and there is what is known as the
Gothic novel, almost unreadable at present. There is, also, the epistolary
form marking the real beginning of the English novel, and the interminable but still-absorbing volumes of Richardson's *Pamela* form, of
course, the classic example. There is, too, the realistic novel, though
every proper piece of fiction should possess the illusion of reality. De-
foe, with his *Moll Flanders*, if I remember my college lectures correctly, was the progenitor of our own Dreiser. Recently, when realism
becomes very hard to take, it turns into the naturalistic. In contrast to
more difficult fiction comes the romantic novel, that was regarded in
the past with a suspicion that often accompanies it to the present. My
great aunt once told me that when she went to school, she used to open
the lid of her desk to peep secretly at pages of *Ivanhoe*, a degenerate
book which she could not bear to put down and for which she was
punished when her schoolmistress finally caught her. Romance and
realism, we are told, divide the novel into two great streams, but why
they cannot blend with each other no one has ever told me, and sometimes by accident our hero, with his cloak and rapier, does become realistic or even naturalistic. There are, too, the novel of nature, and the
novel of manners, and the *roman à clef*, and there are more, too, if I
could remember them.

These forms we are to take seriously, because they are capable of
becoming works of art, but in our prose fiction more recently have

evolved new forms of artisanship and cabinetmaking, mere entertainment that any well-brought-up reader should dismiss with a shrug. In
this category, perhaps, fall the cloak-and-sword or costume story, the
mystery story, and the average magazine serial — works ironically
enough which frequently demand higher technical skill than their more
ambitious betters.

And we cannot leave the novel here. We learn by analysis that there
are certain methods of novel writing — there are the objective and the
subjective methods; there are the stream of consciousness, and the
flashback, and the peephole methods of narration. Fiction, we also
learn, is made up of dialogue, narrative, description, and exposition —
all of which should be blended and balanced. This is about all I can
tell you of what a novel is and of the species of the novel, and what
does this information amount to? Frankly, I think it amounts to almost
nothing. A good novel is still a good novel, whether it is *Robinson
Crusoe, Tom Jones, Clarissa Harlowe,* or *The Great Gatsby.* It does not
matter one iota whether or not it is written in the first person or in the
form of letters or from the point of view of a servant girl or with
God-like omniscience. It does not matter whether it is romantic or
realistic, picaresque or Gothic, if it is a good novel. Furthermore you
and I will know whether it is good or not, without being told in the
classroom. It will be good for certain reasons, some of which are hard
to define and some of which are easily catalogued. Some, but not all,
are attributes common to all good novels. There is one thing about
these attributes which I should like to emphasize. They are beyond
teaching; they arise from the creative, dramatic instinct of the writer.
Nevertheless a few can be analyzed.

In the first place, every novel, except perhaps the picaresque, has a
beginning, a middle, and an end, and this is true with any other dramatic form, whether it is displayed on the stage, on the motion-
picture screen, or in lines of verse. Superficially you may think that
this statement is a hysterical discovery of the obvious, lacking in pro-
fundity, but it is nevertheless valuable. These three component parts
form the essential skeleton of every novel, and each of these parts has
its own peculiarity which makes it different from the others. Mr. John
Gallishaw, who has made several detailed studies of what he terms the
laws of fiction, was the first to point out this fact to me, and as far as
I know, he is the only analyst who ever discovered it. And for this

alone, if not for the rest of his conclusions, I have always felt that I owed him a considerable debt.

There are dozens of ways of writing the beginning of a novel, but every beginning — long or short, tedious or absorbing, brilliant or brittle — performs the same essential function. It presents a series of characters moving in a setting, all of the novelist's creation, and confronted by some sort of problem of life or action, a problem which must be resolved, perhaps by the active deeds of these persons working upon each other, perhaps subconsciously by sheer processes of living and passages of time, or by tricks of destiny beyond an individual's volition. Fortunately for those who love to lose themselves in a world of fiction, there are varieties of problems in the life about us as infinitely varied as individual human beings, but when you think of it, in every drama and in every novel there must be this sort of a beginning.

Roughly, in the beginning the writer is telling you who his people are; and why they are being presented to you is worthy of your attention. This beginning on the stage, being partly visual, is very swift. In fact, a very competent playwright once told me that after one minute and a half, at the longest, the audience must know enough about the main characters to be interested in them and enough about the general direction which the play will take, to wish to follow further. Otherwise, with a longer beginning, the attention of an audience will be permanently lost, no matter how good or how significant the subsequent parts of the play may be. In this respect there is one thing that must never be forgotten. There is no conceivable excuse for boredom, on artistic grounds or on any others whatsoever. If a writer fails to retain the interest and attention of his reader, he had better look back carefully to see what is wrong with his effort, because his creation will contain the elements of failure. Fortunately the author of a novel has much more leisure for his beginning than the playwright. Indeed this sense of leisure is possibly one of the main differences between the novel and other dramatic or fictional forms. Personally, I believe that leisureliness, care in setting the scene and in developing character and motivation tend to produce an illusion of living in a real world with real people. I like a leisurely beginning, but I should not recommend the long descriptions of Sir Walter Scott or heavy paragraphs of exposition, however brilliantly they may be composed, or tedious physical descriptions of an individual's dress or features.

The middle is a simpler subject, and one we may deal with more briefly, although the middle may very well be the longest part of the work. Here we see the characters — the main ones, with whom one should now be completely familiar — in interplay with each other, working out their problem or their destiny, answering the question that was posed by the beginning. In the end of the middle there will always be some sort of result. Our people will win, lose or draw — it makes no difference which, as long as the result is stated clearly, but the result must be clear in order to understand the ending.

A novel is often a long and complicated work. Many contemporary novelists, I fear, confuse length and physical weight with serious stature, forgetting that Edith Wharton's *Ethan Frome* or Willa Cather's *A Lost Lady* or Henry James's *Daisy Miller*, short though they are as novels, might not be benefited by an extra page. But then length does sometimes give dimension if it adds to the life of that temporary world. Long though a novel may be, the end may be very short. Yet even on a short ending, the test of the whole structure, all that the author tries to say by the art of indirection, will finally be determined. The end must show definitely and clearly, with no room for compromise, the effect on our people of the experiences through which they have passed in the beginning and the middle. The ending in a really good novel should finally draw together all the diverse threads of the rest of the work and give them a meaning, an inevitable, indefinable quality that rises above structure in the sum of component parts. Some of the greatest difficulties of fiction and the most egregious failures of otherwise able writers arise from an author's not knowing how and where his characters will finish. Most experienced novelists, I believe, can allow their characters to do what they like in the middle of their novel and the more unpredictably they behave the better they may be as characters, but no experienced novelist, I would also like to wager, ever set pen to paper before considering carefully the beginning and the ending of his work. In fact one of the best novelists who is writing today once told me that he is always thinking of his final scene down to the last words before "finis" is written, through all the months during which he may be drafting his story.

The best fiction, unfortunately, is hardly susceptible of analysis. It is only in the second-rate that a reader is consciously aware of scaffolding or structure, of hesitation, of chinks and creaking joints. If a reader is aware of any of these things or if he is consciously annoyed by repetition or elaborations and eccentricities of style, this indicates that the writer has failed measurably to create a believable world of illusion. This may be the same as saying that he has failed to tell his little lie convincingly, because all that is best in fiction is bound to be now a distortion — now a slight caricature — now an abbreviation — now an oversimplification — of life as it is actually lived.

As Percy Lubbock has pointed out in his interesting book *The Craft of Fiction,* no living reader can remember everything in any novel. The work cannot be stretched before him for his contemplation like a canvas by Veronese. Rather, as he turns the pages he is subjected to a series of impressions, and these impressions will be different for every individual who reads the book. This is why every discussion of technique is very difficult, and tedious, and inaccurate. This is why most professorial critiques have impressed me as a waste of time. A good novelist speaks to the individual, and you and I will always disagree in interpreting his shades of meaning. Nevertheless, before I close I might venture to tell you what I believe a good novel should do to every reader. It is nothing more than a question of emotional impact, no matter what its elements.

A novel is great and good in direct proportion to the illusion it gives of life and a sense of living. It is great in direct proportion to the degree it enfolds the reader and permits him to walk in imagination with the people of an artificial but very real world, sharing their joys and sorrows, understanding their perplexities. There should be no skipping through a great novel, and if a reader skips he should do so with reluctance, knowing that he is the loser. When he finally closes the book, he should do so with more than regret. He should feel that he has been through an experience that may be as real, and more significant, than experiences in his own living. He should feel that he has walked with living people, that he has been in the presence of a vital creative force. He should turn back to this experience again and again if the novel is really great, remembering parts for years, pondering over their significance. This is the ultimate creative gift, and few have attained this goal. Balzac, Tolstoi, Dostoyevsky, Fielding, Smollett, and a very few others, I think, have touched the edges of this sort of perfection. Others have approached it. But always the degree of this sort of impact on you as an individual is a measure of a novel's intrinsic merit. Finally, I say again, I do not care how this effect is created, conventionally or unconventionally, or whether the writer composes with his hands or feet. If you like his book, if it conveys a meaning for you, he is a good writer. If it does not, he is not a good writer as far as you are concerned, and that is all there is to it. There is no excuse, there is no appeal. I do not care how he drives the ball, as long as he hits it and sends it to its destination.

"Merry Christmas, All"

(1942)

This story is an attempt at satire, and was also designed to sell on the larger periodical market. Considering these two divergent purposes, I am surprised that it is as good as it is. Its touch is heavier than it should be. It would have been far better if it had been written in the vein of "Sun, Sea, and Sand," of which I might term "Merry Christmas, All" an ancestor. The truth is that satire is not a popular commodity with most Americans, whose perennial optimism is still undimmed by Yalta, Potsdam, and Geneva. Satire is even less popular with the wide-circulation magazine.

"Merry Christmas, All" would doubtless never have been published if it could not have been read as a straight story that ends with a happy reconciliation between wife and husband. The dangerous heresies voiced here regarding Christmas and the Christmas spirit are acceptable only because they stand as factors in that same reconciliation. With all its faults "Merry Christmas, All" seems to me a very daring piece of work, at least in the matriarchal civilization of the United States. I believe I am right in thinking that Christmas, in its present state of commercial hysteria, is basically a woman's holiday, that most men don't like it, and that they go through this ritual only because they fear public criticism and marital repercussions. Though this may be a wrong conclusion, it is at least a point of view, and one which I am glad I have presented. I only wish that "Merry Christmas, All" were livelier and more suitable for young people, so that it might be read as a companion piece to the Christmas Carol *before Santa comes down the chimney, as he doubtless will continue to do unless we are conquered by Russia.*

" '. . . the two young Cratchits set chairs for everybody, not forgetting themselves, and, mounting guard upon their posts, crammed spoons into their mouths, lest they should shriek for goose before their turn came to be helped.' "

Joe Mills drew in his breath, paused for an instant to allow the dramatic effect of this passage to sink into the minds of his audience, and continued reading Dickens's "Christmas Carol." Nevertheless his mind was wandering somewhat from the lines — not that this made much difference, since he was familiar with the work. It had been read to him every Christmas Eve during his own childhood, just as he read it now to his three children seated before him in their warm woolen dressing gowns. Although he was doubtful about the whole thing, his voice did not waver, because he knew that this work of Charles Dickens's was a part of the holiday ritual in every respectable American home.

His wife had said the same thing only the other day. "It isn't dull," Elsa had said. "It has the true spirit of Christmas in it, and every nice person you know reads it to the children every Christmas Eve."

"I didn't say it was dull," Joe had told her. "I simply said perhaps it was a little dated, Elsa, what with the war and everything. Besides, I'm not sure it's particularly well-written."

Elsa was always very difficult around Christmas, with buying things and making a "list" and wrapping packages.

"Well, I'd like to see you try to write anything like it," Elsa said.

"I didn't say I could write it," Joe answered. "I only mean that it's hysterical in spots. Frankly, I don't think Tiny Tim is very convincing."

"Joe," Elsa said, "I wish you wouldn't argue when there's so much to do. You're always hard to get along with at Christmas time."

"I'm not," Joe said. "I'm just the way I always am. I don't know why you have to lose your perspective, Elsa."

"You're always nasty," Elsa said. "You're just like Scrooge."

"All right," Joe said. "All right, I'm just like Scrooge, and he isn't a convincing character, either."

"You needn't be so horrid," Elsa said. "I'm all tired out. You haven't even bought the stocking presents."

"You don't like them when I buy them, Elsa."

"No," she said, "because you always buy jokes that squirt water in your eye, and things like that. That isn't what Christmas is for."

"Listen, Elsa, what is Christmas for? Except to spend a lot of money."

"Joe, you ought to be glad to spend a little money — glad!"

"A little money?" Joe said. "You don't understand about the income tax. A pair of silk stockings — and that really helps the Japanese — and twenty dollars for each of the maids, ten dollars for the choremen, ten for the policeman, ten for the postman, and then everybody in the office, and then the presents for the family."

"I'm sure," Elsa said, "you needn't buy *me* a present this year if that's the way you feel."

"I didn't say I felt that way about buying you a present."

"And at least," Elsa went on, "you might be nice about the children. If it doesn't mean anything to you, at least it means a great deal to the children. Can't you remember the way you felt about Christmas? You might have bought the stocking presents, instead of making me do it on top of everything else. I don't know what I would have done if Albert Reed hadn't gone with me."

"Who went with you?" Joe asked.

"You heard me," Elsa answered. "Albert Reed. And Albert had wonderful ideas. He knew just where to go for stocking presents."

"I think it would be a very good thing," Joe said, "if Albert minded his own business and didn't get mixed up with the children's stockings."

"Albert is very sweet," Elsa said.

"If you want my frank opinion," Joe answered, "Albert is a meat ball, and he'd better keep out of my children's stockings!"

"A meat ball?" Elsa asked. "What on earth is a meat ball?"

"It's just an expression," Joe said, "that the boys used to have around college. It means someone who tries to do the right thing and never quite makes it."

"I don't see how you can be so limited," Elsa said. "If anyone is just a little different from the narrow orbit in which we live, you call him some sort of name. It's so childish, Joe. It shows that you are inadequate, that you haven't developed."

"It isn't inadequate," Joe said, "to realize that Albert Reed has limitations. And it isn't narrow-minded to like a certain type of person."

"I'm tired of just a certain type of person," Elsa said, "and I'm tired of the way you never deviate. Albert has the spirit of Christmas, and that's more than you have."

"All right," Joe said, "I'm Scrooge. Don't say it."

"You are," Elsa answered, "and the least you can do is to get some rum for the punch. And you can write the cards for your presents — for your father, your mother and your Aunt Eleanor and the children."

"All right," Joe said.

"And you can move back the dining-room table, and help with the wreaths, and you can finish reading the 'Christmas Carol' to the children before they go to bed. That's the very least you can do. And then you can see that the candles in the windows don't burn the curtains; and don't say we ought to have electric candles, either, because it isn't the spirit of Christmas."

"All right," Joe said, "don't get so excited, Elsa. I'm doing what I can. It only comes once a year."

The "Christmas Carol" was nearing its close. The three children seated by the parlor fireplace had become fidgety. Ellen, who was old enough to be familiar with the story, whisked the end of one of her pigtails across her chin, pretending it was a brush. Robert had taken off one of his slippers and had contorted himself into a posture which seemed to indicate that he was trying to place his toe inside his left ear. Little Joe, or Josey, as he was called, had taken a silver paper knife and an ash tray from the table. He was trying without much success to cut the china ash tray with the paper knife.

It seemed to Joe Mills that all this had been going on for quite a while, although he had only started to read the "Christmas Carol" to the children at bedtime the night before.

"Put those down, Josey," he said.

"Yes, Josey," Ellen said. "Daddy's trying to entertain us, because Mummy has so much else to do. And it's almost over now, isn't it, Daddy?"

"Yes," Joe said, "and when it's over, you'll have to go to bed. Where was I? ' "A Merry Christmas, Bob!" said Scrooge. "A merrier Christmas, Bob, my good fellow, than I have given you for many a year! I'll raise your salary and endeavor to assist your struggling family . . ." ' "

The parlor was unnatural, now that the furniture had been moved into unaccustomed places. The punch bowl was already on the table near the wall, and the cake of ice that would eventually repose in it was downstairs by the laundry tubs. The sliding doors to the library were closed, concealing the Christmas tree until Christmas afternoon, because Elsa's family had always done it that way.

It was growing dark, almost time to light the candles, and Christmas was already coming over Boston, and especially Beacon Hill. The police were closing the near-by streets to traffic, and strangers were trooping in from outlying districts to stare at the lighted windows. Joe could hear their voices outside in the street.

"Daddy," Ellen asked, "aren't you glad God lets us spend Christmas on Beacon Hill?"

"Yes," he said, and he felt embarrassed. "Why shouldn't I be?"

"I hope Santa Claus doesn't put oranges in my stocking," Ellen said, "the way he did last Christmas, because there wasn't enough else."

"Now, look here," Joe told them, "you'll be pretty lucky if you get anything in your stockings. If — well, if Santa Claus wants to give you an orange, it's more than he does for a lot of other children." He stopped, feeling that he was being foolish because he was sure Ellen no longer believed in Santa Claus.

Then, before he could continue, he saw Elsa in the doorway. The children were to hang up their stockings in the fireplace in Daddy's and Mummy's room and go to bed, and to come in as early as they wanted for their stockings.

"Wait a minute!" Joe said. "Couldn't we put a time limit on it? You know how it always is around here. We'll be up all night."

"Joe," Elsa said, "don't! Don't mind Daddy, children. You can come in any time you want and wake us up before you open the stockings. Daddy is always cross at Christmas."

Joe closed Dickens's "Christmas Carol" softly. It was one of those hidden rocks which they passed every year in their marriage, and he had negotiated it again. Christmas itself was a recurring cycle. It seemed to him that all the divergences between Elsa's personality and his were always magnified by Christmas. Those little differences had been amusing once, when he and Elsa had first discovered that they loved each other, but that was quite a while ago.

That red-leather book he was holding was a part of a set of Dickens' that had been given to them for a wedding present. Elsa had said then, when they were first engaged, and when he had told her that he was never much good around Christmas time, that he would learn to love Christmas. She had said that she was a Christmas girl, that Christmas had always been the happiest time of her life and that she would make it so when they were married, no matter what happened. It had sounded simple then, and all sorts of other things had also seemed simple — all those dissimilarities in taste and habit.

He remembered Elsa's father had alluded to them once. It was when he had told Elsa's father that he wanted to marry Elsa.

"Father's upstairs," Elsa had said. "Go up and tell him now. You'll have to get it over with, Joe."

"But doesn't he know about it already?" Joe asked.

It seemed to him that it must have been quite obvious to Elsa's family for the better part of a year that he wanted to marry Elsa.

"Of course he knows about it," Elsa said. "Mother and Father have been waiting for you to do something, and it's driven them nearly crazy. They've been sitting in the sewing room nearly every evening all winter. But he expects you to tell him. He's up in the sewing room now."

Joe had actually thought until then that Elsa's father had preferred the sewing room as a place to sit. Until that moment Joe had never considered that the old gentleman might be a personality with a mind of his own.

"There's only one thing that troubles me," the old gentleman had said. "You see, Elsa has very definite ideas. She makes wishful pictures of everyone she knows. She simply thinks of you as the sort of person she would like you to be, and I don't believe you're the sort of person she thinks you are."

Of course it was absurd that anyone should be troubled by such a trivial matter. Elsa was a clever girl, and they had explored each other's character for months and months. It was very obtuse of the old gentleman to think that Elsa did not know him just as well as he knew Elsa.

"Oh, I think she has a pretty good idea of me," Joe had replied, "and if there's anything she doesn't like about me, she can change it."

"By gad," the old man had said, "she'll certainly try. And now that all this is over, maybe I can get out of this damn sewing room."

The scraps of that musty conversation were changed by the perspective of the years; and Elsa was already dressed for the evening. She looked tired, but very pretty, just as pretty as she had looked that evening when she had half pushed him into the sewing room.

"Elsa, what are you looking at?" he asked.

"At you," Elsa said. "I don't see how you can sit sprawled out on that chair when there's so much to do. And Joe, please put the book away just where it came from."

"All right," Joe said, "all right. I was just thinking what your father said when I told him we wanted to get married. He said you didn't know what I was like. I don't see that I'm complicated. I'm just like everybody else."

"No, you're not," Elsa said. "You're very complicated. You're not what I thought you were at all. But let's not go into it now."

"What's wrong with me?" Joe asked.

Elsa sighed. "You never want to do the right thing at the right time," she said. "Here we are, in the middle of everything, and you ask me what's the matter with you! Just when I have to think about the party."

When he wanted to talk about anything important, Elsa could always push it aside. Now it was the party, the same party they gave every Christmas Eve — open house for anyone who wanted to drop in.

Joe smiled at her. "You know, Elsa, you look awfully pretty. You certainly are a Christmas girl." He thought it would please her to be called a Christmas girl, but he seldom was able to say the right thing in the holiday season.

"Joe," Elsa said, "I heard you speaking to the children about Santa Claus. I wish — I know you don't care, but I wish you wouldn't speak to them in quite that way."

"What did I say wrong?" he asked. "I wasn't criticizing Santa Claus."

"That's just it," Elsa said. "It's your tone of voice. I'm used to it, but I do think the children might be allowed to keep a tiny shred of belief. You sounded very bitter about Santa Claus. Joe, what are you laughing at? It isn't funny."

"I'm not laughing, exactly," Joe answered. "I was just thinking. You believe in Santa Claus more than any of the kids. Honestly, Elsa, I don't mean to be bitter. I was just saying — "

"I know what you were saying. It's hard to feel the way I do, and to have someone in the house who feels as you feel."

"Elsa, don't take it so seriously. Let's not quarrel on Christmas Eve."

Elsa smiled at him, but her smile was preoccupied. "Yes," she said, "let's try not to quarrel. Joe, you have a pail of water up here, haven't you? And a pail of water downstairs, in case the curtains catch?"

"Yes," Joe said.

"Well, then you'd better light the candles, and if you say again we ought to have electric candles, I shall scream. Look out the window. The Rogerses have lighted theirs already."

The shades were up, the curtains were drawn back. Rows of candles stood ready on the shelves that had been fitted across each window. Joe stood with Elsa for a moment, looking out into the street. There had been no snow, but there was the sort of atmospheric suspense that comes before snowy weather. The night, the street, the city, the world, perhaps, were waiting.

The candles in the Rogerses' house were already lighted, and the Rogerses would have a punch with frozen strawberries in it. Farther up the street the Caldwells would have a punch with orange peels; and around the corner Martin Jones would throw some white wine and pineapple juice into a bowl. These beverages would not mix well together, yet it would be necessary to sample all of them.

"Joe, what are you thinking about?" Elsa asked, linking her arm through his.

"Just about Christmas," Joe said. "I've got a present for you, Elsa. It's something you wanted. It's — "

"Don't tell me," Elsa said sharply. "You always tell me. It spoils everything, Joe. Don't!"

"All right," Joe said, "all right."

"That colored man will be in in half an hour, to help with the punch. Beatrice has all the sandwiches ready in the pantry. And Joe!" Her voice rose sharply.

"All right," Joe said. "Don't frighten me. What have I forgotten?"

"The ice! The big block of ice that goes in the punch bowl. You forgot about seeing the iceman, didn't you?"

"No," Joe said. "It's down in the laundry tub."

"Oh," Elsa said, "thank heavens! You'd better light the candles now, and don't forget to wrap up your presents. They're on the little table in the guest room. And don't get them mixed up with the stocking presents. They're on the other table. And Joe — "

Her voice had changed. All at once it was casual in an elaborate careless way that did not sound right.

"Yes," he said, "what else?"

"Nothing," Elsa answered, "but Albert Reed is coming in. He promised to come early."

"Albert? What's he coming for?"

Elsa looked out the window and back at him. "He's so sweet, Joe," she said. "I wish you wouldn't be silly about Albert. You know, he's so Christmasy. He's like something out of Dickens."

"I know, I know. All right, he's Christmasy, but what's he coming early for? It strikes me that Albert's been around here enough lately."

"Oh Joe, please — please don't spoil everything. Albert just promised to take me out to see the lights and make a few calls before everything starts."

"Look here," Joe said, "why can't I take you? We've always — "

"Don't look that way," Elsa said. "Albert suggested it. Why, Joe, if I had thought for a *minute* that you would act like this!"

"I'm not acting like anything," Joe said.

"We can't go out together, dear," Elsa said. "Someone has to watch the candles, and besides some people might drop in early. And besides — "

"Besides what?"

"Besides" — there was a break in her voice — "after I've worked so hard, I just want to spend a little time on Christmas Eve with someone who is Christmasy. And I'm going to; no matter what you say."

"All right," Joe said. "Stay out with him all night if you want to. I'm Scrooge."

"All right, if that's the way you feel."

"I don't know how I feel," Joe said. "Give me the matches and let me light those damn candles."

Outside in the streets some carolers were already singing, and he had not lighted the candles.

"God rest you merry, gentlemen," they were singing, "let nothing you dismay. . . ." And then the doorbell rang.

"There's Albert now," Elsa said. "Don't try to manufacture a situation, at least not on Christmas Eve."

There was absolutely no reason to say that. If he did not happen to be particularly congenial with Albert Reed, certainly he had been perfectly congenial with most of Elsa's friends and family. They would all be in the house pretty soon — Elsa's mother, Elsa's father, her brother, and her sister who had married someone from New York, and shortly afterwards would come the New Year's bills, and then it would be time to compute the income tax.

"I don't have to manufacture a situation," he said.

"Now, Joe!" Elsa said.

Whenever he had something on his mind that was really interesting he hadn't the time to say it. The living room, where they were standing, was on the second floor, and he could hear Beatrice, the maid, opening the door in the hall below, and then Albert Reed was calling up to them. Albert invariably shouted up the stairs.

"Merry Christmas," Albert was calling. "Merry Christmas, all."

"There isn't any need for him to say, 'Merry Christmas, all.' Why can't he just say, 'Merry Christmas'?" Joe asked. "That's because he sells life insurance."

"Well, he does it very well," Elsa said. "Why did you ever ask him here if you don't like him?"

"I never did ask him," Joe answered. "He just keeps coming."

"Well, he's a lot nicer than most people you know," Elsa said. "He doesn't keep playing squash and worrying about the war. He's interesting."

"Merry Christmas, all," Joe heard Albert Reed call again. His steps were thudding upward.

If Albert Reed had ever taken any regular exercise, he would not have been winded from his quick trip up the stairs. His face was red and merry, and it was true, he looked like any character you wanted in Dickens's Christmas books. Albert had a sprig of holly in his buttonhole, and a handkerchief and a fountain pen in his outside pocket. It occurred to Joe that he might have done without the pen.

"Well, well, well," said Albert, "here we are!"

"What's the pen for?" Joe asked.

Albert slapped him playfully on the shoulder. "Just to sign up applicants for a little personally conducted tour outside," Albert said. "Seriously, you've never seen such a night. It makes you want to sing. And the lights. They do something to you, those lights. They make you forget — "

"Forget what?" Joe asked.

Elsa laughed, but not spontaneously. "Don't mind him, Albert. You know Joe. He's always like this on Christmas."

Albert laughed without any nervousness whatsoever, as one should who is bubbling over with a sort of mirth which must be shared with everyone. "Ha, ha," Albert said. "But seriously, Joe, you ought to relax. You ought to get out of yourself on Christmas Eve. Seriously, that's the Way to Keep Christmas."

"I'm all right," Joe said. "I've been perfectly genial all day. I just don't want to get out of myself. Why should I?"

"Ha, ha," Albert said again. "Seriously, Joe, you don't know what you're missing, does he, Elsa?"

"It's Puritanism," Elsa said. "The Puritans always hated Christmas, and Joe is almost completely Puritan."

"That isn't fair," Joe said. "I don't hate Christmas, and I'm not as much of a Puritan as you are."

Elsa's cheeks glowed dangerously. "Oh, yes, you are," she said. "And no matter how I try to make Christmas happy — "

Albert raised his forefinger and shook it genially. "Now, now, children, children, not on Christmas Eve!"

"All right," Joe said.

"Don't say you're Scrooge again." Elsa's voice rose sharply. "I just can't stand it when you keep repeating yourself."

"Now, children," Albert said, "children!" Then he laughed again. "Seriously, Joe, it's just getting into the mood. I'll tell you how I interpret Christmas. I guess Elsa and I were brought up the same way; it's — seriously, it's a sort of faith. Think of it this way. Think of the world outside, a world chock-full of happiness." Albert waved his arms to indicate the world. "Now, here's Elsa, making everybody happy. It's all simple. It is, Joe, seriously. The kiddies with their stockings, crinkly red paper, holly berries, mistletoe." Albert looked at Elsa, beaming. "By the way, where is the mistletoe?" He chuckled mischievously. "Now seriously, that's Christmas for you. I'm not good at expressing myself, but Elsa understands, don't you, Elsa?"

"Of course I do," Elsa answered, and she was smiling almost tenderly, "and no one's going to spoil it for me. Albert, let's be going now."

"Yes, let's," said Albert. "Jingle bells, jingle bells." He glanced at Joe and back at Elsa. "By the way, Elsa, there's a box in the hall. I just couldn't resist them — more stocking presents for the kids."

"Hush," Elsa said, "not so loud, Albert. They might be listening."

Joe put his hands in his pockets and walked over to the empty punch bowl, but neither of them noticed him. Albert had picked up Elsa's rabbit-fur coat and was putting it around her shoulders, giving it an affectionate pat. At the moment his mind was obviously not exclusively on Christmas.

"First we'll go down the street with a whole barrage of Merry Christmases," he said, and gave her shoulder another pat. "You don't mind, do you, Joe, if we just snatch a few minutes?"

"Mind?" Joe said. "Why should I? Look, Elsa, how long will you be gone?"

He hoped he did not sound the way he felt, and it had nothing to do with Christmas.

"Oh, I don't know," Elsa said.

"A lot of people are coming in," Joe said. "You asked them." He moved a step nearer to her, and the cool way she looked at him had nothing to do with Christmas either. "Elsa, try to get back as soon as you can, won't you? I've got a Christmas present for you. It cost a lot more — " He stopped, remembering that Albert was there.

"Well, don't boast about it," Elsa said. "It's — it's not how much things cost. Let's be going, Albert."

"Joe," Albert said, "you don't mind, seriously, do you?"

"Mind?" Joe said. "Why, certainly not. Take her out and show her the holly berries. But Elsa, where will you be if I want to get hold of you? If a lot of people come here and begin to ask?"

Her smile was as set and cool as the new wave in her hair. "I don't know," she said. "Anywhere Albert takes me; and you can bring up Albert's stocking presents and put them with the others. Come on, Albert. Let's not stand here spoiling Christmas."

"Here we go," said Albert. "Jingle bells, jingle bells — so long, Joe."

Joe followed them to the head of the stairs and heard Elsa laughing.

"It's like England, isn't it?" he heard her say. "There'll always be a Christmas." And then he heard the front door slam. It echoed through the house with a strange finality, shutting Elsa out and leaving him motionless at the head of the stairs.

There was no answer to what he was thinking from the shadows in the hall. He was trying to think of other Christmas Eves, and memories of them were gathering in the hall. He had inherited the house from his father, and he had spent a good many Christmases in it. The family had always had a tree on Christmas Eve, and you played with your presents all through Christmas Day — a good deal better arrangement for the children than Elsa's innovation of keeping it waiting till Christmas afternoon.

The stockings used to be hung downstairs by the dining-room fireplace, and not in any bedroom. The idea was not to wake up the older people in the house. You tiptoed quietly down the hall, and then you could slide down the banisters, right into the dining-room. But Elsa had said you must have the stockings in the bedroom. Her family always had them there. And Elsa had said you must have the tree on Christmas afternoon.

"All right," Joe said, and his own voice startled him, because he had not meant to speak out loud. "It's a matter of technique." And then he remembered it was time to light the candles.

He had just finished the candles in the dining room when Beatrice came in from the pantry. "Mr. Mills, Guthrie is here," Beatrice said, "and don't know what to do."

For a moment Joe could not think who Guthrie was; then he remembered that Guthrie was the colored man who made a living passing things at parties. Joe walked through the pantry and into the kitchen.

When he had first married Elsa, they had lived in what was known as a "tiny apartment" with a kitchenette, because it had been the fashion in those days for young people to start out that way. Elsa had done the cooking, and someone had "come in" late in the afternoon. As he looked back on it, the ménage had run nicely. It was different, now that he had inherited the town house, and now that they had three children. Now there was Nora, the cook, and Beatrice, the chambermaid-waitress, and Isabelle, the nurse, and Mrs. Flannigan, who did the laundry and who also helped at parties.

They were all in the kitchen. It seemed to Joe that the more people he had working for him, the more he had to do personally. "Well," he said, "Merry Christmas, all." He tried to sound like Albert Reed, but his wish was greeted without enthusiasm.

"Mrs. Mills is out, isn't she?" Beatrice asked. "She hasn't told me what to do about the doilies."

"Maybe it would be just as well to do nothing about them," Joe said.

"Mrs. Mills always puts doilies under the sandwiches," Beatrice began, but Joe was not listening. He was looking at Guthrie. Guthrie's white coat was too small for him and the cuffs of his purple shirt shot out below the sleeves. He had large cuff links in the shape of serpents.

"Maybe I'd better taste the punch," Joe told him. "It's in the pantry."

Guthrie brought him a glass of it. Even without ice, it was very good punch. Joe asked Guthrie to bring him a second glass, and to bring a glass for everyone. He was sure Elsa would not approve.

"Well," Joe said, "Merry Christmas, all." He finished his second glass.

"Mr. Mills," Nora said then, "the furnace has gone out."

It confirmed exactly what he was thinking. The more people you paid to work for you, the more you did yourself.

"What?" he asked. "How did it go out?"

"Mr. MacSweeney didn't put no coal on it," Nora said. "He hasn't been here since morning. It's the way he is on holidays."

"All right," Joe said. "I guess I'd better fix it. Guthrie, give me some more punch, then go upstairs and fill up the bowl."

He could see that no one else was going to fix the furnace, and he did not blame them. He did not even blame Mr. MacSweeney much. Instead, he wished that he were in Mr. MacSweeney's place.

The cellar was growing cool. The children's sleds and all those other things which finally get into a cellar were dusty shapes in the electric light. First it was necessary to shake down the ashes. Then it was necessary to stamp on some boxes, find some newspapers and get the thing going. As he worked, bits of Dickens's "Christmas Carol" came into his mind.

"Such a bustle ensued that you might have thought a goose the rarest of all birds. . . . Mrs. Cratchit, looking slowly all along the carving knife, prepared to plunge it in the breast; but when she did, and when the long-expected gush of stuffing issued forth, one murmur of delight rose all round the board, and even Tiny Tim . . . beat on the table with his knife, and feebly cried, 'Hurrah!' "

In opening the damper, Joe jammed his fingernail.

Now that the coal was ignited, he could go upstairs and clean himself, but he must remember to make frequent visits to the furnace all evening to put on more coal and watch the draft.

When he was washed, he put on a clean shirt in the spare room where Elsa kept the presents, because he could never use his own room when they gave parties. The presents were all around him in red and green wrappers. He saw what he had bought for the children; he was expected to come through, and he had. There was a small writing desk for

Ellen, and a large toy grocery store for Robert, and a box of tools for Joe.

The sight of them aroused in him an unexpected sense of revolt, for they were closely connected with what he had been thinking at the head of the stairs — of Christmas when he was a child. Those large presents were in a corner, because they must be with the Christmas tree. Elsa, the candles, the furnace, and the punch and Dickens's "Christmas Carol" were all related parts of the emotion which surged over him. His finger throbbed where he had jammed it in the furnace, and perhaps the pain in his finger had something to do with it. But it was the punch, he realized, that made him speak out loud.

"They won't have them at the tree," he said; "they'll have them with their stockings!"

Then he opened the right-hand upper drawer in the bureau. Inside was a jeweler's box which held the platinum wrist watch he had bought Elsa. She had always wanted a watch like that.

"She can have it in her stocking or she needn't have it at all," he said.

It did not sound important. It had something to do with Albert Reed, but there was no time to think what it had to do with him, for downstairs he could hear the doorbell ringing, and Elsa was not there.

By the time he reached the parlor, the room was full of neighbors and friends. Elsa's mother and father were there already, and Elsa's sister and her husband and Elsa's brother and his wife.

"Joe, where have you been?" Elsa's mother asked. "And where is Elsa?"

"She just went out for a minute," he said. "Merry Christmas, all." Guthrie brought him a glass of punch, and he drank it quickly.

Elsa's mother looked at him. "Elsa's done something to you," she said. "She's made you look happy on Christmas Eve. I've never seen you look so happy. Don't tell me you don't enjoy it — secretly."

"Of course I do," Joe told her. "I always have liked it."

"Oh, no, you haven't. And now I know Elsa's made you. No one can help loving her on Christmas. Where is Elsa?"

Before he answered, Joe put his empty punch glass on the mantelpiece. There was something disconcerting in his mother-in-law's manner. It seemed to him that she was anxious as she waited for him to answer. Her anxiety made him self-conscious.

"Oh — Elsa," he said. "Why, Elsa just went out to make some calls. You know how it is on Christmas — the wife makes calls, the husband watches the candles."

For some reason Elsa's mother looked more cheerful. She put her hand confidingly on his arm. "Joe, I'm awfully glad everything seems to be going so much better with you and Elsa."

Joe's voice sounded unnatural to him. "Why, what's the matter with me and Elsa?" he asked. "I certainly haven't noticed anything."

"Joe, don't look so serious. A mother always worries, I suppose. It was only when I saw you looking so happy tonight that I even dared to mention it. It has just seemed to me that Elsa has been a tiny bit restless lately."

Joe could not avoid a sense of shock. "That's Christmas," he said. "You know Elsa: she's always restless on Christmas."

"Yes, of course," Elsa's mother said. "I only meant that Elsa was a very sensitive girl, and when life grows a little humdrum she always has reached out for something else. It's only natural for a mother to worry, but this isn't the time to worry, is it?"

"I'm not worried about anything," Joe said. "It's always this way on Christmas. Guthrie, give me some more punch."

The one thing he wanted to keep perfectly clear in his mind was that Christmas was to blame, and the punch made him sure of it. Every minute more people were coming in. The faces in the room made up the whole background of his life; a quiet life, but it certainly was not humdrum, and there certainly was not anything wrong with any of it. All their friends and neighbors were coming in. He was shaking hands with Russell Rogers. He had known Russell always; they had been to school together.

"Hello," Russell said. "Where's Elsa?"

"Oh — Elsa," Joe said. "Why, she just went out for a minute, down the street."

"Oh," Russell said. "Well, that's the way it is. Did you hear about the Brownings?"

"No. What about the Brownings?"

"Didn't you hear?" Russell asked. "They've busted up. Cynthia walked out on him yesterday. You can't tell what's going to happen next, can you? If I'd been asked to name two people who seemed absolutely happy, it would be Bill and Cynthia, and there you are."

"Yes," Joe said, "there you are. Well, Merry Christmas, Russell. Guthrie, come over here with the punch. I've got to go down and fix the furnace."

"A thing like that surprises you," Russell went on. "Why, I couldn't be more surprised if it happened to you and Elsa."

"Well, it hasn't," Joe said.

"My God, Joe, I didn't say it had!"

"Well, let's forget about it," Joe said, "and think of a pleasant topic. I've been reading Dickens's 'Christmas Carol,' and it's unreal. Do you think it's unreal?"

"Of course it is. It's fantasy."

"Well, it's too fantastic for me," Joe said, "and I don't like Bob Cratchit and I do like Scrooge, and the worst of it is, I can say it by heart."

"Well, say it," Russell told him. "Come on, boys, listen. Joe's going to recite the 'Christmas Carol.' "

"All right," Joe said. "I'll recite it as soon as I've fixed the furnace."

Russell took him gently by the arm. "I'll go with you and take some punch along," Russell said. "I'm always interested in other people's furnaces."

His words gave Joe a sense of deep relief. Russell was interested in other people's furnaces, not in other people's wives.

Down in the basement, the cellar was quiet and pleasantly warm. Joe threw open the furnace door, and coals were glowing. If you put on more coal and checked it off, the house would get full of gas, and if you left it open, the house would get too hot, and there you were.

"What you want is an oil burner," Russell said. "Then you could sweep all this out and turn the place into a rumpus room. It could be a place where you could get away, and the kids could have electric trains down here."

"How could I get away if they had electric trains?" Joe asked. With the fire door open, the cellar had a genial glow. "The great thing about a cellar is that it only has to be cleaned once a year and women hardly ever get into it. They all hate cellars."

"That's true," Russell said. "They all hate cellars. Joe, I can't get over the Brownings. They were as happy — "

Joe picked up the shovel. "Never mind," he said. "Russell, you know Albert Reed, don't you? What do you know about him?"

"Reed?" Russell repeated. "Albert Reed? What's he on your mind for?"

"He isn't," Joe answered. "Can't I just be curious about someone who isn't a part of the narrow little orbit in which we live?"

"You needn't sound so complicated," Russell said. "He just doesn't belong in any of my orbits. All I know it that he sings, and the girls like him."

"Well, we ought to know more about people like Albert Reed," Joe said, and he tossed a shovelful of coal into the furnace. "Why do the girls like him?"

"Well, you can't tell about women. Maybe they want a change. Maybe you and I aren't interesting."

Joe scooped up another shovelful of coal. "If you want my frank opinion," he said, "you and I are a lot more interesting than Albert Reed."

"All right," Russell said. "Forget about him."

Joe slammed the furnace door. "I can't forget about him," he answered, "because I don't even remember him. Who brought his name up, anyway?"

"You did," Russell said.

"Let's go upstairs," Joe said. "I'm not aware that I even mentioned him. You must have."

Then they were upstairs again.

"Joe," someone said, "where's Elsa? We've been looking for her everywhere."

Moving about the room, passing the punch and sandwiches, made Joe lose his sense of time. He never knew exactly when Elsa got back, but long before he noticed her he had developed a new technique. If anyone asked where Elsa was, he said that she had been here a minute ago and she must be somewhere.

She must have arrived when he was standing in a corner with a group, just back from another visit to the furnace.

"Come on," someone was saying, "tell us some more about Bob Cratchit."

"What?" Joe asked. "What was I saying about Bob Cratchit?"

"A lot," someone said.

"Oh, yes," Joe said. "All right. 'And while Bob, turning up his cuffs

— as if, poor fellow, they were capable of being made more shabby — compounded some hot mixture in a jug with gin and lemons —'"

He was just going on to tell how Mr. Cratchit put it on the hob to warm, when he saw Elsa in front of him. She must have just come in, because she still had on her rabbit-fur coat.

"Why, hello," Joe said. "Where's Albert? Merry Christmas, all."

As he focused his attention on her, he thought she had never looked so beautiful, although she did not look at all pleased; but then, he did not expect her to be pleased, and he did not care, at that moment, whether Elsa was pleased or not.

"Joe," Elsa said. "Don't say 'Merry Christmas, all.' Just say, 'Merry Christmas.'"

"Why not?" he asked. "Albert says it. Where's Albert?"

"Albert?" she answered. "Why, he's around somewhere. It's all right when Albert says it, but it doesn't sound like you." She put her hand on his arm. "Joe, what *is* the matter with you? Are you angry with me?"

"No," he said, "not exactly, Elsa."

"You must be angry. You must be, or you wouldn't be reciting the 'Christmas Carol.'"

"Not reciting. Only quoting, Elsa."

"You've never done that before in just that way."

"That's so," he said. "It never struck me as funny before, and it is funny. No, I'm not angry. I'm just being natural."

"Joe," she said, "don't shout so."

Joe swayed back on his heels. There was a doubtful look in Elsa's eyes. He could see that she was worried about him, and he was pleased that she was worried.

"It isn't the punch," he said. "I'm being natural, that's all. It's the first time I've ever been myself on Christmas Eve."

"Joe, you're going to have a headache again on Christmas morning. You always do."

"Never mind," he said. "Do you know what I'm going to do? I'm going upstairs to take a nap."

"A nap? You can't do that, with everybody —"

"Oh, yes, I can. You and Albert can run the party. You can wake me up when everybody's gone, and we'll fill those damn stockings, and we're going to have them in the dining room, and my presents for the children are going to be with them — *with the stockings in the dining room*, not with the Christmas tree."

"Joe, aren't you feeling well?" she asked.

"I'm feeling fine," he told her. "Tell them I've gone out somewhere. I'm going to take a nap."

"But Joe, someone might see you."

"No, they won't. I'll be on the spare-room bed, with the presents."

It was the first time he had ever been natural on Christmas Eve, and Elsa was getting ready to do something about it.

"Joe," she began, "I want to tell you something." She stopped before she told him, staring at something behind him. "Oh," she said, "where did Albert get it? What is he going to do now?" and Joe also turned to look. Behind him, near the piano, he saw Albert Reed standing on a Hepplewhite chair, and Albert was dressed like Santa Claus, holding a glass of punch in one hand and a gold wrist watch in the other.

"Stop," Albert was calling. "In just five seconds it's going to be Christmas. Is everybody ready? One — two — "

Joe began moving toward the door.

"Joe," Elsa called after him.

He was out of the room as Albert finished, but Albert's voice followed him.

"Five!" Albert shouted. "Now, all together. 'Merry Christmas, all.'"

"Albert," Joe heard Elsa call, "you're breaking the back of the chair."

He was walking to the guest room, and the voices of Christmas were behind him. Down below he could hear the piano, and he could hear Albert Reed singing in a cheerful baritone.

> Santa Claus will come tonight, if you're good.
> He'll give you a woolly sheep and a doll that
> goes to sleep, if you're good.

Joe closed the guest-room door.

As he lay there in the darkness, he was struggling like Scrooge in the story, with his own conscience, with the Spirit of Christmas and with the Spirit of the Future. He was like Scrooge being wafted over the housetops in the cold Christmas morning.

He must have gone to sleep while he was thinking, for the next thing he was aware of was Elsa's voice. Elsa was shaking his shoulder. "Joe," she said, "wake up, Joe. Everybody's gone."

She had turned on the light, and he was in the guest room with the presents, the stocking presents and the others, some of them tied in red paper, some of them tied in green paper, some with ribbon with green bells, and some with ribbon with red bells.

The house had the same soundless vacancy which it always had when it was time to fill the stockings on Christmas morning. His head was aching, just as Elsa had told him it would. Joe pulled himself to a sitting posture.

"Well," he said, "I'd better go down and put some more coal on the furnace. Mr. MacSweeney let it go out."

"It's all right," Elsa said. "I put some on. We don't have to do anything but fill the stockings."

Joe stood up; his head was still aching. "You didn't have to do that," he said. "I'm not much good at Christmas time, but I always stoke the furnace."

"I know you do," Elsa said. "But I had to do something — definite — after Albert left."

She looked sad and lonely in her party dress. The presents and the ribbons, on the bed and on the floor, looked like pieces of a house which had crumbled and fallen.

"Did you have a nice nap?" she asked.

"Yes," Joe answered, "fine."

"Won't you help me fill the stockings? You don't mind, do you? I can do it myself if you mind."

"Of course I don't," Joe answered. "Haven't I always helped you do it?"

Elsa opened the bureau drawer where she always hid the stockings. "Here's Josey's," she said. "His presents are on the little table, and Joe, we'll hang them in the dining room as long as you want to — and I'll see that the children don't wake you up."

"If you're trying to make me feel mean about it, it doesn't work," he said. "That's fine if they don't wake me up."

"Why, Joe, I thought you'd like it."

"I do like it," Joe said. "It's fine, and I don't feel mean, and I'm not sorry I left the party."

Elsa said, "I don't mind about that. Albert broke the Hepplewhite chair. It's just matchwood."

"Well, well," Joe said.

Elsa looked up from the stocking she was stuffing. "I thought he'd never go home. He kept singing carols."

"Well," Joe said, "that's fine."

"And when he wasn't singing carols he just kept saying, 'Jingle bells.'"

"All right," Joe said. "Jingle bells — that's fine. Haven't we any holly? Stockings never look right without holly."

"Oh, Joe," Elsa said, "don't say that. You sound just like Albert Reed."

Joe stared at her. All the room was different — warmer, brighter. "Don't you *want* me to sound like Albert Reed?"

Then he saw that she was smiling at him, but her voice was unsteady.

"No," she said, "I certainly don't, and next year we'll have electric candles. Merry Christmas, Joe."

"Why, Elsa," Joe said, "Merry Christmas, all."

High Tide

(1932)

As I said in the foreword to this book, most of the short stories contained here illustrate various experiments I once made in the field of social satire. This does not mean that I have not written a great many others outside this classification. Any professional writer who has been in the periodical field as long as I must be able to turn his hand to anything. The only trouble with this sort of dexterity, as the late Joseph Lewis Vance once pointed out, is that finally one uses up all of one's creative inventiveness. Stick to books, Mr. Vance said, and don't knock yourself out with too many short stories.

"High Tide" is included here, among other reasons, as a display of versatility. Once I made a deliberate study of the Civil War as material for fiction, and read the standard sources and visited the Virginia battlefields. Having been in a war myself I felt I knew something of the eccentricities of combat. The results of this endeavor were a Saturday Evening Post *serial and two series of short stories. "High Tide" is one of several dealing with a young Virginian who served with the great Confederate cavalryman J. E. B. Stuart. I was only following in the path of many of my contemporaries. The Civil War was popular in current fiction before Pearl Harbor.*

I like to think that my general historical background for "High Tide" is reasonably accurate. I am sure that I could once give documentary evidence for the minutest piece of detail. I can also trace the sources of my plot, since once as a child I had the privilege of seeing William Gillette in Secret Service. *I am gratified that most of "High Tide," from the angle of craftsmanship, is passable, even including the spy. Indeed I think that "High Tide" is not a bad example of what a reasonably experienced fiction writer can achieve with good historical material. It is disconcerting to perceive that there is nothing much be-*

low its plausible superficiality. Here, I think, lies the trouble with most costume fiction. It is nearly impossible to give events, even as recent, comparatively, as the Civil War, a present-day significance. No living writer can put himself inside the mind of someone like Scott Mattaye. He can only approximate it, provided he has been steeped in the Southern tradition, and I was not. By the way, if I were doing this all over again, I would deprive Captain Mattaye of most of his Southern accent, because dialect, though a crutch, seldom develops character.

SOMETIMES, in the sultry warmth of summer at Deer Bottom, Scott Mattaye could remember the high tide; and sometimes, when he was feeling in the mood, he might even tell of how he went through a hostile country to find an army which was lost, and how the Battle of Gettysburg might have been wholly different if his horse had not gone lame. At such an hour, after his second glass, the old man would sit straighter at the table, and his voice, slightly cracked, but soft and gently drawling, would rise above the whirring of the moths which kept fluttering around the guttering candles like incarnations of the quiet sounds from the warm, dark night outside.

"You follow me, gentlemen?" he would say. "I'm referrin', of co'se, to the lack of cavalry in the opening phases of that engagement — cavalry, the eyes and ears. And I'm referring, above all, to the temp'rary absence — an' I maintain the just and unavoidable absence — of our cavalry general, on whose staff I had the honor of servin'. I'm referrin' to that immortal hero, gentlemen, Major General J. E. B. Stuart — Beauty Stuart — in the Army of Northern Virginia of the Confederate States of America — the ve'y greatest cavalry commander in that army, gentlemen, which, of co'se, is the same as sayin' the greatest cavalry leader in the history of the world."

He meant no exaggeration when he said it. Some impression had been left upon him which transcended time. He would smile beneath his drooping white mustache as though he had a secret, and he had the secret of his days. Strange, unrelated moments were flitting before him like the shadows of the moths upon the wall — plumed hats, boots of yellow leather that came above the knee, girls snipping buttons off gray coats, eggnogs, Virginia hams, black boys dancing the buck and wing beneath the lantern light, a kiss, a lock of hair, the Bower, Frederick, Winchester, high tide.

"High tide," he said: "it all was accident and time."

It was clear what he was thinking, although his words had a way of wandering when his mind was groping in the mazes of his vanished world. He was going back to the hours when the tide of the Confederacy lapped over the Potomac to reach its high-water mark of the war. He was thinking of Rowser's Ford and the captured wagon train at Cooksville — twisted iron rails, staggering horses, men reeling in the saddle, drunk with sleep. He was thinking of a spy, and of Stuart's last great raid. The Army of Northern Virginia was pouring into Pennsylvania. Lee and Longstreet were arguing over plans.

"Sammy," he said to the cook's small boy, "bring refreshment to the gentleman. . . . Now, Gettysburg — of co'se, we should have whipped 'em if Stuart had been there. I should have fetched him — yes, indeed. If that horse had not gone lame near East Berlin, why, sholy I'd have fetched him. If I had not stopped by the stone house near the road. A matter of a spy, you understand — a foul, ugly matter. . . . I share in the responsibility, gentlemen. It all was accident and time."

He did not add that he had nearly died in cold blood in that square stone house.

He could see the beginning, and he knew that the hand of fate was in it, though it happened more than sixty years ago. Stuart had been stroking his fine brown beard, as he did when he was troubled. It was in the cool of an early summer morning, the first day of July. The horses' heads were drooping, and faces were blank from lack of sleep.

"Mattaye," Stuart was saying, "I'm lost. Early's gone. Everybody's gone. I've sent off three officers already. You go out, too, and find the army. You see this map? We're here. Ride out toward that place Gettysburg yonder. Keep riding till you find it."

It was a fine day, he could remember. The fields were green and fresh from early summer, and the land was richer than the land at home. It was a country of fine, rolling fields of pasture and wheat and corn, of neat hedges, neat houses and compact, ungenerous trees. It was a land uncompromising in its plenty, without warmth of welcome. But the dead weight of weariness was what he remembered best. After two days of steady march, men were lying exhausted with bridles in hands, watching horses that stood too tired to eat. There was food in the Yankee wagons they had taken. He could see the white tops of the wagons down the road, but there were many too tired for food.

Scott Mattaye was made of iron and rawhide then, but he was very tired.

"The army, sir?" he said. "Which army, sir?"

His question made Stuart laugh, and the sound of it came back across the years. He was in a hostile country with his column too tired to move. He was lost and he was worried, and he had not slept an hour in the last three days. Yet the general seemed to feel none of the lethargy of exhaustion. The way he wore his sash, the tilt of the plume in his hat, the angle of his cloak about one shoulder made his equipment look as fresh as when he had started. Nothing ever wilted in the general.

"Which army?" he said. "Well, I'm not aiming to encounter Federal troops in force this minute. I'd prefer to meet the Army of Northern Virginia, General Robert E. Lee commanding, now engaged in invasion of Pennsylvania, and due to end this war. I'm out of touch, and I don't like it — not right now. They're somewhere over there — somewhere."

He waved his arm toward the southwest, but there was no dust or smoke or sound; nothing but open rolling fields, stretching to the horizon in the tranquil light of early morning. The very peace was like a disturbing suspicion that something had gone wrong. It could only have been anxiety that made Stuart speak so frankly.

"The corps should be coming together," he said, "and we should be in front. There should be word, you understand? . . . Your horse all right?"

Scott's horse was a light sorrel caked with sweat and dust.

"He's worn down, sir," said Scott. "But he's as good as any in the column, I reckon, sir."

"Take your blankets and saddle off," Stuart said. "Kill him if you have to, but report to General Lee, you understand? Ask for orders and a new horse to take you back."

"Yes, sir," said Scott. "Where will I find you, sir?"

"We're resting here two hours," said Stuart. "Then we're moving on to Carlisle. Watch out for cavalry, and don't get caught. We've lost too many on the staff. Good-by."

Only the impression of small things was left to Scott Mattaye, and the touch of all the great sights meant much less, until all his memory of camp and bivouac came down to little things. Bodies of men, the sound of marching troops and firing were a part of his life, and were blurred into the monotony of days, but the smell of bacon grease in smoke, a voice or the squeal of a horse would be like yesterday. He remembered how his blankets sprawled over the tailboard of the headquarters wagon, inertly, like a dead man's limbs. As they did so, he had a glimpse of fine gray cloth among them. It was his new uniform coat, which he had planned to wear in Washington City, certain they would take Washington.

An impulse made him put it on which was composed of various thoughts — the idea that he might never wear it, through accident or theft, the desire to appear in an enemy country like a gentleman, and the conviction that a staff officer should look his best. The coat had the buff facings of the staff. Though it was wrinkled and still damp from a wetting in the Potomac, it was very well cut. He strapped his belt over it, with his saber and his pistol — a fine, ivory-handled weapon which he had taken from a Yankee colonel in Centerville. His saddle was a Yankee saddle; even his horse had a U.S. brand, but his coat was Richmond, bought with two hundred and fifty dollars of his country's notes.

"You, Jerry," he said to the horse, "step on. We're bound to go." Then he remembered that the animal sighed almost exactly like a man.

He went down the road past the picket at a trot, and half a mile farther on he met a patrol, riding back. He knew the officer. He was Travis Greene, from Maryland, and Scott had always liked him. He liked the way he handled horses; there was something in him which Scott had always trusted — a candor, a vein of sympathy.

"Trav," he said, "seen anything out there?"

Trav shook his head and grinned. The corners of his thin mouth wrinkled.

"No," he answered. "Where yo' headin'?"

"Message," said Scott.

"Seems like the general's getting nervous," Trav said. "Nothing but the staff with messages. Yo' won't get far on that old crock of yours. He's powerful near through."

"Why, boy," said Scott, "this animal can go a week and never drop.

Why, he just craves to run. Why, boy, you've never seen a raid. This is only triflin' up to now."

"Where we headin'?" the other asked. "I reckon you don't know."

Scott felt the importance of his knowledge and smiled. "Don't you wish you knew?" he said. "Where Beauty Stuart wants. That's where. Come to think of it, seems to me you're always asking questions."

"Saucy, aren't you?" said Trav. "I reckon you're out calling in that new coat of yours. I'd take you for a damn Yank if it wasn't for that coat."

"Would you?" said Scott. "Well, you ask Beauty Stuart where I'm going. No doubt he'd just delight to tell you, and call for your advice. I'll be seeing you. Good-by."

Then, almost without thinking, he pulled his watch from his breeches pocket. It was a fine, heavy repeater.

"You, Trav," he called, "keep this, and if I don't get back, send it on to Deer Bottom, and I'll be much obliged."

He could still hear their voices, low and pleasant, and could recall the way Trav started as he reached and caught the watch.

"To Deer Bottom? Certain sure! I'm proud of your confidence," he said. "Good-by!"

Scott Mattaye loosened his revolver in its holster and put his horse to a trot again, not fast, for he had to save the animal's strength, and the horse was tired.

"You, Jerry," he said, "take your time."

Then, as he spoke the word, he knew that he had made a blunder. He had three hundred dollars in Confederate bills in his pocket, which would have been more useful at Deer Bottom than a watch; and now, because of a sentimental impulse, he had no way of judging the distance he was traveling, except by instinct and the sun. He knew that one could conceivably ride all day through an opposing army with a good horse and a knowledge of the road. He had seen enough in the raids around McClellan and Pope to have gained a contempt for Yankee horsemanship. He could get safe away from a regiment of Yankee cavalry.

But now he could detect a difference. He had been in a friendly country on other rides alone, where there had been a careless tangle of woods and grown-over fields. Friendly people had waved to him; girls had brought him milk. His horse beneath him had been like a reservoir of untapped strength, but now his horse was tired. There was no spring in the trot, nor a trace of willingness to increase the pace, and the country itself was foreign. There was a plenty in the Pennsylvania fields, like the rolling land along the Shenandoah, but there was no generosity in that plenty. There was the same sinister threat in the meticulous furrows and the abundance of that earth which he had seen in the armies that sprang from it.

There was a menace in that hostile land, for everything was watching him. He could feel a hatred in that country rising against him like a wave. The sun, glinting on the windows of small farmhouses, made those windows look like eyes, reflecting the hatred of unseen faces, staring toward the road. And the uncertainty of time was weighing on him, because he did not know the time. The uncertainty made him remember Stuart's own uncertainty. "Time," the hoofbeats of his horse were saying, and the humming of the insects and the rustling of the corn were speaking of that flowing, unseen principle which connected life and death.

A sound made him draw his reins, and his horse stopped, obedient and still. It came, a swift, metallic click, from behind a clump of small trees near a bend which shut out his vision to the right. His revolver was cocked in his hand, while he sat staring, listening. He did not know that he was speaking until he heard his voice.

"Pshaw," he heard himself mutter.

A man in overalls was hoeing a potato patch just around the bend. He turned and stared at Scott.

"Morning, friend," said Scott. "It looks like a right fine morning."

The man spat on a potato hill. "I ain't no friend of yourn," he said, "nor any of your kind."

Scott laughed. "Why, mister," he said, "I mean you no harm, and that's why I say 'friend.' I only aim to ask you if you can let me know the time."

"Would it give you comfort," the other asked, "if you was to know the time?"

"Why, sholy," Scott said, still smiling. "I'd like right well to know."

The man's voice became louder.

"Then I'll die before I tell yer, ye nigger-tradin' thief! Two of my sons has died, and I can die before I raise a hand to give one mite of comfort to your lot! I only hope your time is short, and I may see your carcass rotting! Now git on!"

Scott Mattaye put his horse to the trot and hurried down the road, amazed. He saw other men pause to gaze at him from the roadside. Women stared from doorways. Children, when they saw him, ran screaming. He did not stop again to ask the time.

He did not stop again until his horse went lame. By then a high forenoon sun was beating on his plumed felt hat, and the farming country lay before him as beautiful as a picture, incongruously far from war. The horse went lame so suddenly you might have thought he had been shot — a stumble, a sharp snort of pain, and he was limping. After Scott Mattaye was off the saddle, it did not take a half a minute to convince him that his horse was through, and, though he had grown callous to the suffering of animals, he had a pang of sorrow.

The road, he remembered, was sloping down to a ford across a brook. Beyond the ford it wound up again past a rutted lane, which led to a square house of deep-gray limestone, set back perhaps a hundred yards from the roadway.

That house on its little rise of ground always came back to his memory as aloofly pleasant — heavy chimneys, small-paned windows, a fine, arched doorway of an earlier time. It always seemed to him to speak of kindliness and of sober, decent lives, and to be without a taint of anything sinister or bizarre. A long cattle barn stood behind the house, flanked by young apple trees set in even rows. He looked for half a minute, then hooked the bridle through his arm, walking slowly with his limping horse.

"Jerry," he said, "I'm going to leave you yonder."

The windows were blank and impassive as he walked up the lane, and everything was silent — too silent.

"Hello," he called. "Is anybody home?"

The sound of his voice was like the breaking of a spell. Two shepherd dogs rushed at him, snarling. A door had slammed and an old man ran toward them with a stick, a picture of towering strength, half worn away by age. A white shirt, bare, scrawny arms and a fine white beard halfway down his chest, but his height was what Scott remembered best. He was very tall.

"Grandpa!" he heard a child's voice calling from the house. "Don't take on so, grandpa! You'll have another bad turn if you do!"

The noise of the dogs seemed to ebb away. All his memory of the barnyard seemed to ebb away, leaving only that figure of age — something never to forget. The old man was breathing much too heavily.

His shirt and knit suspenders and baggy trousers took nothing from his dignity. Something in his face made his beard like ashes over glowing coals — a mobile, powerful face. His forehead was high. His eyes were serene and steely blue. Scott Mattaye took off his hat and bowed, though the man was plain and not a gentleman.

"I'm intrudin', sir," he said. "My horse — he's broken down. I reckon that — "

"Mary Breen!" the old man shouted. "You, Mary Breen!"

A girl — she could not have been above thirteen — came running from the house. Her gingham dress, her face and eyes, had a washed-out look; her bleached yellow pigtails were slapping on her shoulders.

"Mary Breen," the old man said, "put up that hoss. . . . I made haste, as I always will, to serve the Lord. . . . Young man, you come with me. This is a day of glory."

Scott Mattaye stared at him, bewildered for a moment.

"Put up that horse," the old man said, "and put the saddle on the bay that's waiting. . . . You'll need another horse for sure. Now, please to follow me."

"Sholy, sir," said Scott. "With great pleasure. I'll be pleased to settle for another animal, of co'se. Excuse me. Could you let me know the time?"

He had no premonition on entering the house. He had seen enough peculiar people and places in that war. The tide of war had pushed him into mean kitchens and stables for a night, or just as strangely it had whirled him into dining rooms of plantation houses, where he had touched on lives which he would never touch again. He did not bother to put an implication on the old man's words, except that they were friendly. The friendliness brought back Scott's confidence in inevitable fortune, and he straightened his sash and dusted off his coat.

"Yes," the old man said again, "this is a day of glory. I'm glad I've lived to see it, because I'm gittin' old."

The kitchen was very neat. A kettle was humming on the stove, so that the steam made the air humidly pleasant. There were two strong wooden chairs and a deal table, but what he noticed first was the asthmatic, hurried ticking of a clock above the humming of the boiling water. He turned to glance at it where it stood on a shelf between two windows. A dingy clock in a veneered mahogany case — he could shut his eyes and see it still. The hour was just eleven.

"No," the old man said, "not here. The parlor's just this way."

He had opened a door to the front entry, and Scott began to smile, amused by the formality which led him to the parlor. He had a glimpse of himself in the entry mirror; his face was thin and brown, and his coat, he was pleased to notice, fitted very well.

"Here you be," the old man said, "and we give thanks you're here."

He opened the parlor door as he spoke, and Scott had a whiff of fresh cigar smoke and a blurred vision of a horsehair sofa and of faded floral wallpaper, but he only half saw the room. For a second — the time could not have been long — he stood on the threshold stonily.

A saber and a revolver were lying on the parlor table, and behind the table, smoking a cigar, his coat half unbuttoned and his black hat slouched over his eyes, a Federal major was sitting. In that instant of surprise Scott could think of nothing. A sharp nose and deep-brown eyes, florid cheeks, a drooping black mustache half covering a lantern jaw, clean linen, dark-blue broadcloth, gold on the shoulders — Scott Mattaye saw it all in an instant, and then, before speech or motion could touch him, the major began to smile.

"Howdy, Captain James," the major said. "I saw you from the window. I'm from — you know where. Let's get down to business. I've got a way to ride. Do you want to see my papers?"

"No," said Scott; his voice was hoarse. "No, Major."

"No doubt about you," the major said. "New coat, Yankee saddle, Yankee boots. You've got your nerve to go among 'em so, and, by gad, you're young to be in a game like this."

The major was watching him curiously, but not suspiciously, beneath the brim of his black hat, and Scott Mattaye had learned to read the capabilities of an individual. Something told him that this officer was an accurate and dangerous man. The major's hand, with thick, blunt fingers, was resting on the table just six inches away from his pistol butt. Scott could see it from the corner of his eye, and he could notice four notches cut in the black walnut of the butt, telling him in silent voices that the chances were the major could shoot him dead if he made a sudden move. Scott was standing in the doorway, with the old man just behind him. If he should make a move to draw his weapon, before his pistol was out of the holster he knew he would be dead.

"A dirty game," the major said with his cigar between his teeth, "a thankless game. You should be more careful, Captain. Your uniform's too new."

Scott Mattaye was not a fool. He knew, if he had not known before, what he was supposed to be and why the major was waiting.

"Thank you, sir," said Scott, and he contrived to smile. A little talk, a word, a gesture, and he might have a chance to snatch that pistol from the table. "I agree, sir, it's a right dirty business, and I detest a — scout. . . . But, excuse me, we'd better be alone."

It would help to get the old man out. He turned slowly, until their eyes met — the old man's eyes were as blue as a china plate at home — and he heard the major laughing.

"Don't worry about Pa Breen," he said. "He's as straight as string. . . . Father, you go out and close the door."

"Young man," old Mr. Breen said, "don't fret about me none. I can die for a cause as good as you, I guess. Amen."

When he closed the door, there was no sound outside in the entry, but the farmer must have had the tread of an Indian, because, five seconds later, Scott heard the kitchen door slam shut.

"The old man's cracked," the major said. "You know, one of those fanatic abolitionists — agent in the underground, friend of Garrison and Whittier, leader of the party hereabouts. Why, he'd kill a man in gray as easily as he'd stick a pig, and he's in the butcher business. They had to hide his pants so he wouldn't go to Harpers Ferry with Brown."

"Yes, sir," said Scott. "It's been my observation that he's a right smart old man."

The major tapped his fingers on the table, but some perversity kept them close to the revolver butt.

"Mad," said the major. "Ideas drive men mad, when ideas and religion mix. . . . What's your notion of their strength, James? . . . Sit down. There's a chair."

Scott Mattaye drew his chair carefully to the opposite side of the table. Being an officer of the staff, he had heard enough rumors and secrets to enable him to twist them plausibly into lies. It surprised him how quickly his mind was working, and as smoothly as his voice.

"Major," said Scott, "Marse Bob, he has a heap of men. Reserves have been drawn from the state garrisons. I'm safe saying General Lee's across the river with a hundred and ten thousand. It's high tide."

He tossed out the number glibly, though he knew he was naming twice the strength. He did so from his knowledge of the Yankee obsession of superior numbers, and he saw that his guess was right. The major whistled softly.

"You're high," he said, "I hope. Can you name the strength of corps?"

He had never thought of the meaning of information until he sat there, waiting for the Yankee major to move his hand. As he spoke, he could think of armies moving like blind monsters, each groping toward the other to the tune of lies like this. He paused and leaned a trifle across the table.

"Major," he said, "have you another of those cigars? I'm perishin' for a smoke."

He gathered his feet under him noiselessly. He could not sit there talking. If he could make the major move his hand, he could push the table over.

"Beg pardon," the major said, and reached with his left hand inside his coat and tossed a leather case across the table. "A light?" The major pushed across a silver match safe, still with his left hand. "Believe me, your information's worth a box of those cigars."

A tap on the door made him stop. It was the little girl with the bleached pigtails; she was carrying two glasses and a small stone jug.

"Why," said Scott Mattaye, "hello, honeybee!"

"Grandpop," said the little girl, "he said to fetch you this."

"Set it on the floor," the major said, "and close the door behind you. We're not thirsty, sister."

"Grandpop," said the little girl, "he don't touch it since he was took with spells. Somethin' 'pears to git aholt of him, like a rope acrost the chest. First a pain under his arm, like, and then acrost the chest."

"You tell your grandpop to take a pill," the major said, "and go out and close the door."

The major leaned back in his chair. His deliberation set Scott's nerves on edge, but the major did not move his hand.

"Well," he said, "It's a quaint, strange world. Here you and I are sitting, smoking good Havanas. There an old man is 'took with spells.' And somewhere else two armies are jockeying for position. Suppose they ran into each other blind, neither of them ready. War's like walking in the dark."

"Believe me, sir," Scott said, and he half forgot what he was supposed to be, "Robert E. Lee is never in the dark. He's the greatest man alive."

"You've got the cant," said the major. "But you don't believe that, do you? Where's his cavalry? Off with Stuart, when it should be in front of his army. Either Lee or Stuart's a plain fool."

Scott Mattaye half rose from his chair, and sat down again. Just in time he remembered where he was.

"Yes, sir," the major was saying, as though he were reading from a textbook. "Cavalry should form a screen in front of any army of invasion, as any plebe knows at the Point, instead of being detached on a needless mission, moving northwest when the main body's thirty miles south."

Then Scott Mattaye forgot, and spoke before he thought. "Here," he asked sharply. "How did you know that?"

The major's head went forward; his eyes were suddenly sharp: "Why, you sent us word from Hanover yourself."

"Hanover?" said Scott, but the major was not listening. At last he had raised his right hand from the table.

"Hush!" the major said. "Hush! Listen!"

For a second Scott forgot the hand. The major had good ears. Through the closed windows Scott became conscious of what the major heard, though it was not a sound exactly. It was rather a very faint concussion, a stirring in the air, which might have been summer thunder if the sun were not shining. Even in the parlor Scott could feel its strength.

"I hear 'em. Guns," he said.

Though the major was looking at him, his eyes were blank from listening.

"Yes," he said, "a scad of guns. We've struck into something heavy. . . . There. You hear?"

Scott could hear, and he could see. In that same instant the officer turned his head toward the direction of the sound, and then Scott moved. He was very quick in those days, when a sudden motion might make the difference between life and death. That Yankee moved also, but he was not fast enough. Scott had snatched the pistol up, and he was stepping backward.

"Here, you!" the major shouted. "Set that down!"

"Mister major," Scott told him, "yo' step backward from that table and keep down yo' voice, if yo' want to save yo' skin. . . . That's better, Major. . . . You've told me somethin' right valuable. General

Stuart will be pleased to know he's got a spy out with him. I'll be surprised if that spy keeps livin' long."

The major was a cool man. He leaned against the wall, twisting an end of his mustache and speaking in a careful nasal drawl.

"All right for now," the major said, 'but you listen to me, staff officer. A spy's more valuable than you or me. I hope you realize I'll do my best to stop you if I can."

Scott smiled back at him. "I realize," he said. "That's why I beg of you to stand right still. If there's a battle yonder, I'm goin' to it, mister major, and yo' horse is goin' with me."

"You've got a most consoling voice," the major said.

"Put your hands above your head," said Scott.

Then he knew that there was something wrong. The major's eyes had narrowed and he was looking across Scott's shoulder toward the little parlor door.

"Certainly," the major said. "Don't get excited, Johnny."

There was a creak of a floor board behind him. He remembered the impulse to turn and the certainty that something was just behind him, but almost with the impulse a weight landed on his back and he was pitching forward.

Scott fired just as he was falling, so that the crash of the shot and the smell of black powder blended with a taste of sulfur in his mouth. Someone had him by the throat. He kicked to free himself, but someone held his legs.

"Tie his hands," he heard the major say. "Steady. He's all right."

He was choking; flashes of searing light were darting across his eyes.

"Breen" — another voice was speaking — a soft Southern voice — "take yo' hands off him. We've got him all right now."

Then he was struggling to his feet. His hands were tied behind him, and he noticed that a cloud of powder smoke was rising softly toward the ceiling. There was a haze before his eyes and a drumming in his ears.

"Scott," someone was saying, "I'm right sorry it is you."

The haze was lifting like a curtain, until he could see the room again. The major was perhaps four feet away, lighting another of his cigars. Old Breen, with one of his braces snapped, leaned against the table. Scott could hear the old man's breath.

"Hush, hush," it seemed to say. "Hush, hush."

There was a fourth man in the room, in Confederate uniform. Scott felt a wave of nausea as he saw him. The man was Travis Greene, whom he had met that very morning."

"Johnny," the major said, "you stand still."

"So it's you, Trav, is it?" Scott Mattaye was saying.

The other cleared his throat, looked at Scott and then away.

"Scott," he said, "I reported to the general your horse looked mighty bad. He sent me on to follow you. I was looking for a chance to get away. Scott, I'm sorry it should be you."

Scott Mattaye answered dully. "Trav," he said, "I won't say what I think."

"I reckon I don't mind," said Greene. "That's part of it."

Scott drew in his breath. The old man's breathing, with its wheezing haste, was all that disturbed him.

"Trav," he said, "you better keep out of our lines, if once I get away."

"Scott," said Greene again, "it makes me sick it's you."

Then the major was speaking impersonally, almost kindly: "Listen, Johnny. I'd take you back as prisoner if I dared to run the risk, but we're too close to rebel cavalry for anything like that. This officer" — he waved his cigar slowly and was careful with his words — "this officer is going back where he's useful, son. You see my point. There's no hard feeling in it; you and I don't amount to shucks. This officer is going back, and there must be no — er — chance of your going. See my point?"

Scott moistened his lips.

"I understand," he said. "Well, I'd be pleased if you get it over with. Perhaps we'd all be pleased."

There was a silence. He heard Greene start to speak, and stop. The old man's breathing was easier. He became aware that the old man was watching him with his steady light-blue eyes.

"Gentlemen," said Grandpa Breen, "you leave this yere to me. There's been enough goin's on to attract attention. I'll gladly mind this yere."

There was no doubt of his meaning or any doubt that the major took his meaning. The major was buttoning his coat with steady, rapid fingers.

"There's a time," the old man said, "and a place for everything under the sun. Take him to the kitchen and tie him to the hick'ry chair. I'll fetch rope."

"Major," said Greene, "you take him."

"Oh," the major said, "let's get out of this! Come on."

The major was a good hand with the ropes. He lashed Scott to the kitchen chair so efficiently that there was no chance of moving. Just above his head, where he could not see it, the clock was ticking, and the kettle was bubbling on the stove. Once he was alone, he found himself searching the pine floor for a speck of dust. They were in the parlor, talking. He could hear the murmur of their voices.

". . . soon's it's dark," he heard the old man say.

"Major!" he shouted. "Here, you, Major!"

The door from the entry opened, he remembered, and the major stood there pulling on his gloves.

"Johnny," he said, "you keep your nerve."

"Yes, sir," said Scott, "I've got my nerve. I simply wish to ask you, are you leaving me alone?"

"Yes," the major said. "Johnny, keep your nerve."

Their glances met, but only for a fraction of a second, as though they saw something indecent in each other's eyes.

"I'm not letting your friend come in," the major said.

"You tell him good-by," said Scott.

"Good-by," the major said. "I should have shot you, Johnny, when you were rolling on the floor."

Then the kitchen door opened, letting in warm air that was sweet with the scent of hay. Old Mr. Breen, still in his shirt sleeves, was standing in the doorway with a shovel in his hand. The homeliness of the kitchen and the peaceful warmth from outdoors made everything grotesque.

"Brother," said Mr. Breen to the major, "the hosses are ready. You'd best be gittin' on. . . . And you, young man, I wish you no pain, but I know what you are figurin'. It won't do no good to holler. No one'll hear who cares. It won't do no good to tip over in the chair. I made it. It won't break. But I'll be near if you should call."

Scott Mattaye did not speak again, and the door slammed shut. He tried to move, but he was as helpless as a hog tied by the legs. First the dogs were yelping, and then there was a sound of hoofs outside the door, and then the place was still except for the humming of the kettle and the ticking of the clock, and in back of everything was that almost soundless vibration of cannon a long way off. He closed his eyes, but even when he closed them he could see Mr. Breen.

He had no proper sense of sequence, for his mind was like a sick man's; but there was one thing in his thoughts, Scott Mattaye remembered. He could not divide an hour from the next when his mind was carrying him to a hundred places. Bits of his life would whirl about him. He was shooting wild turkey at Deer Bottom; he was with the cavalry again; but there was one thing on his mind. He must not let the old man know that he was in deathly fear.

The light was growing softer outside the kitchen windows when the kitchen door opened again and Mr. Breen came in. Clay was smeared on his hands and over his gaunt, bare arms. He walked past the chair and began washing at the kitchen sink.

"Young man," said Mr. Breen, "do you need water?"

"No," said Scott. . . . "So you're going to kill me, mister?"

The old man walked in front of him with a clean towel in his hands.

"Yes," he said, "I'm the Lord's poor instrument. Young man, are you afraid?"

"No," said Scott, "but if I were you, I reckon I'd be afraid."

Old Mr. Breen stared down at him and began to wipe his hands.

"Did your people fear," he asked, "when they sent an anointed saint to heaven?"

"Mister," said Scott — and he kept his voice even — "I'd be pleased to know, for the comfort of my mind, when you propose to kill me."

"After dark," said Mr. Breen. "I don't aim to lug you out for burial in daylight. I'm pleased you ain't afraid. I ain't afraid, and I'll die presently. There's somethin' gits me — here."

Suddenly his eyes were childlike, Scott remembered. He was drawing his hand across his chest.

"Mister," said Scott quickly, "I've seen a heap of illness. Step here and show me where."

"Young man," said Mr. Breen, "I can read your mind, I guess. You want to tip your chair and yourself atop of me. No, young man. I'll be goin', but I'll be ready in case you call."

The light outside the kitchen windows was growing soft and mellow, and he could hear the cannon. The time was going past him like a flood again, leaving him motionless like a rock against that flow. For a long while he was entirely alone. As the dusk came down he heard the low-ing of cows and the clatter of the milk pails which had stood beside the barn. It must have been when the old man had started milking that the little girl came in through the doorway from the entry. The door squeaked and opened just a crack at first.

"Why, hello, honeybee," said Scott. "Come in. Don' go away. Sholy I can't hurt you, honeybee."

She came tiptoeing toward him. He did not blame her for being frightened.

"Honeybee," he said — the child was not attractive, but he could see she liked the name — "I'm powerful thirsty. Could you fetch a cup of water from the sink?"

"I'm scared," the little girl whispered.

"Why, shucks!" said Scott. "You scared — a saucy girl like you? You fetch that cup now, honeybee. Isn't your grandpop milking? How'll he know? . . . There . . . And I've got something for you in my coat. Just ease this rope off my hand so I can reach — "

"No," she whispered, "I'm too scared."

He could hear his own voice still, not like his own, with its under-current of appeal beneath its ridiculous pretense at playfulness, as he pleaded for life. He was ashamed of that moment always — his begging from a child so that one hand could be free.

"I dassent," she whispered, but he knew better. She would dare, because there was something inside his coat. All the repression of her life gleamed in her pale-blue eyes in little points of light.

"Honeybee," said Scott, "it's something mighty fine — something you won't guess."

There was no sound which made him look up, but he had the sense that there was something different in the gathering of the dusk. The dusk seemed to settle over him like a blanket thrown about his head. He looked up to see the old man, standing in the doorway, watching. There was something in the way he stood that made Scott sure that he had planned that scene for his own pleasure. He must have been there for several minutes, as inevitable as the figure with the hourglass and the scythe.

"Mary Breen," the old man said, "you step away. Now, Mary Breen, you fetch the papers by the wood box. . . . So. Now lay 'em on the floor around the chair — under it. . . . You'd best lay on some more. And now go up to your chamber and close your door tight shut."

They were silent for a while. Old Mr. Breen seemed taller in the dark — more like an immense abstraction than a man.

"It's gittin' dark," he said. "Young man, I'll leave you five minutes to say your prayers."

He turned on his heel silently, walked out and closed the door.

"Time," the clock was whispering, "time!"

Inside the stove a piece of wood snapped sharply. He could see the glow of coals through the lids on top. The homely smells of the kitchen came around him in a rush. He strained sideways at his ropes, and the heaviness of his breathing drowned every other sound.

"Help!" he shouted.

The dogs in the yard began to bark, so that his shout mingled with the wave of barking.

"Help!" he shouted. "Murder!"

He hitched forward, and the chair fell forward, throwing him head-first into the dusky whiteness of the paper on the floor. The blow on his head must have stunned him, but he could not have been out long. There was still a little daylight when he found himself, lying sideways, still lashed to the kitchen chair.

"Mister soldier!" someone was calling. "You hear me, mister soldier?" It was the little girl in the gingham dress again.

"Yes," he said, "I hear you, honeybee."

"It's grandpop," she was sobbing. "He's took again. He's flopped flat down right on the parlor floor. When you hollered, he flopped down."

"Yo' get a knife and cut me loose," said Scott. "I reckon I can help your grandpop then."

"Mister," she sobbed, "please, you won't hurt him?"

"No," he answered, "I won't hurt him."

Once he was loose, his arms and legs were useless for a while. They burned and ached, once the blood came back, until tears stood in his eyes.

"Strike a candle light," he said, "and help me up. I'm very pressed for time."

He hobbled through the entry. Old Mr. Breen was lying on the parlor floor, face up, flat out. The candle which the girl was holding made a frame about the high head and the flowing beard. He was conscious, in great pain, staring up at Scott Mattaye. Scott's own ivory-handled revolver was lying on the floor, where it must have fallen from old Breen's hand. He stooped painfully and picked it up, but for half a minute no one spoke.

"Your heart, sir?" said Scott. He was incomprehensibly courteous and polite, but the old man did not speak.

"Something gits him right across the chest," said Mary Breen. "It pulls him down."

"Set that candle on the table," Scott was speaking gently. He saw his belt and saber in the corner. He walked over and strapped on his belt.

"Sir," he said, still gently, "I'm sorry to leave you in distress, but you and I don't matter. You've a horse in the barn, I recall yo' saying. I'm leaving you a hundred dollars on this table for the horse. I'll call at a neighbor's to send you help. . . . And now good night."

He was in the barnyard among the snarling dogs, holding a stable lantern. There was a heavy smell from hay and from the soft, warm breath of cattle. There was a drumming in his ears like the hurry of the clock.

"Time," it was saying, "time."

He heard himself speaking to Mary Breen, and then he was mounted and in the yard again. The horse was coarse and wild.

"Scuse me," Mary Breen was calling. "Ain't you forgot — somethin' in your pocket?"

He pulled out the rest of his bills. "There," he said, "take 'em, honey-bee."

He saw the house like a sharp, ungainly blot against the sky where a deep-red gash of something burning in the west made the outline clear. As he moved down the lane toward that distant glow, he did not know what he felt or thought, except that he must hurry, but suddenly he leaned forward on the neck of the farm horse. He felt sick — deathly sick.

There he was, sitting at his table at Deer Bottom, too old by any right to feel the force of memory. The wings of death were hovering near him, but no such death as that. He had the consolation from the knowledge he had gained that life was all dirt cheap.

"Only two things," he said, "matter — accident and time. Now, Gettysburg — all that mattered were accident and time."

His mind was back on the night again. It always seemed to him that most of the Gettysburg affair was night — mistaken roads and Union pickets, and other roads choked by ammunition trains and infantry, and wounded moving back — two crawling, passing lines. Through the discipline was good, roads were always confused in the rear of a line of battle. There was the vagueness of a dream when one rode at such a time. There was no hope in haste or wishing.

"You come from Stuart?" someone said. "Well, it's too late for cavalry until we drive 'em. Where've you been? We've been fighting here since yesterday."

The night was never clear, but when he saw the leader of the army, that was clear enough. He reported to General Lee at a quarter before ten in the morning, outside a half-demolished house on the outskirts of the town of Gettysburg.

Curriers were holding horses, and staff officers were standing a few paces back, so that he always thought of the general as entirely alone. He could remember a tall, solitary man with a graying beard and deep, dark eyes, whose face was passionless. He was looking, Scott remembered, across a valley of fine green fields to a long, gentle slope, which was held by the Union lines about half a mile away.

He was speaking to a dusty, worried officer, Scott remembered, unhurriedly, except for one short gesture, and Scott could hear the words:

"Is he ready to attack, sir?"

"No, sir."

"Very well," the general said. "Hurry back; tell him he's very late already."

He stared back across the valley as Scott stood waiting. The stones of a cemetery were visible upon the ridge opposite, and an ugly building, which would be some sort of school. The ridge was heavy with troops, throwing up lines of earthworks. Beyond were the dust clouds of more troops moving up, and more. That ridge was a fine position, which was growing stronger every hour. Now and then there would be a burst of rifle fire, but there was no forward movement.

He stood waiting while the general looked, forgetting his fatigue as he watched. Then Scott saw him strike his hands together in a sudden, swift motion, and he heard him say:

"It's too bad — too bad."

Scott had a wish to be somewhere else. He felt like an eavesdropper who had heard a dangerous secret, but the general was turning toward him slowly.

"Well," he said, "what is it, Captain?"

"Captain Mattaye, sir," began Scott, "from General Stuart's staff — "

"Yes," the general stopped him, "When did you leave the general, Captain? How far is he along?"

"Six o'clock yesterday morning, sir," said Scott. "General Stuart was at Dover then."

For a moment the general looked at him, and it seemed to Scott that the general was very tired, though his expression did not change.

"Captain," the general said, "you're very late."

Scott felt his face grow red. "Sir — " he began, but the general stopped him.

"Never mind," he said. "Of course, you were delayed."

"Sir," said Scott, "will the general send me back with orders?"

"No" — the voice was tranquil and very courteous — "General Stuart has his orders. It's too late to make it better. . . . It would have been too late unless he had come yesterday." He raised his voice, and Scott knew again that he was thinking of time: "Colonel, send another officer to General Longstreet to find out his delay. And give this officer food and rest. He's too tired to go on."

Where Are You, Prince?

(1939)

THERE is a gentleman whom I have had a good deal on my mind lately, although I never knew him very well and though we never had much in common during our short acquaintance — not even a mutual language. When I saw him last he was watching a dozen of his soldiers assemble five machine guns which had just arrived on camel back. He was dressed in a rich sapphire-blue silk gown that came down to his ankles, and the gown was quilted, since the spring weather was still cold, and his long hands were snuggled in the warm capacious sleeves. The pointed upturned toes of his beautifully embroidered riding boots protruded elegantly from beneath the gown. His peaked fur-lined cap was also blue. His face was yellowed, genial and moonlike, but the high cheekbones made him seem more like an American Indian than Chinese. His hair was braided in a beautiful black queue. Behind him his secretary was standing, a pale young man with a pock-marked nose, wearing a hat with a peacock plume and with a fine glass button on top of it, the palace insignia of his station. From the courtyard not far away there came a gurgling, shrieking sound. It was the complaining noise of the gentleman's camels, each being loaded with five hundred pounds of his traveling equipment.

When he saw me he looked up from the men kneeling about the machine guns and his black narrow eyes grew narrower and he smiled. When I took off my hat and bowed he seemed puzzled by the gesture, but he removed his hands from his sleeves, clasped them together and shook them gently, like a prize fighter acknowledging the greetings of the crowd.

The Swedish medical missionary who was with me began speaking in a language more explosive and guttural than Chinese.

"Well," I said, when he had finished, "I guess we'd better be going,"

and the Swiss who was with me, who knew a great deal more about
that sort of thing than I did, said it was right — that we'd better be
going.

"Ought we to give him a present?" I asked.

"The silk banner is enough," Mr. Bosshard said. "We gave it to the
secretary."

"Well," I said to the Swedish missionary, "say good-by to His High-
ness, will you, and thank him very much."

The missionary spoke again and our host nodded and held out a
hand to me very graciously.

"Well," I said, "good-by, Prince," and he said something, which of
course I could not understand, and we shook hands.

Then we walked past two sentries in sheepskin robes, facing each
other by the courtyard gate, leaning on their rifles, out through another court past two more sentries then around the High Spirit screen
of the great main court, and out through the main gateway, with its
sculptures and its garishly painted wooden carvings. In front of us
was a stagnant lake and beyond it a rolling buckskin-colored country
of sand and gravel and dead grass, bare and bleak and deserted, except
for a pile of rock on the horizon supporting a pole that bore ragged
prayer flags, which whipped and waved in the knifelike cold of the
desert air.

That was the last I ever saw of Teh Wang, hereditary prince of
West Senurt, whose lands reached to the southern edge of the Gobi
Desert, who owned all the herds of horses and camels, goats and sheep
in his principality and who held feudal sway over his nomadic subjects.
It was the last I saw of him and the last I probably will ever see, but
in spite of the time that has elapsed he remains in my mind as a lonely
and magnificent figure, surrounded by ceremonial much older than
Genghis Khan. His father by right of birth could sit once a year at table with the emperor of China. He owed allegiance to no one, since
the Chinese Empire was dead. He was walking alone on a precarious
road, with the Japanese, the Chinese and the Russians pressing on him.
He wished to be allied to none of them. It was his desire, he told me,
to establish an independent state of Mongolia. I sometimes think of him
at night and say to myself, "Where are you, Prince?" I think of him
and he is part of a fantastic dream, a part of as strange a land as you
can hope to see. A traveler in that region has described it rather pret-

tily, saying that the clock has struck twelve in all the rest of the world, but it is still five minutes of twelve in Mongolia. And it has always seemed to me that it was even earlier when we ate boiled mutton and drank rice wine with the prince.

When I think of the prince I usually think also of another character, quite different, but an integrated part in the wild life on the steppes beyond the Great Wall of China. In the town of Kalgan with its mud and gray-brick houses, the beginning of the old caravan route across Mongolia into Urga, there dwelt a man named Adams Purpiss. He was the head of a trading company which operated under a German charter, but which was just as Communist Russian as Mr. Purpiss himself. It was the only company in the troubled period of 1934 which was allowed by Russia to cross with trading goods into Outer Mongolia. It was the last of the great trading companies operating from Kalgan, and a year back they told me it had gone with the wind and Mr. Adams Purpiss and his German and Russian employees had gone with it.

I remember very clearly our first meeting, because it was the first time that I began to feel that I was close to what is called getting off the beaten track. It was the first time that I had the remotest idea of life in central Asia. It was not interesting to my traveling companion, Walter Bosshard, a Swiss newspaper photographer, because he had crossed Mongolia before and had traveled the caravan route across Turkestan into Tibet.

"Since we do not leave until tomorrow," he said, "we might go down and call on Mr. Adams Purpiss."

"Will he give us a drink?" I asked.

"That is why I suggested it," Bosshard answered. "I do not know him very well, but he always has vodka."

As a matter of fact, both Bosshard and I needed refreshment that afternoon, since we had been spending all that day and the night before in a missionary compound with a Mr. Soudarbaum, an aged melancholy missionary, who was endeavoring to get us across the line into Mongolia. We had said prayers with Mr. and Mrs. Soudarbaum the night before and the morning had been spent in religious ways. There was something about the whole Soudarbaum atmosphere that was completely removed from the rugged mountain ranges of North China. Bosshard remarked that wherever you traveled all missionaries were the same, dwelling in comfortable European houses, making as much money as they could and singing hymns. I was inclined to agree with him, though I felt that his views might be superficial. At any rate I wanted a change. Our rickshaws pulled us through the gate of the wall of the old city down narrow lanes, where our runners' feet tossed up clouds of choking yellow dust, past streets of shops, past rows of men bending under loads of soft coal on their backs, past old men taking their song birds for an airing, past the military barracks, to an enormous walled enclosure where Mr. Purpiss lived. The yard or compound of his company, once we were through his gate, must have been ten acres in area. Around the edge of this great enclosure were low warehouses. In the center seated in lines and munching hay were seven hundred and fifty camels. The rest of the yard was filled with camel boys and Chinese workmen wrapping up bales of goods, because on the next day the Purpiss camels would be on their way to Urga. They were packing up great bricklike slabs of compressed tea leaves, wrapping them in bales of Chinese matting. They were filling bags and boxes with Chinese copper and pewter ware. They were packing up bolts of cloth and dozens of high leather Mongol riding boots. Above the hammering came the chant of clerks keeping a tally of the merchandise.

Mr. Purpiss was a short fat man with beetling eyebrows, close-cropped black hair and very white teeth. He received us in the social hall and seemed very glad to see us. A pleasant detail of the Orient is that Europeans there are generally glad to see each other. We began conversing about the situation in North China while more and more of his employees flocked into the social hall.

"So you gentlemen are going to Mongolia," Mr. Purpiss said. "Where in Mongolia?"

We explained that we were going to West Senurt, that we had letters to a Mr. Larson there.

"Oh," Mr. Purpiss said, "Larson. Then he will send you on to the prince. You will be visiting at the palace. Let us have some more vodka. It is very interesting in Mongolia."

Mr. Purpiss was able to drink vodka very quickly with no visible effect.

"The prince is a very nice man," he said. "The Japanese are troubling him and he gives too much of his money to the lama temple. How are you going to travel to Mr. Larson's?"

It was a problem which had taken me about four weeks to work out and so I was glad to tell him. Larson was living four hundred miles away over a trackless country. We were making the trip the next morning with a missionary in a C-model Ford coupe. We had been warned of bandits and other difficulties, but we were going, if the Chinese general would let us through the Wall.

"It seems strange to me," Mr. Purpiss said, "that you gentlemen should like to travel with a missionary." He swallowed his glass of vodka. "How would it be if you motored there in my new car?"

Bosshard and I both laughed heartily and told him it would be very nice.

"Please," Mr. Purpiss said, "believe me, I am not joking. I have a new Buick. It was sent on the railroad from Tientsin. Do not disappoint me. I should love to have you take it. Seigi, my chauffeur, can drive you. He has driven for the Panchon lama. I believe you will be more comfortable than with a missionary."

He rose and walked to the door of the social hall and shouted across the courtyard.

"I shall have the Buick brought around so that you can see," he said. Bosshard looked confused.

"Think nothing of it," he told me. "Purpiss is drunk. That's all."

I got up and walked to the door where Mr. Purpiss was standing. He might have been under the influence of liquor and I might have been also, but a Buick limousine had appeared from somewhere. It was in the middle of the court under a cold North China sky, winding its way between the bales of bricked tea and the camels, and it stopped in front of the door where we were standing — about as incongruous a sight as you could imagine against a background that was like something in the Old Testament. I remember the smell of the camels and the dust and the yellow mud walls and the Chinese voices behind it. But there it was, the very latest model, driven by a young Slav in an embroidered Russian blouse. The car was full of chromium-steel gadgets, spare tires, glass vases, cigarette lighters, windshield wipers and fawn-colored upholstery.

"What are you going to do with a car like that?" I asked. "There aren't any roads here to drive it on."

My question delighted Mr. Purpiss, for he went into peals of hearty laughter.

"Mongolia is like a tennis court," he said. "Everywhere you drive is a road. You will see when Seigi takes you out tomorrow."

"Has there ever been a car like this up here before?" I asked.

"No," said Mr. Purpiss. "You can drive at seventy miles an hour in Mongolia. If you gentlemen will give me your passports the Chinese general is a friend of mine and there will be no trouble. Seigi will call for you at six in the morning."

"You're not serious," Bosshard asked, "that we should take your car?"

"Please," said Mr. Purpiss, "do not hurt my feelings. What is a car for but to run? Take it and enjoy yourselves. Take it for ten days or two weeks. Seigi will take care of you."

It took Mr. Purpiss quite a while to make us understand that he was serious, and even when he did I could not understand it and Bosshard could not either.

"What is he doing it for?" I asked Bosshard. "You can't tell me he isn't going to get something out of it and what is he going to get?"

"I do not understand," Bosshard said, "but let us not argue. Perhaps he is going mad, but we have got the car."

I might add incidentally that no one could have had a better companion on a trip through Central Asia than Walter Bosshard. He was six feet four and had the icy blue eye of a Nordic and the crude but effective humor of a German funny-paper. He was an expert photographer. On his expedition to Tibet two of his European companions had died. He had been obliged to fight off bandits in Turkestan and he had flown over the North Pole with General Nobile in his dirigible. He had a rough and patronizing air which the natives seemed to enjoy. It was his idea never to try to speak their language, because he said you only made a fool of yourself and lost face. He said if necessary you could get on anywhere with a few simple signs, followed up possibly by a kick. It seemed to work very well in Mongolia. Once when our car was stuck in a mud slough near the Chinese border Bosshard induced fifty Chinese peasants to push us out. He first tried signs, and when these didn't work he resorted to more vigorous methods in which Seigi, the chauffeur, and I finally assisted. I suddenly found myself coming into physical collision with a shrieking Chinese peasant the size of a Harvard fullback.

"Take his stick away," Bosshard shouted, "and hit him." I was frankly afraid that I could not do it, but I did take his stick away and hit him in the stomach. The great advantage was that all the farmers must have been frightened of us, and when they pulled the car out we gave them a Chinese dollar to divide between them. This was only an incident on the way, but it made me admire and appreciate Bosshard. I was genuinely touched when Bosshard asked me a year later to travel with him to Tibet in a Mongol camel caravan. It showed that we got on rather well.

I have not intended to make this into a travel paper and there is not room to go into details about the country and the people, but anyone who has been through the last spur of the Great Wall north of Kalgan will never forget his first startlingly unexpected vision of the Mongolian plateau. We arrived at the deserted gate tower at seven o'clock on an early April morning, riding in Mr. Purpiss's brand new Buick, wrapped in bearskin rugs, with sheepskin coats, crowded between petrol tins which occupied every inch of available space in the car. We had made our way along a ravine that cuts through the bare, brown mountains to the north of the city, where great heaps of loess dust froze on either side of the road in high unsubstantial cliffs. This is the dust that blows back and forth in choking clouds over all of North China. It is the top soil, many believe, caused by the deforestation of the Mongolian plains. When the vegetation was either cut away or was eliminated there through climatic changes this soil was caught in the heavy gales from the Gobi Desert, so that now the surface of Mongolia is hardpan, so hard that a car may pass on any line you like over the rolling country. There was no warning of the Mongolian plateau. As we climbed toward the mountain through the Wall it seemed that we might journey indefinitely through a forbidding, hilly country, but suddenly at the Wall at an altitude close to seven thousand feet the mountains stopped. It was as abrupt as the change of scene in a motion picture, as decisive as the turning of a page. At the gate of the Great Wall a cold wind struck us and everything in front of us was clear and cold. The mountains had leveled off as though the Wall had checked them, and as far as you could see to north and west and east was spread the faintly, undulating land of Central Asia. A land which extended with hardly a variation north to Siberia and west to the Himalayas. It was like struggling through the sand dunes and coming upon the sea. It gave you the same impression of loneliness and limitless distance. It stretched out in low waves like the sea in bare, tawny-colored undulations, monotonous and indescribably lonely. The early-morning sun shone upon it, making it golden brown, tinged with the soft faint green of spring.

Bosshard nudged me in the ribs.

"It surprises you, what?" he asked. "What do you think of it?"

It was impossible to express what you thought of that first sight of limitless, treeless land. It would have been easier to comment on something as concrete as the Grand Canyon, but here there were no boundaries except infinity. I told him it was the damnedest thing I had ever seen.

"Yes," Bosshard said, "it is exactly that."

A rough track cut through the sand and gravel and tufted grass. Seigi stepped on the gas and we began moving in Mr. Purpiss's Buick at forty-five miles an hour seemingly into nowhere.

"Very nice," Seigi said. It was about all the English he knew. "Nice — nice — nice."

"Is he traveling by the sun?" I asked Bosshard.

"No," Bosshard said. "It is easy. We are on the Urga road."

And then I could see by the worn track in front of us that we were on one of those caravan routes, older than the earliest civilization, over which bolts of silk had started on their way to Babylon and Thebes. It was an anachronism to be traveling in Mr. Purpiss's Buick. An hour later it was clear that Mongolia was aware of the anachronism. We swooped over a rise of ground into a wretched mud town on the edge of a dried-up watercourse. It was the last outpost of Chinese culture, a town of immigrant farmers who were trying to make a living, like our Dust Bowl farmers, out of sandy soil that was good only for grazing. When we stopped there to get water for the Buick the entire population of the town surrounded us; hundreds of Chinese in ragged quilted blue denim pressed about the car, wide-eyed, open-mouthed, jabbering with excitement. You did not have to know the language to tell that they had never seen anything like a limousine. They touched it timidly. They pointed with awed exclamations at the brightwork. They touched our clothes gently when we got out. When Seigi blew the horn there was a stampede for cover and women and children ran and screamed. We were making a day's journey that would have taken several weeks by oxcart or by camel.

It was the same fifty miles farther on when we stopped at another sort of village, the first Mongol settlement I had ever seen. It was a group of hive-shaped felt huts of the nomads in the lee of a low hill. First we were met by a pack of shaggy black dogs that circled around the car, snapping and snarling, until the dogs' masters came running from the yurts and called them off. Then the car was surrounded by wild grinning men in peaked hats and belted gowns, wearing long greasy pigtails. Their high cheekbones shone with grease. They smelt of rancid butter and of smoke from fires made of cattle dung, the only fuel in Mongolia. They had none of the timidity nor the politeness of the Chinese. They looked you straight in the eye and laughed and talked loudly.

"They never bathe here," Bosshard said, "except the day they are born."

When we went inside one of the large circular yurts the succession of smells showed he was not exaggerating. A fire was burning in the center of a great circular room. Around the edge were wooden cabinets and brass utensils with rugs and cushions placed near them. By the door was a pen of newborn lambs. In the center was a fire of cattle dung, the smoke of which eddied chokingly through an opening in the ceiling. A woman with a heavy headdress made of silver and coral beads offered us each a bowl of tea with rancid butter floating on the top. We drank it, signifying pleasure, and presented our host with a package of Camel cigarettes. Seigi chatted amiably, as though they were old acquaintances.

"Say car very nice," he said. "Oh, so nice."

It was plain that we were looked upon as very important people, as travelers of infinite resources. It was not difficult to understand their point of view. No viceroy of the great Khan had ever crossed the plains in an automobile like ours.

We were on our way to stop with a trader named Larson who dwelt behind the walls of an abandoned lama temple some four hundred miles from Kalgan, not far from the beginning of the Gobi Desert. The existing maps of Mongolia have few details, none of them accurate, but Seigi knew the track out to the crumbling walls of Larson's place, the only solid habitation which we had seen after fourteen hours of travel. Once on the low hills that grew light and dark as the clouds scudded over them we saw eight or ten men on horseback about half a mile from the track who shouted and galloped toward us. We had been warned of bandits in the region, but if they were bandits they had no chance with us, for Seigi stepped on the gas and put the Buick up to fifty-five. Except for that single interruption the life along the route was old and slow. Once we passed a row of twenty or thirty bullock carts, loaded with brick tea and rice, plodding seemingly into nowhere, the drivers limping by the animals' heads. Now and then we saw the red robes and the yellow robes of lama priests on vows of solitary pilgrimage and twice we passed bands of Chinese immigrant farmers, ragged and emaciated, searching for new land, though it seemed hard to believe that they could raise crops on that watery sandy grass-tufted plateau. Some of them drove bullock carts loaded with a few poor house furnishings. Others, less happy, pulled their carts themselves, men and women and children stretching out fanwise, each holding a rope. Others stumbled forward, carrying their belongings on their backs. They represented the restless borderline of China, the migration from some famine-stricken area into a semi-hostile land. They were the latest wave of a Chinese tide which had beaten against the plains of Mongolia for millenniums. It is possible on a day's ride to see the ancient stones of Chinese hand mills, scores of them, each representing a house and farm, the last monuments of a civilization in a howling, arid wilderness where once there must have been trees and streams, but now Mongolia is dry and lonely and very wild. Twice on the hills we saw herds of antelope which flashed away from us as fast as birds upon the wing, and once we saw a wolf. It must have been after the noon hour, I think, that we came upon a camel caravan. It is hard to explain if you have never seen one the sort of excitement that you feel at the sight of a string of shaggy animals walking in single file, neither fast nor slow, to the monotonous tune of the lead camel's bell. They moved like a primitive freight train, each back loaded with five hundred pounds of hides and wool. The drivers in peaked caps rode along the flanks and when they saw us half a dozen of them whipped up their camels and loped toward the car. When they stopped they made their camels kneel and slipped off and hurried toward us, awkwardly in their high boots, grinning and pointing their thumbs upward to signify approval. When we gave them cigarettes they pulled flint and steel from their pouches and lighted them and squatted on their heels. It was a caravan coming down from Urga and we waited by the road as they went by, four hundred beasts in lines of fifty, like the sections of a train.

My notebook shows that it took us fourteen hours to reach Larson's temple, most of it fast and steady driving. We saw the white walls in the starlight and the peaked roofs of the old pavilions above the walls. Nearby was the small wooden house of a missionary station, with a shadowy group of yurts around it. There was the usual baying of dogs and the shouts of their owners. The temple gate was opened and a Mongol appeared carrying a lantern, followed by Larson himself in a heavy Mongol robe.

A year ago Larson stopped with me two days in New York. The Japanese had driven him out of Mongolia and he was on his way home to Sweden. It was strange to see him in New York — a gentle, bewildered, rather elderly Swede — when I thought of him standing at his gate that evening with a rifle in the crook of his arm. He had given up his temple — the Japs had squeezed him out. He was willing to sell the temple for a hundred dollars the last time I saw him, but when I offered to buy it from him — I liked the idea of owning a temple in Mongolia — he refused.

"The Yaps," he said, "would never let you back."

He stood there that evening staring at the Buick car.

"Where did you get that?" he asked, and we said that Mr. Purpiss had loaned it to us.

"Why did he do that?" Mr. Larson asked, and we said we did not know why.

"There has never been anything like it," Mr. Larson said, "not in Mongolia. Tomorrow you must go to see the prince."

I have not intended, as I have said before, to write an account of travel, but I wish you might have seen the prince's palace — another five hours by car into nowhere. One minute you would have thought there was no one living within a thousand miles and in the next you came over a rise of ground and there was the prince's palace by the half-dried bed of a lake. Its walls and pavilions were like a miniature forbidden city and the life inside it was conducted along the lines of the ancients' Chinese court — nomads and traders living beyond the walls in yurts. Secretaries, seneschals, lama priests with shaven heads, soldiers, camels, neighing Mongol horses — they all crowded around us when we came and the prince's son, a sallow, dissipated young man,

and the prince's secretary made us welcome. The servants took our
bags and bedding and led us through the gates to the courtyard reserved for distinguished guests. We slept upon a raised kang in a room
furnished with red lacquer. The attendants brought us warm water in
shallow brass basins and stood at the door fascinated while we shaved.
Then in came a boiled lamb and rice and chopsticks and rice wine and
then the prince in his sapphire-blue silk gown. He sat beside us on the
kang watching while we ate, conversing with us through the offices of
the medical missionary whom Mr. Larson had sent with us on the
trip. The prince was very curious about the outer world — how was it
going in Peking, was it true that there was great poverty and revolution in the United States, what was our present relation with Japan,
would we make an alliance with Russia, did we think that Hitler would
rule Europe? Then he answered our own questions about Mongolia.
The Russians, he said, the Japanese and Chinese, all wanted him to
make an alliance. It was hard to make up his mind, very hard. He
wanted to know where we had ever found the automobile — it was
more beautiful than any he had ever seen, even in Shanghai. He had
been to Shanghai once eight years before. We told him it was loaned
to us.

"Tomorrow," the prince said, "you must see my army. My wife and
I shall ride with you in your car. I shall be displeased if you do not
stay for two days at least."

I remember how the prince sat back in the cushions of the Buick
and examined the cigarette lighter and the clock and blew the horn.

"You must be very rich," he said, "to travel in such a car as this.
How much did it cost?"

It was hard to translate the figure into Chinese money. Such a car,
we said, would cost at least twelve thousand Chinese dollars.

"The owner of the machine," the prince said, "must be magnificently
rich. I could not afford such a vehicle."

There is no room to continue with our trip to Mongolia. We saw a
great deal of the country and I never hope to have a better time. The
Mongols are an open-hearted, friendly people. They took us riding,
they wrestled with us. We sat in the evening singing songs. We drank
a good many gallons of tea and rancid butter and ate rice cakes and
rock candy. They had the hospitality of a primitive, nomadic people.
I keep hoping I may see them again if their country is ever quiet, but,

as I say, there is not much room to talk about them. We were ten days in the domain of West Senurt. We traveled several hundred miles farther on. We stopped for a while at Larson's. The Buick car was spattered with mud and caked with dirt when we turned back on the track to Kalgan. By the time we drove through the gates of Mr. Purpiss's trading company late one afternoon the car did not look new at all, but if Mr. Purpiss was displeased he did not show it.

"It is only to be expected," he said, "that the car should suffer some slight dents and scratches. My men will put it into shape. They are working on it now. Let us have some vodka and tell me about your trip."

Mr. Purpiss urged us to drink more vodka. We must stay to dinner with him and sing Russian songs. He seemed delighted that we had enjoyed ourselves — delighted that we liked the Buick.

"And you saw Mr. Larson and the prince?" he asked.

"Yes," we said, "we saw the prince."

"Such a delightful man," Mr. Purpiss said. "Was he surprised when he saw the Buick?"

We told him he was very much surprised; in fact, deeply impressed.

"Ah," Mr. Purpiss said, "I hope you told him that it cost a great deal of money."

By that time I felt most grateful to Mr. Purpiss, puzzled but very grateful. The room was beginning to fill with smoke and some camel drivers were doing a dance.

"Of course we can't thank you enough," I told him.

I wanted to make this clear to him while there was still time, because Mr. Purpiss seemed to be doing his best to drink Bosshard and me under the table — and either we or Mr. Purpiss would be under it pretty soon. I tipped over the vodka bottle by mistake.

"Ha, ha," said Mr. Purpiss, "you are getting drunk! We Russians can drink more than Americans."

"We can't thank you enough, Mr. Purpiss," I said, "for letting us have the automobile. The least I can do is to pay you some rent for it."

Mr. Purpiss looked hurt. He waved his hands in front of him and tipped over the vodka bottle.

"Do not insult me," he said, "when we are friends, dear friends. You and Mr. Bosshard are so charming. Let us not talk of money."

"My dear Mr. Purpiss," Bosshard said, "at least we should pay for the petrol and the oil."

"Please," Mr. Purpiss said, "do not hurt me when I endeavor to do a little kindness to friends. It is an insult to talk of money. The car was yours for your pleasure. If it was satisfactory I am repaid by your happiness."

"Now, wait a minute, Mr. Purpiss," I said, because it seemed to me that it had all gone far enough about the car. "I don't know you and you don't know me and in this world we don't do anything for nothing."

"Oh," said Mr. Purpiss, "let us not be so crude."

"Well, it's true," I said. "Let us be frank as long as we're friends. You got something out of letting us use that car. Will you tell us what it was?"

Mr. Purpiss began to smile.

"As long as you are leaving Kalgan tomorrow," he said, "I do not mind telling. Bring us more vodka and play more music. I was sure you would like the prince."

"Go ahead," Bosshard said, "and tell us why you let us have the car."

"Oh, yes," Purpiss answered, "the car. Well, frankly I don't mind telling you. Each month I send seven hundred and fifty camels in a caravan to Urga. You followed the route. It crosses the territory of the prince. Perhaps you follow me now — seven hundred and fifty camels through the territory of the prince."

"No," I said, " I don't see the connection."

"If you would stay here for a year, you would understand so clearly," Mr. Purpiss said. "The camels must eat. The prince usually makes a grazing charge of ten dollars per animal crossing through his country, but so far he has rendered me no bill and I have considered it necessary to give him a present. You see, the Buick is for the prince."

Mr. Purpiss smiled again and shrugged his shoulders. "And very cheap at that, but it seemed to me how much better it would be if the prince were to admire that Buick sufficiently before he had it. That is why I loaned it to you. The prince and all his people have admired it, and now when he gets it he will really value it. I hope you understand."

Rainbows

(1930)

This early effort is again an experiment in form, and proves again, in part, that it is just as well to know about what one is writing. I was familiar with the technique of radio announcers even back in those days, but then who wasn't? I was also sufficiently familiar with popular songs to achieve a presentable parody, but I knew nothing whatsoever about professional fighters except from distant observation. I also still felt that dialect might be useful in depicting character. I do not believe this now. In fact, I rather think that a good mental picture could have been achieved of Uncle Remus if his author had made him speak less like the end man in a minstrel show. The medium of a broadcast is of course not a good medium for fiction, since the point of view is very rigid and the time is wholly the present — facts which are proved by the end of "Rainbows."

Good evening, everybody. This is Arthur McQuilloch speaking on the coast-to-coast hookup tonight. And here we are, ladies and gentlemen of the radio audience, waiting for the boys to come on to settle the decision for the light-heavyweight championship of the world.

It is a fine night here at Thirty Acres, and whilst we wait, let me try just to paint a little picture of the scene, remembering all the while that the report of this spectacle is being conveyed to you tonight by the courtesy of the makers of Mellow Sweet Cigars, chock full of goodness and sun-cured Kentucky leaf, and also by the courtesy of the Oronoco House and Cottages, that internationally known resort hotel nestled 'midst the ozone of Virginia's Blue Ridge Mountains.

It certainly looks like a big night tonight. That's the way it looks to me out here at Thirty Acres. The darkness is like velvet, and in about two minutes Sammy Small, the handsome and much-talked-of champion, who tipped the scales this afternoon at 172, will meet in fifteen rounds the challenger, Johnny Jones, the rocky-jawed baker's boy, who is tougher than the buns he used to heave and who did 173 on those same scales.

Now, I want to say right here and now, there isn't any love lost between these contestants tonight. Somehow — maybe you know why — the boys have got it in for Sammy Small, the dapper Apollo who heads his class. For instance, just before leaving his training quarters this morning, Johnny Jones made the following announcement:

"I may not be good at this book thing," Johnny Jones is reported to have said, "but I simply ask to be let in with this alleged Big Panic. He's kept me waiting two years, and it won't be long now."

And now it seems there's a touch of romance in this fight tonight, the same genuine romance that you can sense in the smoke of Mellow Sweet Cigars, made from those rich sun-cured leaves that you know all about. It happens to be my privilege to be able to let you in for something. They say — Dame Rumor hath it — that with the last blow tonight, wedding bells are going to ring for Sammy Small; and that Sammy is going to wed none other than a little lady who is the daughter of a large magnate whose name I will not mention.

Right at the ringside in back of Sammy's corner is a vacant seat, and, according to prevailing talk, it's for the little lady herself, who's coming to see this fight. If I was to mention her name now, I'm sure you'd be surprised, since it has a familiar ring in Newport, Southampton, Palm Beach and Aiken. But maybe you saw the tale yourselves in the paper this morning, when you lolled back over the empty coffee cups and lighted up one of those Mellow Sweet Cigars we were speaking about.

It seems — as is natural with class — that Sammy Small chanced to be last winter at the Oronoco House down at Boiling Springs, Virginia. And, folks, you'd better write that down, as the Oronoco House is helping to defray the expenses of this big coast-to-coast hookup. Nestled 'midst the heart of the old Blue Ridge Mountains, so famed in story and song and romance, the Oronoco House offers that distinctive and discriminating hospitality so sought by the men of the world whose nerves are frayed by the cares of modern business. Its natural mineral baths, under the supervision of trained attendants, offer that priceless gift of home, amidst fastidious surroundings.

It seems — as Dame Rumor hath it — that Sammy Small was enjoying those crystal baths at the Oronoco House, having twisted the nerve of his left elbow. Naturally enough — I say naturally enough, because there is that aristocracy of fellowship in that homelike place — he fell into conversation with a gentleman on the rubbing table next him, who was endeavoring to reduce his weight. And one thing led to another. You know and I know that the old-fashioned bruising barroom type is out of date, and we both know that Sammy is addicted to reading Plato and similar book writers, though the muscle element, which infests this game both in the ring and in the cheaper seats out back, don't like the idea of Sammy's lecturing on Keats to the women's club out West.

Didn't I tell you it was my privilege to let you in for something? That party on the rubbing table next to Sammy Small was the very magnate of whom I was speaking, the sort who frequent the Oronoco House. For various reasons it is not well to mention his name, but it's going to come out all right. And when it does, I repeat, you'll be surprised. The automotive industry wouldn't be the same without him. . . . And who said there isn't poetry in the world? As Sammy was lying on the rubbing table getting his tendons stretched, pretty soon the man on the next table commenced looking over toward him, as you may have read last week in the Sunday supplement.

"I say," he says, "whatever are you reading?"

Now, as I have intimated, whatever the coarser element in this racket may say, Sammy can take and give.

"Marcus Aurelius," Sammy told him, just like that. "Hughie, would you kindly go to work again on my lumbar muscles?"

"Who's Marcus Aurelius?" says this millionaire, immediately interested, of course. And don't forget Sammy's just a great big-hearted kid; natural, not stuckup.

"Marcus Aurelius," says Sammy, "was an emperor of the Roman Empire whose philosophical writings, to me, seem best to reflect that clear spirit of natural paganism, in contrast to the new humanism of to-day; and this, to me, seems the greatest intellectual contribution of pre-Christian Rome."

"May I ask," says the stranger, "how did you know that?"

"Out of the front of the book," says Sammy.

It may be I haven't got this right, but that's how Sammy's publicity man put the words into his mouth. He does love books — and, really, I'm not joking when I say it.

Now, as Dame Rumor hath it, one 'thing led to another after that. Quick to be impressed — all right, I won't be long now; I've got to give 'em this, don't I? — quick to be impressed with Sammy, this gentleman introduced him to none other than his daughter, the little lady whose name is now linked so romantically with pugilistic circles. And what happened is nobody's business — now, is it? But maybe you can guess.

Friends, honestly now, as we pause here at this great ringside, surrounded by a pulsing throng in a velvet night, I want to ask, is this the first time that Dan Cupid has played his tricks? It has happened before, hasn't it, that a boy has hitched his wagon to a star in love's sweet dream? The little lady with her millions and Sammy Small in his dapper tweeds — it gives a bit of romance just to think of it. Frequently last winter Sammy has been seen with the little lady in question, riding, dancing in the moonlight, and more than once at a prominent table in a Broadway night club. And what happened is nobody's business. . . . And here's a seat waiting for her so she can see her dream man fight. . . . That's romance, friends; the same romance you get in the smoke of the Mellow Sweet Cigar. . . .

When interviewed yesterday at his training quarters, Sammy Small was discovered sitting on the front porch of his bungalow, reading to himself from a limp leather volume. When questioned regarding the prevalent rumor, he seemed ill at ease, and some noticed a blush beneath his tan. At this point his private secretary appeared in natty doeskin trousers and passed each visitor a piece of typewritten paper which read as follows:

"Though fully realizing my duty as a public figure, I must decline to discuss the rumors of my forthcoming engagement. The press has had a lot of fun with me lately, and fight fans seem to have gained an impression of me which is unfortunate. Won't you, the fairest public in the world, give me an even break and let what I do speak for itself?"

As this statement was being read, Sammy Small, who gave evidences of being trained too fine, exhibited traces of nervousness.

"Will she be present tomorrow evening?" one of the boys is said to have inquired.

"Fellows," said Sammy Small, "I wish we could talk fighting, but that is a fair question. There will be a seat reserved for the lady in question, if she chooses to be present. I can't say any more than that, and I want to ask you for an even break."

Well, there's the whole picture painted for you with this bit of local color and romance which gives this battle a note not usually connected with modern fistic exhibits . . . and you can listen, if you want to, while everyone is stamping and whistling. They want the thing to start, and do you blame them?

There's something happening now. It's Benny Rheinstein, the popular cold-tonic boy with the nightingale voice, climbing through the ropes. Benny is going to croon one for the crowd through his megaphone to keep 'em quiet while we wait, and I'm going to put him on for you too. This is Benny Rheinstein now. And Benny is going to let one go — his famous one about rainbows. Hold on tight now and light one of those Mellow Sweet Cigars. . . . "Rainbows" — spring it, Benny!

> I'm not fit — that's it;
> I'll say I know
> You're high — way up in duh sky-y-y —
> I'm down bee-low,
> So it seems
> That I gotta build a ladder outa dreams;
> That's the only way that I can go
> To ye-e-e-ew.
>
> Rainbows — rainbows,
> That's where my brain goes,
> Climbing the ladder to you;
> Blue skies, blue eyes — that's all, I guess —
> Sobs, tears, groans, sighs and happiness,
> All go to make my ladder outa rainbows,
> The ladder of my dreams that be-eams
> For y-e-e-e-ew.
>
> Rainbows — rainbows,
> That's where the pain goes,
> And my tears' stain shows
> Just rainbows — rainbows — rainbows!
> And I get sadder — madder — gladder,
> Climbing up my rainbow ladder
> Into the blue
> To y-e-e-e-ew.

You have just been listening — we've all been — to Benny Rhein-stein, the popular cold-tonic boy, who has just been giving us so much pleasure. If you have enjoyed that bit of colorful whimsey, send him an applause card, and maybe if he gets enough, perhaps he'll get out of here and start a night club of his own. . . . "Rainbows!" . . . Maybe Sammy Small is building his ladder out of rainbows in his dressing room out back. . . . I don't know what else he's doing.

Wait a minute . . . something's happening out here. . . .

All right, we can cut out this stuff now. Here comes Johnny Jones, the challenger. He's climbing through the ropes, and I want to say he looks good, even under wraps. Short hair, a day's growth of beard like Dempsey, and nice legs — heh, heh! — his looks are in his legs, I'd say. The crowd is giving him a hand now. Don't tell me Johnny isn't popu-lar — listen for yourselves. . . . Johnny's shaking hands in the air now. Now he's on his stool with his hands on his knees, hunching his neck into his shoulders. . . .

And now here comes Sammy. You can spot that fancy Japanese ki-mono Sammy wears like a whisky breath in a Sunday concert. Sammy has now reached the ring, surrounded by a platoon of athletic valets. He certainly has that matinee look — light curly hair, and boy-scout complexion, and financial polish, and strong — oh, my — and yet so gentle. No wonder some little lady has lost her heart to him. Will you listen to the raspberry this champion is getting? All the floor is booing, and the back counties are returning the Bronx cheer.

Seemingly surprised he hasn't got a hand, he looks around, worried, and gives the appearance of not having slept all night. And now some of these cutups are starting to sing "Rainbows, that's where the pain goes." He's looking over in back of his corner, like he expected some-body who isn't there, while that catchy tune of "Rainbows" is being taken up on all sides. Don't tell me there isn't romance in this angle. He's looking over at that empty seat. Is she going to let him down? Maybe she will, but I'll tell you something that won't, and that's one of those Mellow Sweet Cigars.

Now they're in the middle of the ring for those formalities that are inseparable from the commencement of these arguments. The boys are posing for the news photos, shaking hands. Johnny is giving Sammy a dirty look. He said something to Sammy then, and it couldn't have been just "heigh-ho," because Sammy's face is getting red. He's looking back of his corner again at that empty seat.

Here we are at the ringside of Thirty Acres through the courtesy of the Mellow Sweet Cigar Company and the Oronoco House and Cottages. Jack Hamlin — that solon who is refereeing tonight — has beckoned Johnny and Sammy to the center of the canvas for the usual talky-talky about not doing a thing he wouldn't do, and . . . something tells me Jones will try for a quick finish.

All right, now we're down to brass tacks. . . . The boys are doing the shoe-and-rosin act, and there's the bell. . . . They meet in the center of the ring and fool around, and Sammy leads with a straight left. Johnny slips it and comes in, but Sammy ties him up. They are now locked in a close embrace, and Johnny is saying something in Sammy's ear, and Sammy gives the impression of having a pain, and not having his mind on this. He's looking at that empty chair. Now Sammy jabs his left and misses, and shoots a pretty right to Johnny's jaw, but there isn't any steam to it, and Johnny laughs, and then he wades in and . . . fetches a right-hand sock to the middle . . . and buries another right and left. Sammy's mouth drops open. . . . Sammy backs away and Johnny is right there after him. . . . Jones — wait a minute — as Jones bores in, he take a right from Small to the back of the head, and lands a wild right . . . flush to the face . . . which sends the champion rocking on his heels . . . and as Jones sets himself . . . Sammy Small staggers into a clinch and hangs on with his head on Johnny's shoulder, staring toward his corner, his face a bloody smear. . . . And now everybody's on their feet, and Jones is fighting to get away. . . . And now they break, and Sammy pushes out a left, and he's a sight. . . . It's just as well his girl can't see him now. . . . Johnny tears at him, ripping in rights and lefts, and Small, half blinded, is trying to fight back. . . . And there's such a noise you can't hear yourself think. . . . And now Jones is rushing again, and — there's the bell!

Folks, you have the Mellow Sweet Cigar Company and the Oronoco House and Cottages to thank for a first round which nearly tipped the champion's crown off the wabbling head of Sammy Small in the fifteen-stanza bout here at Thirty Acres.

Small is wandering toward his corner like a sleepwalker, wiping his eyes with his glove and staring over a sea of yelling faces toward a single empty chair. He doesn't seem to know what's happened when he sees that chair is empty. His seconds are pulling him onto his stool. And the gossip is that something has happened out back before the boys came on. There's some talk about legal worries, but the inside money says the worries aren't legal. It's a certain little lady who is letting Sammy down. Sammy is saying something to Jake Ledoux, his manager, and looks like he's going to cry. . . . And now the boys are singing "Rainbows." There's no sympathy for a champ that's going down . . . and there's the bell!

Right here before the eyes of a million-dollar throng, through the courtesy of the Mellow Sweet Cigars and the Oronoco House, the hopes of a champion are going. Jones is out of his corner with the gong, and tearing into Sammy. . . . They're in a clinch, and Sammy's mouth is open like a fish. Can you beat it? He's still looking at that empty seat. The referee is breaking 'em. He's got blood on his white silk shirt. . . . Rainbows . . . rainbows . . . It's all a dream to Sammy in that rain of blows . . . heh, heh! . . . And now he's backing off . . . and Jones is after him . . . and now they're yelling "Why don't he fight, the punk?" . . . and Sammy shoots a right to the head with a flash of his old form, as Jones tries to work him into a corner . . . and he bounces a right on Jones's jaw . . . but there's no steam to it. . . . As they clinch, it is clear that one good sock will finish this show. . . . Put . . . him . . . out. . . . Everybody's yelling to put him out.

In one desperate effort to stave off the inevitable, Small steps in and they trade lefts to the heads. . . . Rainbows . . . rainbows . . . he's up there with them now. The welts on Sammy's body look like pancakes. . . . He's hanging on, and now the crowd is yelling, "Yellow." . . .

He don't hear 'em. He's looking out over the first rows, and Jack Hamlin has to holler in his ear. Now they're breaking . . . Jones takes his time . . . he's getting set . . . there he goes. . . . A left to the midsection bends Sammy over, and he tries to cover up; then . . . with a beautiful right . . . Jones connects with the jaw . . . and Small . . . sinks forward . . . on his hands and knees. . . . Hamlin waves Jones to a corner. . . . Jones skips over quick. . . . Oh, baby, hear 'em yell! . . . Hamlin's over Sammy. . . . He's counting in his ear . . . and a champ is going out . . . three . . . a champ is going out . . . five . . . Sammy's bending up . . . seven . . . no — yes, he's coming out of the rainbows . . . eight . . . nine . . . he's up and rocking, and Jones is diving at him, and — there's the bell!

The best minds here agree that the bell saved Sammy Small in the second round, through the courtesy of the Mellow Sweet Cigar Company and the Oronoco House and Cottages. And maybe Sammy doesn't wish he was right there now, nestled 'midst the Blue Ridge ozone, doing the tango instead of smelling the salts.

Jack Hamlin's coming over. I think . . . yes, he's going to stop it. No, Sammy's sitting up! He looks sick, but he's talking fast. . . . Yes, they're going on with it. . . . Ledoux is hollering at Sammy, and Sammy is looking back at that seat. Ledoux has grabbed Sammy's head and turned it away . . . and now the handlers are slapping his face. What with all the color and the romance that I've tried to give you, we find ourselves sitting to watch a light go out.

But . . . say . . . wait a minute. . . . Something's going on. A boy's just come to Sammy's corner with a telegram. Sammy sees it. Ledoux is tearing it open. . . . Now he's reading it out loud. . . . Now Sammy's sitting up like he's had a shot in the arm, and just gazing at that scrap of paper . . . just gazing . . . and now he is sighing . . . relief . . . romance . . . rainbows. . . . As they give him another sniff of the bottle, he pushes it away and — here we go; there's the bell.

I don't know what that wire said — maybe it's nobody's business. . . . Jones comes in with his usual rush . . . and . . . Small straightens him up with a left jab, and now they're in the center of the ring swapping punches . . . and Jones misses . . . and Sammy comes in with a nice right. . . . Don't tell me there isn't anything to love. . . . Sammy jars Jones with two straight lefts. . . . Jones looks startled . . . he can't understand it any more than we do. . . . He comes in just in time to take a right hander . . . and now they're in a clinch . . . and Jones is tired! . . . Yes, Jones is tired. . . . As he attempts to nail Small in another rush, Sammy uncorks an uppercut that sends Jones back a step. . . . The crowd is on its feet . . . and Small follows with a swing to the jaw. . . . Sammy has Jones on the ropes, and Jones tries to clinch as Small pounds at his body. . . . I've never seen an act like this, nor has anybody else. . . . As they break, the crowd is yelling for Sammy, and Small connects with his right. . . . Jones is boring in . . . and . . . Sammy props him off and . . . there he goes again . . . and Sammy nails him with another right to the jaw. . . . And . . .

Jones . . . is . . . down . . . and . . . Sammy takes one look at him
. . . and now he's walking away . . . and Hamlin's counting. . . .
Five . . . six . . . Jones is on his face . . . eight. . . . Sammy looks
over just to see and looks away . . . and now he's commencing to grin
in that boyish way you've seen in his photos and . . . Jones is out!

And Sammy Small, snappy, dapper light-heavy champion of the
world, retains his title by a knockout in the middle of the third round —
I wish I knew what that telegram said — in the middle of the third
round, and you have been present at a first-class fight, through the
courtesy of the Mellow Sweet Cigar Company and the Oronoco House
and Cottages. . . . And now they're dragging out Johnny Jones, the
rocky-jawed contender, still unconscious through the auspices of
Small's sleep-inducing right. . . . And Small is donning his gold-and-
purple kimono, so loved by the followers of good, clean sports. . . .
And I wonder what someone is thinking now . . . I wonder . . . as
another dream man has built another rainbow ladder to the skies. . . .

And now . . . wouldn't we all like to know what Sammy Small has
to say about it? . . . Hey, Sammy! Sammy, will you say a few words
to the radio audience?

Did you hear Sammy Small kindly agreeing to say a few words? And
here he is now, right beside the microphone, with that smile which has
endeared him to so many!

"Aw — shut up!"

Did you hear what Sammy said, friends? That was his own voice.

"G'wan — gimme dat t'ing, for the luva Pete. I can't wait all night."

Did you hear him? That was Sammy Small himself, speaking of the
big treat he has in store for you. Now Sammy will say a word, and
maybe he will tell you something about the rare aroma of the Mellow
Sweet Cigar, and maybe he will tell you something else that every sport
fan wants to hear. . . .

"Aw — cut out that hoke."

That was Sammy Small again. He's in a hurry to get back to his library — eh, Sammy?

All right. I'm giving up the microphone to our own Punching Apollo
— and champion of the world and fighter all the time. Listen to them
giving a hand . . . a big hand . . . to Sammy Small. . . .

"Good evenin', folks. This is Sammy Small speaking. I can't shovel
hoke like that guy can, because socking is my racket — see? I guess

you heard a lot of hooey about me tonight — and I ask you — kindly forget it, see? I don't blame 'em. They're paid for it — no, I ain't gonna give this back. They been telling you off a lot of hooey — see?

"Ladies and gents, I wanta thank you one and all for your kind attention. This has been a good fight and Jones did his best. I wasn't going so good when I got in here, but I'm going all right now. . . . Something is off my mind, which is nobody's business. . . . Well, all I gotta say is I want to thank you one and all for your kind attention. Especially any personal friends who may be listenin' in. They know who. . . . And especially — yeh, especially — I wanna thank a certain little lady, who sent me the telegram tonight. It did me a lot of good to know she took everything I said the way I meant it — see? She understands a guy says things sometimes, I'll say. But I want to thank her for getting it straight, because I think maybe she didn't — see? And I want to thank her particularly for getting what I wish other birds would get — that I'm not the marryin' kind!"

Poor Pan

(1947)

Once I believed, and I fear many writers do still, that one only needed to travel about the world collecting "local color" in order to write of distant places like a Kipling or a Conrad. This, I venture to assert, is not the case. No matter how skilled the author is and no matter what exceptional material he may encounter, his short story or his novel, though accurate and even perceptive, will lack in final authority if he simply goes about the world observing and taking notes and then returning home to put them in finished form. Perhaps it is necessary to make the experiment oneself before realizing that one must have a living stake in the community in order to convey a deep impression of it to others.

I wish heartily that I might have lived for a while in Peking, which was, before the bamboo curtain fell, the most diverting and beautiful city in the world. Unfortunately I have only been there several times as a tourist, though I like to think that I learned more than some of my fellow travelers about the city and its people. If "Poor Pan" has any merit it is because it attempts only to describe China through the eyes of recent arrivals.

You could get air transportation to almost any place you wanted in the postwar Orient, if you were an American, especially if you were a magazine writer, and knew the right people. Jack Spycer had found this out shortly after reaching Manila on his way home from India. There was still room for Americans and American ideas in Manila. It was the first time in weeks that he felt that he was getting close to home.

The man he met who said he could get him to Peking was a sunburned civilian, in a beautifully starched white suit, whose name, Spycer thought, was Chapman Ricks. He either had something to do with the embassy or something to do with surplus war materials. It did not matter which, and his name did not matter either, except that Jack Spycer wished he could be sure of it so that he could write and thank him. The main thing appeared to be that they had some friends in common — the Greens from Westport, Connecticut, who had once told Mr. Ricks all about Jack Spycer. Jack could not remember the Greens very well either, now that their names were pulled out of the past and tossed into Manila, but it seemed that the Greens had told Mr. Ricks, if that was his name, that Jack Spycer was quite a character. At any rate that was what Mr. Ricks kept saying at a cocktail party which Jack Spycer attended on his second afternoon in Manila.

"This is Jack Spycer," Mr. Ricks kept saying. "You know, the writer. He once did a piece about something in China for *Fortune* magazine. I read it personally. We have mutual friends in Westport, Connecticut. Mr. Spycer is quite a character."

The party was out of doors on a lawn in front of one of the few undamaged houses on Dewey Boulevard. The sweltering sun shone on the rusted hulks of sunken ships in Manila Bay, and there was a banyan tree and some oleanders, and a small orchestra was playing from a corner of a veranda. Filipino houseboys were passing cool drinks and *canapés* to unmingling groups of people who gathered in the shade of other unknown trees, a strange assortment of individuals — Filipinos who stood tentatively on the sidelines, American civilians, and army and navy officers and their wives.

"Do you have these parties often here?" Jack Spycer asked.

"Yes, all the time," Mr. Ricks answered. "Do you see that little fat man over there? He personally killed a hundred Japanese. He was one of the key Philippine guerrillas."

"You mean the one in that lace shirt?"

"Yes, that's the one," Mr. Ricks answered. "Now you must meet everyone. Everyone likes to meet strangers."

"Never mind," Jack Spycer said. "I just like to stand here and watch. Don't have me on your mind."

"Of course I have you on my mind," Mr. Ricks said. "What would they say in Westport if you told them you hadn't met everyone? Mrs. Blessington, do you know Jack Spycer? He's the writer, you know. He's quite a character."

Jack Spycer smiled and bowed to Mrs. Blessington, a stoutish lady in lavender who looked very hot.

"Have you ever been in Manila before, Mr. Spycer?" Mrs. Blessington asked.

"No," Jack Spycer answered, "I'm sorry to say I haven't."

"It's a pity you didn't see it before the war. It's so heartbreaking now. It used to be a beautiful city. How long are you going to stay in Manila, Mr. Spycer?"

"Only for a little while, I'm sorry to say," he answered. "You see, I'm on my way home."

"If you're a writer, I suppose you're collecting local color. Have you ever been in the East before, Mr. Spycer?"

"Yes," he said, "I was in China once — in Peking. That was around 1936, but it doesn't seem as long ago as that."

"They call it Peiping now, don't they?" Mrs. Blessington asked.

"Yes," he said, "I know, but I like the old name better. I hoped I might see Peking again, but it seems pretty hard to get there."

"It isn't hard to get anywhere," said Mr. Ricks, "if you want to go badly enough. Do you really want to go to Peking, enough to leave tonight?"

"Tonight?" Jack Spycer repeated.

Mr. Ricks grasped him by the arm. "Just come with me," he said. "You can go anywhere you want to these days."

He led the way across the lawn toward a group of army officers who stood on the veranda.

"Oh, General," Mr. Ricks said, "may I interrupt you for a minute?"

Mr. Ricks clearly knew his way around. He was addressing a three-star general whose gray hair was clipped in a crew cut.

"Why, of course, Chapman," the general said. "You can interrupt me any time, Chapman."

"Then just step over here for a minute, will you?" said Mr. Ricks. "I want you to meet a close personal friend of mine. This is Jack Spycer, you know, the writer. We have mutual friends in Westport, Connecticut. You know who General Jenks is, don't you, Jack?"

Obviously neither of them knew who the other was.

"Now, General," Mr. Ricks said, "have you got any room in that plane of yours tonight?"

"Yes," the general answered, "a little room."

"All right," Mr. Ricks answered, "that's all I wanted to know. Jack here wants to get to Peking. You're going to Peking, aren't you?"

"Yes," the general answered, "Peking is on my itinerary."

"Well, Jack here wants to see it," Mr. Ricks said. "He's a close personal friend of mine. He used to live in Peking. If you've got room, you wouldn't mind taking him, would you?"

"You say he's a writer, Chapman?" the general asked.

"Yes," Mr. Ricks said. "You know, Jack Spycer, the well-known writer. He's an old China hand. He can tell you all about Peking."

"All right," the general said. "If you can clear him and get him on the plane by ten tonight."

"You see," Mr. Ricks said, "if you just stick around with me you can hook a ride almost anywhere. Don't thank me. I'll get you to the airport. Now let's go around and meet some more people. This is Jack Spycer, the writer. He wrote a piece about China once in *Fortune* magazine."

That was how Jack Spycer started back to Peking after an eleven years' absence — being introduced by an almost complete stranger to a three-star general named Jenks who happened to have Peking on his itinerary. They would be in Peking for a few hours and back in Manila in four days' time.

"It's all right," Mr. Ricks said. "You're cleared, and you won't have any trouble if you stay with the party."

It was all out of his hands and there was nothing that he had to do.

"It's good luck," Mr. Ricks said. "This is about the last army plane that will go there. We're closing operations at the airport. The rollup's nearly over in North China."

Yes, they were telling him in Manila, the rollup was nearly over. The last of the marines were due to leave at almost any time. In a few weeks there would be no more legation guard, no nothing, in Peking.

"If everybody's leaving," Jack Spycer asked, "why does the general want to go there?" But Chapman Ricks did not know why, except that of course there was some reason, and he added:

"Maybe he wants to see someone, or maybe some friend of his left something at the Wagons-Lits Hotel and asked him to pick it up. I wouldn't ask why he's going if I were you."

He was only convinced that he was going to Peking when the door closed and the plane was moving down the runway for the take-off.

The plane's interior was very comfortable, obviously especially designed for high officers, who needed rest. It had two washrooms, a small kitchen, curtained berths, and seats facing each other with tables between them. The general, three officers, and he were the only passengers, and the general had gone forward to his own quarters. The officers, who glanced at Jack Spycer without any curiosity, had not been introduced to him, and now they had withdrawn to a table to start a game of gin rummy. Only one of them spoke to him after the plane leveled off, a sallow lieutenant colonel with a close-cropped mustache.

"I'm afraid you'll have to sit up," the lieutenant colonel said, raising his voice above the drumming of the motors. "There aren't enough berths to go around."

He answered, raising his voice also, that he did not mind in the least sitting up, and that he was very grateful they were taking him at all.

"Oh, it's no trouble," the lieutenant colonel said. "Someone often gets aboard the last minute." Then he returned to the card game, leaving Jack Spycer alone, looking out of a window into blackness.

As a civilian of course he had no rank, and he could see that he would be no trouble as long as he did not need a bed.

The plane was carrying him not only over dark islands and oceans but backward also through time. The sound of the motors and their vibration reminded him of the drumming in his ears when an ether cone had once been placed over his face. He had said that he would come back to Peking again — and a great many people must have made the same promise in their last hours in that city — and he had meant it quite seriously at the time. It was only after you had left there that such a promise faded into unreality like one's memory of the pavilions of the Forbidden City or the white dagoba near the marble bridge. You said and you meant certain things in Peking that had no validity afterwards. They were all left with their echoes to form a part of the brooding silence of the clear North China air, a silence which somehow persisted in spite of the ceaseless human hum that rose above the city day and night.

There was an excuse for not being consistent about what you said or did there, because everyone in some small way was a part of a work of art. Looking back, it was as though one had actually dwelt for a while in one of those magnificent landscapes of the Sung Dynasty, removed from fact but giving at the same time a complete illusion of naturalistic reality. The mountains, on those silken scrolls, the temples on the hill-tops, the little villages, you would realize were exactly like the mountains and villages and temples of the Western Hills. There were no other hills in the world as bare or as dusty, no colors like their colors in a sunset. There was nothing quite like the ageless serenity that set Peking apart from other cities. War and famine might disturb its surface but never its tolerance, which was as pure and indestructible as the thought of ancient Greece. There was hidden meaning everywhere that the mind could sense without grasping. There was mysticism, in the angles of the broad streets. The Imperial City, the Tartar City, and the Chinese City, and the Bell Tower and the Drum Tower, were all units in an occult plan. Even the Legation Quarter, and the railroad station by the water gate, did not affect its unity. Every day there were new sights and sounds that one had never seen or heard before, and yet nothing ever changed essentially.

Chinese, and Europeans, too, beginning with Marco Polo, have tried to express something of what Jack Spycer was thinking, without very much success. All he was sure of was that anyone who had ever been to Peking had left something of himself there that belonged nowhere else.

He could see himself in the two courtyards he had rented of what had once been a small fraction of a Manchu bannerman's house. He could see the dusty hutung winding between the grimy gray walls that shut out so successfully all the varied life behind them. He could see his own freshly painted red door in one of the walls swing open, and there was the spirit screen behind it, with the potted flowers on either side, and behind that was a ginko tree and his goldfish pool. He had bought some beautiful goldfish, he remembered. He could see them still in the greenish water beneath the lily pads. There was a Dragon Fish, and a Heaven Aspiring Fish with a triple tail and bulging upturned eyes. He could see his Number One Boy Chang in his white gown and slippers, a tall man with the high cheekbones of the North Chinese, ten years his senior although he was his boy. Spycer had only been twenty-six at the time and he had been a fool ever to come to Peking in the first place, and Chang had probably often thought he was a fool, although he had never said so or implied it. But Chang had known everything about him, more than anyone else had ever known, down to the last copper in his bank account. Chang had to keep track of these matters out of self-interest, because he was a frugal, ambitious boy.

"When your money go, you no stop," Chang said.

He remembered that Chang had three long whiskers jutting from his chin, a sign of erudition.

"I can easily make some more," he would tell him in those times when Chang was worried.

"Oh, yes, marster," Chang said, and he never knew whether Chang believed him or not.

He had intended to support himself by writing, which was his reason for coming to Peking in the first place. It was amazing how many people had drifted there with similar ideas. There was his friend Arthur White, for instance, but then Arthur had an independent income. He remembered the room he called his study, with the Tibetan carpets and the red-lacquered desk, which he had bought himself on Furniture Street. His portable typewriter always rested on it, ready with pencils and a heap of yellow paper. Furthermore, he knew just what he was going to do, and he had always intended to start the next morning. His main effort was to be expended on a long book, the first volume of a trilogy. He was even able to quote unwritten parts of it at evening parties.

"I came here to do some writing," he used to say. "I had to get away from Hollywood." It gave Jack a place in the little European world that once had existed so happily within the Chinese city — and in its broadest sense the statement had been almost true. Just before he had come to Peking, and when he was still twenty-five, he had written a short story which had been accepted by the *Saturday Evening Post*, and furthermore its motion picture rights had actually been purchased by a Hollywood studio for five thousand dollars. That was his only contact with Hollywood — a tenuous connection. Yet he often found himself implying that he had to escape because he was a literary artist who could not prostitute his intellect.

He had to get away from Hollywood, but if he had ever faced facts squarely he would have known two weeks after he had left the Wagons-Lits Hotel and had sublet those two courtyards from a strange lady named Mrs. Percival Clyde — the one who had that curio shop called

Things Chinese in the Legation Quarter — that he never was going to write a word in Peking. It would have been a waste of time to have sat writing, even at a red-lacquer desk, when there was so much going on outside. He was distracted by all the mysterious noises beyond the walls, the song of the melon vender, the gong of the barber, and the tap tap of the rag merchant. He always started thinking of Hatamen Street and the Ch'ienmun Gate, of the shaggy lines of camels with their panniers full of coals, of the rickshaws and the creaking carts pulled by sweating men, and the intricate pageantry of weddings and funerals, and then there were the parties and the races and the week ends in the Western Hills. The truth was, in Peking he was an acknowledged literary figure without having to write. Besides, there was plenty of precedent among many brilliant people there for doing nothing. Yes, he had been a literary figure and a patron of the arts, in the city of Peking. And all that side of him was left there, along with his heavy possessions, as fresh in his memory still as moss in the moss jade from Jade Street.

Of course when he had finished his trilogy, or perhaps when he had it all blocked clearly in his mind, he had also planned to write about Peking, as he often announced at those late-evening parties. Distance had made him a man of letters and anyone in the Legation Quarter who cared to might examine the copy of the *Saturday Evening Post* with his story in it. And since they threw money around in Hollywood, the motion picture rights had obviously been snapped up for a fabulous sum. Also there was a rumor that Colman and Garbo were going to star in the script, and when he denied knowing anything about it, he was not sure that even Arthur White quite believed him. Five thousand dollars, though not a large sum in America, used to go a long way in Peking.

The beauty of it was that he could gain a perspective in Peking on his trilogy, which dealt with American life, while at the same time he could gather all sorts of new ideas from a stimulating environment. People kept asking — it was strange how polite conversation invariably fell into a pattern — when they might expect to see a book from Mr. Spycer's pen on China. Well, well . . . give him time. Time was what ripens apples.

He would shine especially at the end of long evenings when congenial people, like Arthur White, and Hugh Garrity, who represented one of the wire services, and Elsie Fentress, who did the etchings that

Mr. Vetch had for sale at his shop in the Hotel de Pekin, and Waldron Summerfield, who was there to buy porcelain for a New York dealer, and the Desborough girls, and Captain and Fifi Gordon from the British Embassy (and later, of course, Cynthia Mark), used to gather in someone's courtyard.

"I suppose you're gathering material," one of the Desborough girls, or someone else, would say. Cynthia Mark had referred to it as local color, but he could not recall that it had grated on his nerves when Cynthia had used this amateurish phrase.

Of course he was collecting *material* — not local color. He could catalogue and collate this material, too, particularly when he was a little tight. (It was remarkable how much you could drink in that climate without its really affecting you. In fact people in the British-American Tobacco crowd at the Peking Club, and other old inhabitants, were careful to point out that whisky and water killed dysentery germs.) Of course he was collecting material, and those people in the lantern light were too naïve to understand that they were contributing as much to his creative future as the acrobats and jugglers on the Road to the Temple of Heaven, or the old men taking their song birds out for an airing on the edge of the Nan Hai, or the young men practicing with their two-handed swords. Of course he was going to write a book about it someday. Next week he would really start making notes while all these new sights and sounds were fresh. He had his notebooks ready, with his Chinese name embossed upon them.

He was tired of the trite remark that everyone when he first came to Peking wanted to write a book and later found he could not because Chinese life became too confusing. Confusion would not interfere with his book. It was not going to be one of those superficial, Anglicized novels, like *Peking Picnic*, or a fragile tale, like *Wang the Ninth*, or a portentous generality, like *The Good Earth*. Admitting that Pearl Buck knew "her" China, she did not know the right part of it, unfortunately. His book would be a distillation of all the sights and sounds, of the patience that dealt in centuries, of the perennial beauty that was around him, but on original lines. It would be the one work which would at last capture the spirit of that city and subtly contrast its cultivation to the posturings of vapid Europeans who could neither see nor understand what riches lay before them. Even Arthur White, Jack Spycer was afraid, could not understand China, though he had a Chinese teacher every morning and kept cards of Chinese characters in his pockets.

There was lots of time for thought, but curiously little for serious writing in Peking, because the physical act of writing impeded observation. He wanted to know the city first and to evaluate his impressions. It was a city of impeccable manners and of such successive layers of polite precedent derived from its thousand-year contact with Chinese imperial courts that courtesy and formality governed the life of the lowest sweeper. When you came to learn a little Chinese, you found that the simplest phrases reflected a millennium of culture. If men jostled each other, passing through the crowded gates, they said — and it was not so hard to pick up Chinese phrases — "I disturb your chariot."

"Monseigneur," the beggars chanted, exquisitely trained beggars, members of a proud and ancient guild. "Monseigneur," and they held out their hands or displayed their deformities and abrasions. The Peking carts with their blue awnings and nail-studded wheels were exactly the same as the cart models exhumed from tombs in the Han Dynasty. Then there were all those busy craftsmen, working in cinnabar lacquer, jade and ivory, whose forebears were brought to Peking by Yung Lo and later Ch'ien Lung to ply their trades for the emperor's amusement. You could watch them in the back streets if you wanted, and did you know that the crossbow makers still made good and handy crossbows somewhere near the Drum Tower?

There was everything in Peking if you had time to find it. There were connoisseurs of chrysanthemums, collectors of rare goldfish, the calligraphers who spent secluded lives, with their ink blocks and brushes, perfecting their skill in writing Chinese characters. They were all there in Peking. Small skills and great (but each an art in itself) were all exquisitely mingled. There were the stilt dancers, the conjurers, the fortune tellers. There was the man with the trained mice, and the famous cooks in the ancient restaurants, and actors who represented the almost agonizing refinements of the drama. There were the sellers of singing crickets and fighting crickets, each insect in its tiny wicker cage. Each of these men contributed to make life there, if you only had the time to taste it all and understand it, infinitely polite and leisurely. There might be war outside the walls and bandits in the Western Hills, but the life within the walls went on. Of course there was no time for writing. There was only time to live.

Later, back at home, especially during the hectic years just before Pearl Harbor, Jack Spycer kept hearing about "gracious living," but nobody understood gracious living as he had known it in Peking. Once in the house of one of his Chinese acquaintances, a Mr. Wong, who collected and sometimes sold scroll paintings, Jack had met an American missionary named Quentin Bock, who had disapproved of certain aspects of European conduct in Peking. Foreign residents there, Mr. Bock said, were being blinded and weakened by a conspiracy of Chinese service. It was well to remember, Mr. Bock said, that this insinuating service, always pandering to the foreigner's tastes and natural sloth, was an instinct with Chinese. It was the greatest weapon of this passive people, one with which they had reduced the Ming invaders and the Manchus to helplessness after a few generations. In time, if you let your Chinese boys have their way, you would be maneuvered inscrutably into a beautiful cell, insulated from all reality, growing so dependent on the ministrations of others as to become incapable of independent thought or action. That was what happened, Mr. Bock said, to many foreigners in Peking.

It was an unpleasant way of putting it, but true or not, it was a glorious surrender. Jack Spycer had never known there could be so many nuances in daily routine until Chang, his Number One Boy, had taught him — Chang's family had been Legation Quarter servants for two generations.

Jack Spycer had previously been accustomed to family life in an American small town, and later to a straitened existence in New York apartments and restaurants. He had never before been introduced to the complications of a perfectly appointed dinner table. There had never been a man in a white robe and slippers to run his tub and to lay out his clothing and to help him with his dressing. There had never been a man to hurry with a drink when he called for it or to run anywhere on little errands, fetching the tailor or small merchants to display their wares, bringing potted plants or song birds or crickets, anything he desired. It only took a little while to become accustomed to all this in Peking. This was the pattern of life, and it would have been ridiculous to have lived otherwise; and Chang would have been very much hurt had he attempted it because Chang had his own reputation to maintain that depended directly on his master's.

When Jack Spycer gave an incorrect order or demanded some un-

orthodox economy, he was grateful when Chang set him right, not that
Chang was ever impertinent or pushing. Chang simply pointed out that
certain ways of doing things were *bu shing*, not suitable for someone in
the master's scholarly position. Chang knew the proper wines and where
to get them, and the correct courses for a small dinner or for a larger
buffet luncheon, and if a larger party were indicated, Chang's family
and friends would always help with it. You could leave it all to Chang.
Chang knew the proper tailor and the way a dinner coat should hang,
though surely he had never worn one. When Jack Spycer took up riding, Chang even knew how riding breeches should be cut and where
two white northern ponies could be bought for very little money. You
could leave it all to Chang.

When Jack Spycer grew to be proud and fond of Chang, he liked to
think that Chang was sometimes proud and a little fond of him. He
never forgot Chang's smile when the first invitation came from Sir
Stanford Gates to a dinner at the Legation Quarter. He was aware of
Chang's intense relief when Lady Maud asked him to sit in her pavilion
at the races and when he became a member of the Club. He could remember the happy faces of Chang and all the other boys when Sir Stanford and Lady Maud and the American explorer Dr. Bixby came to
dinner. He could leave it all to Chang. The soup was always perfect,
the sherry was always dry, and though the bills kept rising, it was
worth it.

He could still remember how all his servants had looked as they
waited near the gate before he left for somewhere in the evening. There
was Ma, the rickshaw boy, and Sung, the yardboy, and Ho, the cook,
and Liu, his assistant. They would all be standing by the gate, in the
cool of a summer evening, and Chang would speak for all of them, in
his quaint, telegraphic English.

"Be happy, marster," Chang would say, and Ma would step between
the rickshaw shafts. Ma was a beautiful runner.

It made him proud to be asked how he had ever found a boy like
Chang, and prouder still when others sometimes said, after one of those
little dinners, that Chang was one of the best Number One Boys in Peking. Older residents also asked shrewd questions about Chang's ac-
counting methods, and how much squeeze Chang got. Of course he was
aware that Chang had his fingers in every piece of household business,
like every other Number One Boy, but Chang surely did not cheat

him much. At least Chang had a perfect instinct of just how far to go. Chang had given him more than he had ever given Chang. Chang had given him a sense of personal dignity, something he had never known before and something that one often needed when one was twenty-six. If it had not been for Chang, and that sense of assurance which Chang had given him, Jack Spycer would never have thought it possible that he could be interesting to anyone like Cynthia Mark, or to her parents, Mr. and Mrs. Jerrod Mark.

In any other place in the world, their wealth would have made it impossible for him to have met them on an equal footing. In any other place, as he understood often afterwards, Mr. and Mrs. Mark, and perhaps Cynthia, too, would have seen him as he was, a gauche, shy boy, with no prospects and with mediocre abilities and ambitions, but it was different in Peking. There, he could actually afford to be condescending to the Marks. He was an old inhabitant, that amazing spring, with his own house and servants, with his own position, and the Marks were only simple tourists, with a suite in the Wagons-Lits.

Arthur White introduced them, he remembered. Arthur always had an absurd and slightly objectionable way of seeking out people off cruise boats. He appeared with the Mark family one morning in mid May just after ten o'clock, a surprising hour for Arthur or anyone else to come to call. Though Jack was still in his pajamas and a blue-silk Chinese robe, he had finished his breakfast. He was sitting at his desk doing something that he had meant to do for some weeks, examining his balance in the North China Bank and planning what to about it. There was only a little over eighteen hundred dollars gold left in his account, enough to keep him for a while but not enough for an easy mind. It was high time that he wrote another story for the *Saturday Evening Post*, and perhaps, he was thinking, this should be the morning to start it.

He had several ideas for stories, and the best, in his opinion, was one in which the action took place on an ocean liner. He had the beginning quite clear in his mind, the smoking room and four men playing bridge, one of them a professional gambler. He could even think of the opening sentence. "The fat, pale man with the heavy, nimble fingers allowed the lids to droop lazily over his eyes as he arranged the cards." This, of course, would be the gambler. The gambler's name would be Sam Rood, and he was such a promising character that one could conceivably build a series of stories around his activities, at five hundred dollars a story, turning one out each ten days. Jack had gone this far and he might have gone even further if Arthur White had not entered unannounced from the sunny courtyard, raising his feet over the high threshold almost like a Chinese actor.

"Hello, Jack," Arthur said. "You're not in the throes of composition, are you?"

He and Arthur were always talking about writing, but he could not recall that either had ever discovered the other in the throes of composition.

"Well, not exactly," Jack answered. "I was just getting some ideas together. It's about time I did something. You see, Chang is getting worried."

"Chang's always worried," Arthur said. "Go ahead and put on some clothes. Don't worry."

They were old friends by then and there was no reason not to be frank so he picked up the North China Bank envelope and explained that more than half his savings were gone. Of course Arthur did not have to be bothered by those things because Arthur had an independent income, but it was time to do some work.

"Listen," Arthur said, "I hate to be a disrupting influence, and you know I'm usually not, don't you, but you have to help me today, really. It's a picnic to the Summer Palace."

This was a side of Arthur that he could not understand. Those picnics at the Summer Palace were something to be indulged in by newcomers to Peking. It even occurred to him that Arthur had lately been developing a domineering manner that was increasingly difficult to contend with. Without wanting to be disagreeable, Jack did want for once to do some work.

"Now don't say you can't," Arthur said, "because of course you can. Get up and put on some clothes. I have some people outside and a car and everything, and I can't leave them out there waiting."

"People?" Jack said. "What people?"

"I've told them all about you," Arthur said. "Please don't argue but go and get dressed, and hurry, and I'll bring them in, and I think it would be nice if Chang got them some tea, don't you! I wish you'd pull yourself together, Jack. They might be disturbed if they saw you in that robe. Their name is Mark. They are positively rolling in riches and they want to see a Chinese house. They're just in off the boat. They're staying at the Wagons-Lits. They had letters to Elizabeth Llewellyn. I met them at Elizabeth's."

Arthur looked self-conscious, and for no good reason, because everyone knew Arthur and Mrs. Llewellyn and everyone kept wondering how anyone her age could so attract young men. Jack was very glad that it was Arthur who was in her orbit and that he had avoided any such complication.

"I'm doing it for Elizabeth," Arthur went on. "Elizabeth can't go today because she has a touch of Peking guts and I promised her that I'd get you. It's Mr. and Mrs. Jerrod Mark — he's a banker from St. Louis — and their daughter Cynthia. They want to see a Chinese house, and Elizabeth wants you to be nice to Cynthia."

It was annoying because, unlike Arthur, he did not have to do everything that Mrs. Llewellyn wanted, and though she had asked him to he had never called her Elizabeth. She was Arthur's problem, not his problem, and if she wanted him to be nice to a strange girl named Cynthia it must have been because she was afraid that Arthur would be.

"If they wanted to see a Chinese house, why didn't you show them yours?" he asked.

"Because they wanted to see a palace," Arthur said, "and Elizabeth told them yours was part of a Manchu palace. Please get dressed while I bring them in, and please ask for some tea. They are very nice people, even if they do come from St. Louis."

It occurred to him that this was inappropriate coming from Arthur, since Arthur had arrived in Peking from Cedar Rapids, but then Arthur was trying, as many others in Peking were, to be a citizen of the world.

"And I think," Arthur said, "or at least Elizabeth thinks, that they're a little worried about Cynthia, and you know how Elizabeth is when strangers come with letters. She does everything for them, simply everything."

"Did you have a letter to Elizabeth?" Jack asked. It was not entirely kind, though he said it in a jovial way, and Arthur, though he was a man of the world, blushed slightly.

"I wish you wouldn't be so funny," Arthur said. "You have such a mordant wit, haven't you? If you want to know the story, or what Elizabeth thinks is the story, they've come out here because they want Cynthia to forget some man."

Whether it was true or not, that would be the story, and there had to be a story about everyone in Peking. Jack Spycer rose and called to Chang.

"Chang," he said, "get tea. Some people are coming in."

That was what he called them, some people. Some strange, vulgar people from St. Louis were coming in, and he had to get dressed and entertain them just because Arthur's great friend, Mrs. Elizabeth Llewellyn, had eaten something which was giving her intestinal difficulties. It was annoying, but after all an old inhabitant like himself, who had been six months in the city, had to be kind, and tolerant toward fellow countrymen.

The window in his bedroom had paper panes, so that he could hear them clearly in the courtyard. They were saying those obvious things that tourists always said. He could hear a man's deep, resonant voice asking why there was a short brick wall built in front of the main gate.

"Now, Jerrod," he heard a woman answer, "it's what they called a spirit screen. It's what keeps evil spirits from the house."

Then he heard another voice, lighter and more musical.

"Oh, Mums, look at the popeyed goldfish, except he isn't gold, he's black."

He was getting into the pepper-and-salt suit which he had brought with him from New York, standing before the mirror looking for a tie, when he saw Chang's face behind him.

"More better, more ploper, you wear the new suit, marster," Chang said, in a soothing, beguiling tone.

It was the first hint Jack received that the Marks might become more than tourists in his life. Chang had already opened the closet and was getting out the dove-gray suit which Mr. Wu, the tailor, had made, largely under Chang's direction. Now Chang was dusting invisible specks from it. Now he was holding the neatly creased trousers in front of Jack Spycer, giving them an inviting little shake.

"Very ploper number one people," Chang said. "Very rich."

It would have done no good to have asked Chang how he knew. There was a grapevine of communication with every European house, and Chang was always right. Chang was getting out his gray-suède shoes. He was picking out his tie.

"More better I tie it, marster," Chang said.

It was more better. Ties never wrinkled or drifted to one side when Chang arranged them. There was no doubt that the suit fitted well, though the cut was more European than American. There was no doubt that it looked much better than the ready-made clothes he had discarded. In fact he looked unfamiliar to himself in the mirror, slender, prosperous, and aesthetic.

"Number one nice suit," Chang said.

The visitors were still in the courtyard when Jack stepped over the high red threshold of his living room and walked down the steps to meet them.

"Well, here he is," Arthur said, and he remembered what Cynthia said some time afterwards.

"You looked so impressive, dear, suddenly emerging out of that Chinese building, with Chang, all in white, just behind you. Mums said you didn't look American at all."

But Mr. Mark looked American. He was heavy-jowled, with dark hair receding from his temples, and dark-gray eyes under bushy eyebrows. He wore a herringbone business suit and he fanned himself with an expensive panama hat. Beside him, Mrs. Mark looked small, active and uncertain.

"It's kind of you to let Mr. White bring us here so suddenly," Mrs. Mark said. "It's such a privilege to have a glimpse of native life instead of just seeing temples and temples. Isn't it, Jerrod?"

"It certainly is," Mr. Mark said. "You look comfortable here, Mr. Spycer. I wouldn't have thought there'd be a hideaway like this off a little back alley like the one outside."

Jack found himself laughing easily and saying that the hutungs all looked like that, nothing but gray walls and gates.

"What's that word?" Mr. Mark asked. "Hutung?"

Arthur was the one who explained it. The side streets in Peking were all called hutungs, and the most beautiful places were on the most unprepossessing streets.

"And this is our daughter, Cynthia," Mrs. Mark said.

Her voice suggested that Cynthia must be their only child and that Mrs. Llewellyn was probably right — the Marks were worried about Cynthia. She was small and straight, like Mrs. Mark. Her dress was white. Her hands were delicate and slender. Her dark-blue eyes at the moment had a guileless look that was contradicted by the self-conscious twist of her deep-red lips. Her hair must have been light once, but now it was a dark rich gold.

"Oh, hello," Cynthia said.

"How do you do," Jack answered. "It's so nice of you to come."

"Thanks for saying so," Cynthia answered. She smiled faintly, and Mrs. Mark spoke hastily.

"Cynthia was admiring the fish in that little pool, Mr. Spycer."

"Oh, yes," said Cynthia. "Take me over and tell me about those poor popeyed fish." And she turned on her heel and walked toward the fish pond.

"Cynthia," Mr. Mark said.

"Now, Jerrod," Mrs. Mark said softly.

"I wouldn't call them poor fish, exactly," Jack said as he followed her. "As a matter of fact, they're rather elaborate fish, with long pedigrees. Those ones with popeyes are called Heaven Aspiring Fish, and those with big heads I think are Imperial Dragons."

She did not answer but kept gazing at the greenish water of the pool.

"Cynthia," Mr. Mark was calling.

"Yes," Cynthia called back, and then she asked, "Who's this White person who's guiding us around?"

"Arthur?" Jack answered. "Oh, Arthur's a friend of mine, a writer."

"Are you a writer?"

"Well, just in a small way," Jack said. "I'm trying to be a writer."

"Well, he has a mother complex with that Llewellyn woman. Yes, Dad," she called, "we're coming. . . ."

"Mrs. Llewellyn is kind to young people," Jack said, and he laughed. "Wait, here's your tea."

Chang was in front of them, with two cups on his tray.

"Missy like tea?" he asked softly. "Number one nice China tea."

"This is Chang," Jack told her. "Chang's my Number One Boy. I couldn't get on without Chang."

"Missy like fish?" Chang asked. "Marster will send Missy two number one fish to the Wagons-Lits Hotel."

"Cynthia," Mr. Mark called across the courtyard, "we ought to leave now, and you haven't seen the house."

Arthur White and the Marks were coming down the steps from the living room. Chang called out an order and Sung, the yardboy, trotted to the gate and Ho and Liu came out of the kitchen. When Chang handed him his hat, his face was expressionless and serene, but at the same time approving.

"Good-by," Chang said. "Be happy, marster."

When Jack Spycer saw an antiquated limousine outside the gate and a smaller car behind it to convey picnic hampers and two of Mrs. Llewellyn's houseboys, he knew that this would be one of Arthur's more ambitious Summer Palace picnics. The Marks sat on the musty back seat of the limousine and Arthur and Jack on the folding seats. When the cars emerged from the hutung into Hatamen Street there was not much opportunity for connected conversation, for every word was punctuated by the sound of the horns, which the Chinese chauffeurs loved to operate.

"Do they always keep tooting like this?" Mr. Mark asked.

"Yes, sir, and there doesn't seem to be any way to stop them," Arthur answered.

"Well, I can stand it if they can," Mr. Mark said.

Jack always disliked listening to strangers talk while riding through Peking. A large wedding procession was moving under a wooden arch called a *peilo*, by the Hotel de Pekin but the inevitable questions and Arthur's answers spoiled the glittering pageant. He wanted to stare in silence at the marble causeway leading to the pink walls and the shining yellow-tiled pavilions of the Forbidden City, but Mr. Mark did not allow him the chance.

"What is it you do, Mr. Spycer?"

"Well, I try to write, sir."

"You must do well at it," Mr. Mark said, "to keep up an establishment like that."

"Well, I've had a little luck lately, sir."

"Where do your writings appear, Mr. Spycer?"

"Well, occasionally," Jack said, "I write for the *Saturday Evening Post*." Now he wanted to watch the walls of the Imperial City, and the trees bordering the Nan Hai.

"I've always heard they pay well," Mr. Mark said. "When is your next article coming out in the *Post?*"

The word article made Jack wince.

"I write short stories, sir. I'm just starting another one."

"What are those men making over there?" Cynthia asked. "They look like coffins."

"Yes," Arthur answered, "they are coffins."

"Peking must be a wonderful place to write in," Mrs. Mark said. "There's so much local color, so many odd sights and sounds."

"And smells," Mr. Mark said. "Don't forget the smells. What are those men eating, those ones with the skullcaps squatting on the sidewalk?"

"Bean curd, sir," Jack said.

"Well, I'll be waiting to see it in a story, but don't forget the smells."

It seemed to be the fixed idea of tourists that Peking should smell. They kept insisting that it smelled, when it didn't. It was dusty in the shadow of the Hsi Chih Men Gate, but even with all the sweating tangle of the farmers and their produce it did not smell.

"Oh," Mrs. Mark said, "why, we're outside the city."

Of course they were outside the city. The gate and the curtain of the city wall were directly behind them. These outlanders did not even know that the Imperial Summer Palace was seven miles beyond the city on the way to the Western Hills. Arthur was beginning his lecture on the Summer Palace, its history and its plan. Jack felt himself squirming in his folding seat. Arthur always enjoyed lecturing. Jack could not avoid hearing scraps of it, even when he tried to keep his full attention on the Peking carts and the peasants in blue-denim gowns carrying their burdens along the dusty road. The Hill of the Ten Thousand Ancients, the Garden of Peaceful Enjoyment. There would be no great crowd today. They would have lunch at the Pleasure Garden, by the summer houses at the edge of the deep pool, beloved by Ch'ien Lung and about which he had written a verse. The Dowager Empress . . . she was the last one to rebuild the Summer Palace . . . the marble boat . . . she built that with the appropriations intended for the Chinese navy. He listened with his back turned, still studying the sights along the road.

He was sure that it would be a terrible day until he realized that nothing could entirely spoil the Summer Palace. It was the most perfect scene for escape in the world. Its steps and gardens, its pools and temples and pavilions, always revealed some new refinement. Its courtyards and its galleries, its magnolia trees, the artificial lake with its Dragon King's Island, made Marie Antoinette's Petit Trianon seem a poor thing by comparison. There was always a curtain of oblivion around the Summer Palace that made you forget the disturbed condition of the rest of China, just as the old empress had been able to forget.

It may have been that plans were made that left him and Cynthia Mark alone together after lunch, or perhaps he had asked her if she cared to walk awhile. At any rate, Mrs. Mark had said it would be lovely for Cynthia to drink in quietly some of the beauty of the place, because she could see Mr. Spycer drinking in the beauty. He could not remember step by step because the day had seemed to start when he and Cynthia were walking alone, behind a group of Chinese students, through a long gallery with oddly shaped latticed windows, to the marble boat. He remembered being relieved that they simply walked and stopped and looked without her asking questions. She said that she did not want to be told anything more, that she was tired of lectures, she always forgot them.

"I don't care if they arranged it for us," Cynthia said, "as long as we can stay away."

She said the only way to make the family happy was for her to pretend to be amused, and now, thank heaven, she could take a little time off from pretending.

"They want me to get my mind off something that happened," she said, "and the more they try, the more my mind stays on it."

They were walking along the edge of the lake, toward the Seventeen Arch Bridge leading to the Dragon King's Island, when he finally asked her point-blank what it was that had happened, not that she had to tell him. But she did not mind telling him at all. She had met a Man in New York who had wanted to marry her, and it really would not have made so much difference if the family had just taken it naturally. If you wanted to know the truth, she had not dreamed of taking this Man seriously until the family got hot and bothered and began making scenes about him, because they said he was a mere adventurer who was after money. And then one day they went off together, she and this Man. She did it just to show the family, and Pops caught them right in front of the minister's house at Elkton. She did it just to show them, and then they had sent her to Dr. Shrewsbury, a psychiatrist, who had told the family that she needed a change of scene, in order to orient herself, and an opportunity to meet more Men in a natural way.

"I don't know why I should tell you all this," she said, "except it does me good to think out loud. You can put it in a story sometime."

Artistically, it was not much of a story. He often thought he would not have been impressed by it at any other place, but at the Summer Palace her artless true confession, with all its irrelevant details, mingled with pictures of the willows and the sunlight on the lake and with the shadows of the pagoda and the temples on the hill. Walking through the grounds of the Summer Palace was always like walking through the scenes on a Chinese screen. None of it would have happened, she said, if the family had ever let her alone to develop. They must have been near the arched bridge and just about to cross over to the Dragon King's Island when he realized that he was jealous of that other man.

"What's his name?" he asked.

It didn't matter what his name was. His first name was Charlie. By the time they were halfway across the bridge, the shade of Charlie was following them.

"I wish you'd get him out of your mind," he said. "Look over at the mountain, and forget about Charlie."

"He was out of my mind until you brought him up," she said. "I like your tie." She raised her long-fingered hand and touched it. "It stays straight. Charlie could never tie his tie right."

It made very little sense — perhaps those boy-meets-girl dialogues never did — but somewhere in the Summer Palace their shadows must be walking still, with other greater shadows.

They were sitting in a summer house that was shabby from the weather, gazing across the lake, neither saying anything, but contented with their silence, and he kissed Cynthia Mark. For the first time in a long while no one had been near them, no Chinese women with their children, no Japanese in their European clothes, no noisy little boys. He remembered thinking that something of the sort might do her good and cheer her up, but his philanthropic attitude changed as soon as she was in his arms.

"Oh, dear," Cynthia whispered, "I've come off all over you," and she had laughed when he did not understand her.

"Lipstick, silly," she said. "Here. Give me your handkerchief. No, don't you do it. I can."

It was strange how little the years had impaired the memory of those trivial details.

"It's just what Mums used to do when I had a smudge on the end of my nose," she said. "Now I've got to fix my face. Here." And she gave him back his handkerchief.

Then she said they'd better see the Temple of the Dragon. Then, as they were walking back across the bridge, she told him that they would be in Peking for two months and that there would be a dance at the hotel that night and the family would love it if he took her. She felt sure that they approved of him. She was glad they had stopped at his house and had seen the way he lived.

"And now," she said, "is my face on straight?"

Her face was on very straight. A dab of powder had been neatly distributed over her thin little nose, and fresh carmine on her lips traveled in a cautious line to the tight smiling corners of her mouth. Not a curve of her dark-gold bob was out of place. Her eyes were shining. She looked very, very happy. It was wonderful to be able to make anyone so happy so easily. That was when Jack Spycer first considered the possibility of marrying Cynthia Mark. Anything could happen in Peking.

He felt dubious about asking Mr. and Mrs. Mark whether he might take Cynthia to the dance that night, but as it happened he did not have to ask for Mr. and Mrs. Mark suggested it themselves, in a tentative, almost a humble way. Mrs. Mark said she knew that he must be busy with his writing, and must be flooded with all sorts of alluring invitations, but if he were free . . . ? The whole negotiation was conducted furtively and hastily while Arthur was fussing with the cars and the picnic hamper, which meant that Arthur would not be included, and this was just as well, because he had often told Arthur that he hated those hotel dances.

When Chang had drawn his bath and he had told Chang that he was going out that night, he found himself wondering how Cynthia would look in the evening. They knew so little about each other. They might weary of each other in half an hour. Yet the uncertainty itself was delightful. There was no necessity to tell Chang where he was going, but he was sure Chang must have known.

When he went to the Chinese theater with Mr. Bock, the missionary, or when he joined Chinese students to attend some useful lecture at the university, Chang had a number of annoying ways of showing his disapproval. But now there was a whisky and soda waiting when he had finished his bath. His best studs were in his newest shirt. Chang made solicitous noises as he selected the very best silk socks, and he said it would be more better to press again that dinner coat which Mr. Wu had made.

All the stars were twinkling in a velvet North China sky that evening. The lanterns were lighted on the rickshaws and their bells joined the raucous blare of Chinese music from the little shops. He did not even mind the strong garlic on Ma's breath as Ma's slippered feet padded with unusual speed through the Legation Quarter.

Cynthia was in green organdy and she wore a string of pearls and a diamond bracelet. From the very first moment he had a sense of being accepted, and of having moved out of the category of a mere acquaintance, which showed that the Marks must have made further and satisfactory inquiries about him as soon as they had reached the Wagons-Lits. That was the great thing about Peking. You could learn a great deal about anyone in a very little while.

"Here's to Hollywood," Mr. Mark said, when they had champagne before dinner. "I've always heard they just throw money at you in Hollywood."

He felt more and more at home with the Marks. He wanted to help the Marks. He found himself drawing thoughtfully on his own experience as he advised them what to see and do in Peking. He would take them himself to buy embroidery and jade and curios, or better still he would send his boy Chang, who knew where you could get anything. Any time they wanted Chang, all they had to do was let him know. He found himself telling amusing anecdotes about Chinese housekeeping and servants, about the Chinese system of squeeze, and what was meant by "face." Then, after a second glass of champagne, it seemed natural that he should be describing the volumes of his trilogy and the novel he was blocking out on Peking life. All these were on the stocks, of course. That was the way he put it, on the stocks. You had to get a novel organized and planned before you wrote it.

"Jack," Mr. Mark said. "You don't mind if I call you Jack, do you? I think it's pretty smart of you to pick out China to write about. How about showing us something you've written?"

He had not finished organizing anything about China yet, but he did have a copy of the *Saturday Evening Post* somewhere with one of his stories in it. He would send it over tomorrow if Mr. Mark really wanted to wade through it, but better yet, how would it be if they all had dinner at his house? His cook was not bad at all. If they liked they could have a Chinese dinner, pigeon eggs and sweet-sour fish and Peking duck, and if they liked there would be a conjurer and a fortune teller after dinner, to give them some idea of Chinese life.

While he and Cynthia danced together, she told him, when he asked, that her hair had a natural wave. There was a downward droop to one corner of her mouth that he had never noticed, and in spite of powder he discovered the faintest sprinkle of freckles on the bridge of her nose. He could not understand why her nose had impressed him as sharp when he had first seen it.

"Do you still like me," she asked, "a little?"

If he had told them, he often thought, if he had only told them when there was still time. When he lay awake in his bed that night, he knew, instead of having talked of his servants, instead of implying that he was a financially successful writer, that it would have been just as easy if he had told the truth. He could have said frankly that he was still only trying to write, while he lived on his savings, and that more than half his money was gone and the rest of it going fast. He could not understand why he had not done so, except that it would not have fitted with the general picture of himself that existed in Peking, and he was loyal to that picture. He must have been living in a world of wishful thinking ever since he had entered the gates of the city and he had been blindly secure behind its walls.

When he rang for his tea the next morning, he told Chang that three people were coming to dinner. For entertainment he wanted a conjurer or some acrobats or the man with the trained dogs, something that would amuse strangers. Mr. and Mrs. Mark and Miss Mark were coming.

"You remember," he said, "the people who were here yesterday."

"Yes, marster," Chang said. "No need you worry."

Communication between them was necessarily rudimentary since Chang's English was bad and his own Chinese consisted of only a few crudely pronounced conventional phrases. There was no need for words, however, when his glance met Chang's. He had never realized until then that Chang, too, had his world of wishful thinking.

"Marster," Chang said, "you like small piece of number one fine jade? Jade man is here."

"What's the idea?" Jack asked. "What do I want with jade?"

Chang's eyes met his again. For a moment he was not an American or Chang his servant. Chang's voice was soft and gentle. He was folding Jack Spycer's blue-silk gown.

"Maybe you buy present for Missy. Little present." Chang was speaking English but he might as well have said Little Lotus Blossom in Chinese. You could never tell how the Chinese discovered things.

"I can't buy her a present," Jack said. "I only met her yesterday. Americans don't give presents to missys they met yesterday."

"Two small piece jade," Chang said. "One for Missy, one for Tai Tai." By Tai Tai, Chang meant Mrs. Mark. Chang had even selected what he was to buy — two ducks of greenish jade, small, but exceptionally good in quality and workmanship, from the shop of one of the best Jade Street merchants.

"Very nice piece," Chang said. "Number one fine piece. Suitable for lady."

There was a festive air all through the house as Jack sat down to breakfast. He could hear Ma and Sung the yardboy telling jokes, and Ho and Liu were singing in the kitchen.

"More better," Chang said, "you wear new suit again. Already pressed. More better."

It was only when he got into the trousers of the dove-gray suit that he thought of his lipstick-covered handkerchief and discovered it was gone. Only then did he understand the reason for the jade merchant and for that merry atmosphere of impending good fortune.

There was no better place for daydreams than a courtyard in Peking, where you could sit beneath a gingko tree, listening to the signals of the barber and the rice-cake merchant and the charcoal seller as they went their rounds through the hutung. No discordant thought intruded itself on Jack as he waited by the fish pool for his guests. There was no necessity to think of the future except in terms of a triumphal pageant, with larger courtyards, more mountainous rock gardens, and perhaps a temple in the Western Hills. There was no occasion, then, to cope with doubts as to whether he was in love with Cynthia or in love with gilded thoughts. There was no fear, then, of ending as a train-bearer or an appendage. Such fears came only when the evening was over, when he realized that he suddenly had risen above himself and had become an unduly glamorous individual, shining in a borrowed setting.

Jack Spycer was the perfect image, that night, of what he had always wanted to be, a man who understood all the niceties of an exotic, free existence, whose own wit and taste had allowed him to escape successfully from the trammeling crudities of a humdrum American culture, as exemplified by the pedestrian Marks. Of course, it was Chang who ordered the new lanterns for the courtyards. It was Chang who set the table outdoors, with red-lacquer chairs which had never belonged to the house and with a whole new service of antique porcelains and silver which must have been on loan from some dealer friend of Chang's. It was Chang who arranged for the series of wines and the flowers in the courtyards, who had decorated the rooms with new scrolls and carvings, and who supplied the extra servants and the Chinese musicians and the jugglers.

There was no wonder that the Marks were impressed by it, because he was impressed himself. He had never seen anything like that effortless, prodigal dinner.

"I really didn't have much to do with this," he remembered himself saying. "Chang arranged it all."

Yet it would all have been a failure if he himself had not fitted so perfectly into the setting.

"This isn't the way I usually live," he also said. "This is Chang's special effort. Chang is a genius in a way." And he found himself smiling serenely, with a blasé sort of wisdom, as he watched the jugglers. "You can see, can't you, why I love it here? There's nothing just like Peking."

He was amused but not surprised when Mr. Mark wanted to go into financial details. It interjected a crass note, but it was easy to explain that all this sort of thing cost very little — the servants' wages were very little, life was very inexpensive in China.

"It's an ideal place," he heard himself telling Mr. Mark, "for a poor boy like me."

It was consoling to remember that at least he did tell Mr. Mark part of the truth. If Mr. Mark did not believe it, he should have. He was a banker, who investigated risks.

It was only to be expected that he should drift away with Cynthia and sit beside her in the shade of the gingko tree, looking at the moon.

There were two more of those red-lacquer chairs that he had never seen before placed side by side in the shadows.

"Jack," Cynthia said, "I have an idea. It's been coming over me all day."

"What sort of an idea?" he asked.

"That I'd really like to live here. I really think I would."

Troubles always started when a dream was on the verge of coming true. That definiteness of Cynthia's, her descent to the practical, gave him a sudden, indefinable qualm.

"I'm awfully glad you feel that way," he said.

"Why, darling," she answered, and in spite of his qualm he found himself holding her hand, "I'm awfully glad you're glad."

It could not be construed as a definite proposal. That was one thing about which he was always positive. He had never proposed to Cynthia Mark. In the days that followed, those strange breathless days and nights when he and Cynthia kept moving from one thing to another, during their rides together, during their walks along the wall, during their hours alone and at all the parties where they kept meeting, he was sure that he had never proposed to Cynthia, but admittedly there was some sort of understanding in which everyone had shared, Arthur and Mrs. Llewellyn and all the Legation crowd. He had certainly not objected when Cynthia began referring to them as "we" in speaking of the future. He was pushed along in those days and weeks faster and faster by insistent implication . . . we could do this and that, we could go here and there. But was it ever worth while going into the details of why something did not work? Such a situation must have always contained in itself the grim seeds of self-destruction.

The end came on a very hot July morning. He and Cynthia were to visit Arthur and Mrs. Llewellyn at Peitaiho, the beach resort where so many people in Peking spent the summer. Chang was getting his bags packed and Cynthia had sent him a little note by messenger from the hotel:

"Darling, I can't wait to go with you to the sea. Sometime we must have a place of our own there. Sometime."

Jack was reading it for the third time when the yardboy brought in the morning mail and laid it on his desk. On top of the little pile was a message from the North China Bank, announcing that his account was down to six hundred dollars. There was a letter, also, from the editorial rooms of the *Saturday Evening Post*. He remembered that when he opened it his hands had grown moist and clammy. The *Post* did not like the story about the gambler on the boat, and so six hundred dollars was all he had left in the world — less than that when he subtracted his outstanding bills.

He supposed, and he had plenty of time to think, afterwards, that there were certain different steps he might have taken, but perhaps it was just as well that instead of taking them he felt as though a thread had snapped and everything was over. It was amazing that he had not realized until that morning that this was bound to happen eventually, but then one never did much thinking when one was twenty-six. He was sometimes sorry that he ran away and did not face the situation squarely. Yet at least he had acted. He opened the drawer of his desk and pulled out envelope and paper and found his fountain pen.

"Dear Cynthia," he wrote, "I can't go with you because I have to go home. My money has run out and I'm not even sure I have the price of a steamship ticket. I've loved the time we've spent together and I hope you have, too — a little. Please forgive me." He folded the paper and sealed it in the envelope. Next he looked in the *Peking Chronicle* for sailing dates from Shanghai.

"Chang," he called. His voice was perfectly steady and so was his hand when he handed Chang the note.

"Give this chit to Missy," he said. "Get the accounts ready. Get a man to buy my furniture and pictures. I'm going home."

He would never forget Chang's stricken look and his high, broken voice.

"You go home?" Chang asked. "Why, marster?"

"No money," he answered. "Just enough money to go home."

In the short silence that followed, he watched Chang fondle the three long hairs growing from his chin.

"Marster," Chang said, "it not necessary."

"Oh, yes, it is," Jack said.

"No, please," Chang said. "You marry Missy."

Jack Spycer was sure that Chang would never have been so crude if he had not been upset.

"No, I can't do it, Chang. I haven't any money. You see, they think I'm rich," he answered, and it was not the right time to laugh but somehow it was funny. "You made them think so just as much as I did, Chang."

"Please," Chang said. His voice was higher. "You marry Missy quick, then you have money."

He knew that it might have been possible, too, if only everything had started in a different way.

"No, Chang," he said. "You send that note to Missy, Chang." But Chang was speaking again.

"Please," Chang said, "I give you face, marster."

"Face?" Jack repeated after him. He never did wholly understand the word's true meaning, but he saw that from the beginning it had been a question of face. He was involved, he saw, in oriental values, cast into a European mold — face or façade, but face was a good definition.

"I give you face, marster," Chang said again. "You marry Missy. I find you plenty money."

That was why he was always fond of Chang. Although Chang was only making a sound business proposition, he always thought it was generous of him. But not a loan from Chang, only the turning back of the clock, could have given that situation face.

"No, Chang," he said. "Take that letter. Someday I'll be back."

Someday he would be back, but he knew he would never see the Marks again.

"No funny business, Chang," he said. "Don't you talk to Missy. Just you leave that chit."

"Marster," Chang began again.

"No," he said. "Be quiet, Chang."

He could hear the song of the melon vender, sweet and enticing, beyond his wall. He could feel the Tibetan carpet beneath his feet and he could hear the English sparrows chattering in the gingko tree, but salt had lost its savor. He was leaving Peking already.

There it was, that tawdry little episode, as clearly as he could recollect it after a lapse of eleven years. It was nothing but some wasted time, a kiss at the Summer Palace and certain more amorous kisses elsewhere, and pretense and conceit combined with debt and doubt. His own career, in Hollywood and New York, put it into shadow, and then the war and the postwar years helped to blur but not erase the scribblings on that slate. What was there, he sometimes wondered, that caused parts of that affair (but it was not an affair, and it was not an encounter, either) to remain so vivid when he had forgotten so many more important things? It was lacking in balance and unity. He could not even remember what Cynthia had been like any longer, except that she was a blonde. He could not envisage her as a person, like other people in his life, because, frankly, she was only a symbol of unformed desire, a sort of attribute of temptation like one of Bunyan's characters, in a shady kind of Pilgrim's Progress. There had been no orderly progress, either. Two lines of Keats kept running through his mind when the wheels of the general's plane left the ground at Tientsin.

> Poor nymph — poor Pan — how he did weep to find
> Naught but a lovely sighing of the wind.

When the plane had leveled off, the door of the general's compartment opened and the chief of staff stepped out. Jack Spycer was surprised to learn that the general wanted to speak to him. The general had hardly noticed him on the trip and Spycer had not minded because he had never done well with generals, but a reflex from the war made him start up hastily as though he were not a civilian. The general was staring out of the window. The plane was flying low, not much above three thousand feet, so that Jack Spycer could see the green and brown squares and rectangles of the Chinese farms and the mud walls and the willow trees around the tiny buildings. From the air as from the ground, ages of human occupancy made the landscape as conventional as the scene on a willowware plate. It was a sunny day, but there was a haze that indicated that a few days ago one of those storms of yellow dust must have blown down from the north.

"Good morning, Mr. Spycer," the general said. "Sit down," and he patted the seat beside him. "It's a bare-looking terrain, isn't it? They've cut down all the trees."

The general, he supposed, was analyzing that countryside as the possible scene of military maneuvers, and thus the lack of trees presented an interesting concealment problem. Jack, on the other hand, still thought of it as something in blue and white glaze.

"That's the trouble with China, sir," Jack Spycer answered in the loud monotone one always used on planes. "No trees. They were all cut down a thousand years ago."

"Why were they cut down?"

"To fire the bricks for the Great Wall. At least that's what I've heard, sir."

"The Chinese are a funny people," the general said. "Getting on with them is like punching a pillow."

"Yes, sir."

There was never any use arguing with a three-star general.

"Now in Chungking — " the general began. "Were you ever in Chungking, Mr. Spycer?"

"Yes, sir. I was in the C.B.I. Theatre for a while." But the general was not interested.

"Didn't someone in Manila say you had something to do with Hollywood?"

"Yes, sir," Jack Spycer answered. "I'm out there now and then."

"Do you know Joe E. Brown?"

"No, sir."

"I met Joe in the Pacific. Didn't someone say you know Peking?"

"I lived there once about eleven years ago," Jack Spycer said. "Have you ever been there, sir?"

"No, but they tell me it's quite a city. It seems to get under your skin if you stay there."

"Yes, sir, more than other Chinese cities."

The loudness of their voices overemphasized everything and gave the conversation a queer monotony.

"There was a friend of mine, a classmate," the general said. "When he was a language officer he stayed two years in Peking. He had a whole houseful of servants and ran it on a captain's pay. He was always talking about his Number One Boy in Peking."

"Yes, sir."

"I saw him at Sill afterwards. He never was the same afterwards. Neither was his wife."

"Peking has a way of spoiling you. The Chinese like to spoil you," Jack Spycer answered. Poor nymph, poor Pan, he was thinking, and he leaned forward to watch the field unrolling beneath them, like one of those scroll paintings that you used to be able to buy in Peking which were meant to unroll just a little at a time.

"We're going to circle the city before we land," the general said. "Tell me if you see anything I ought to see."

"I'll do the best I can, sir. I've never seen it from the air," Jack Spycer answered.

He was glad that the general had fallen silent. Talking above the motors was always difficult and besides he wanted to think of the trilogy that he had never written and never would. But the general continued his belated effort to be gracious.

"I'm sorry we have to take off again this evening," he said.

"So am I, sir," Jack answered. There was an air pocket and the plane was unsteady for a moment but the stomach-searching drop did not stop the general.

"Are you married, Spycer?"

"Yes, sir."

"Children?"

"Yes, sir, two. They're in New York."

"I've got three myself," the general said. "They're grown up now."

"They always tell me that children grow up before you know it," Jack Spycer said.

"You want some gum?" the general asked.

"No, thank you, sir."

"I suppose you get a lot of local color on a trip like this," the general said. "I suppose it helps with the articles you write, but personally I've seen enough of local color."

Then he saw the city in the distance, a blur at first on the North China plain, but growing sharper every second.

"There it is, the wall," he said.

"What, the Great Wall?" The general had pushed himself forward in his seat to look.

"No, sir, the city wall. The city."

"Oh, I see now. It looks damn flat," the general said.

But he was forgetting the general. He had never seen all the walls of Peking at once, the thousands of walls, great ones and small ones, enclosing secrets which were revealed at last if you had time to look — but of course there was not enough time. It was all there, tranquil in the sun, untouched by time and contemptuous of change. The tiles of the Forbidden City glistened like tribute silk. As the plane circled, it was all there, the broad streets, the Bell Tower, the Drum Tower, Coal Hill and the lakes and the Temple of Heaven.

"The Japs didn't burn it, did they?" the general said.

But he had forgotten about the general. Poor nymph, the words were running through his mind again, poor Pan — but he could not blame himself for anything, now that he had seen Peking. Given a second chance, he knew he would repeat it all with pleasure. It did not matter so much whether you had spent your time there wisely or foolishly. As long as you had lived there, you had been a part of a great company. You had shared the place with Kublai Khan and Marco Polo and the Jesuits and Yung Lo.

He saw the general looking at him curiously.

"Did you have a good time down there?" the general asked.

The Same Old Bird

(1945)

EXPERTS familiar with the subject of public speaking have often told
me that the happiest way of beginning a discourse is achieved by telling a story or anecdote. This, they have said, sets the audience in a
genial and receptive mood, and such a genial bit when suitably selected, will lead unsuspecting minds more easily into more serious matters. Now, I've sat through a great many speeches, as you will too, because you will find it very hard consistently to keep out of lecture halls
or to slip away quickly enough from public dinners. And I have heard
a great many of these stories, most of which I cannot possibly remember. In fact, I honestly believe that the only people who do remember
them are other public speakers, who jot them down for future use. It
is my opinion, not that it is worth much because I am not an expert,
that this sort of sugar-coated introduction might very well be skipped
and that most people are intelligent enough to do without it. Yet here
I find myself adhering to the party line, about to ask you to hold tight
to your chairs while I, too, tell a story. I must add, frankly, that it is
not a very good one, but this is my only reason for telling it, because
through its very dullness it illustrates a phase in my life and yours
which perhaps is worth considering.

You have probably heard this one yourselves but I am asking you
please not to stop me. It was told last year over the radio by a returned
war correspondent from England who also wrote it scintillatingly in
the pages of a useful news weekly. This episode, as he sketched it,
dealt with maneuvers which the army has been holding in Britain in
preparation for the invasion of the European continent. These maneuvers were done with such realism that even the higher officers, such as
major generals, who engaged in them frequently did not know whether
the orders calling for the sudden massing of large bodies of troops
might not actually mean that D day had arrived. It seems, on one of

these occasions, that an American general and his staff were much exercised by such uncertainties. They stood on a knoll on the English downs watching roads filled with troops all moving toward the Channel. They were waiting for definite information but, as so often happens in the army, they could get no word from anyone. Suddenly a plane appeared above their position and circled several times above headquarters. It was obvious that the plane was about to drop a message, and it did. The pilot, it seems, tossed out a carrier pigeon. Now I doubt very much if anyone tosses pigeons out of planes — does it matter? This pigeon, being very well trained, flew right down and permitted a member of this general's staff to catch it and, as might be expected, attached to the bird's leg was a message. The message was instantly removed and handed to the expectant general, who read it and was angry. The message read: "I am being sent down because I was naughty in my cage."

I told you that this was not a very good story and personally I was rather bored with it at the time, and somewhat annoyed by all the cumbersome build-up and military inaccuracy that led up to this anticlimax. Then I found myself thinking that sometime, somewhere, I had heard all this before, although I could not recall where, and it remained uncomfortably and uselessly in my mind for several days as such things do. Then suddenly the recollection came back very clearly.

I had heard that story when I was in the Café de la Paix in Paris in the autumn of 1918. The story at that time was not streamlined. I wouldn't bore you now with repeating it except that I am laboring to make what is called a point. It seems back there in 1918, that an American general commanding a division in the Argonne drive had sent his infantry into a heavy attack. His regiments had jumped off at the zero hour, which had been close to dawn, and now it was noon and they had not been heard from since. Back there at division headquarters the telephone outlines had been smashed; no runners had returned for hours; and so there was no news of the fighting up front. Then suddenly, if you will believe it, out of the sky appeared a very badly battered carrier pigeon which fluttered weakly to the portable coop at headquarters. Aides, the chief of staff, and the general himself rushed to catch it, and sure enough the pigeon was carrying a message. They unfolded the flimsy bit of paper and this is what the worried general read, back there in 1918: "I am tired of carrying this damned bird."

So you can see, it is not only a rather dull story but a very old one. In fact, all that is interesting is its age, for its age poses two questions: Has such a mediocre effort as this been lying dusty on the shelf of someone's mind for a quarter of a century waiting to be brushed off and taken down again, or was it a new 1943 invention conceived by new creative thought? Personally I cannot believe that originality is such a scarce commodity that such a story could persist in tradition. I think it is safer to assume that there is nothing new under the sun; that there are no new stories, no contrivances of plot; that the few which exist all lie fallow in the mind of each generation, waiting to be conjured up by the pressure of outside circumstance. If this is so, as I hope, given a war you have war anecdotes, and no war is very much different essentially from any other. There are the same sorts of terror, the same species of hardship, the same rather incongruous discipline, and the same sort of humor.

"Come on, boys," the sergeant says, "do you want to live forever?"

"Do you know who you're speaking to?" the general roars at the lieutenant over the telephone.

"Do you know who you're speaking to?" the frightened young man answers.

"No," the general says.

"Well," the lieutenant answers, "thank God you don't."

These are samples of stories that come out of every war, and I only brought up the one about the pigeons, because it illustrates the fashion of creative thought. Writing, like stale jokes, has a way of changing, as life and as the economic structure changes. This is not so true with wartime writing, as this has a static quality, but it indicates what may happen to the play, and to the novel and to poetry here in America, after this war is over.

There is naturally no way of hazarding any sort of prophecy at such a moment in which we are now living. Emotionally, creatively, economically and socially the lines of our civilization are now in what the military strategists like to call a fluid state. There is a sense of breathless pause today, which all of us here must feel; a certain knowledge that everything tomorrow must be different — our manner of thought, our manner of expression, everything. You here are going to be an active part in that new thought. You are going to help to form it, both from your experiences today and from those you will have tomorrow. You are going to live the most active part of your lives in a postwar world. I don't know how this world will shape itself any more than you do, but when I was about your age, I lived in a postwar world myself and I believe that all postwar epochs must have certain similarities. I have led most of my life in a postwar world of letters, and I have been somewhat intimately associated with its reactions. I venture to tell you a little about it because what happened to my generation may happen in a measure to yours also.

On the second of November, 1918, I sailed on a very shopworn ship from the harbor of Brest, in France, back to the United States. I was a first lieutenant, recommended for a captaincy, at the time I was ordered back to join a new division in America which was about to embark for France. The ship was crowded with casual officers and with wounded. All of us had seen a good deal of fighting. It was such a slow trip that when we arrived in New York harbor, the Armistice had been signed and the show was over; but I still can remember very vividly the first shock of coming home to America after having lived a life for some little time in which being killed or wounded was accepted as a conventional ending.

Last autumn I relived that same experience vicariously, for last autumn I returned from India in a C-54 army transport. This plane was also filled with wounded men and returning officers, one of whom sat next me — a bomber pilot — who had been on raids for the last eighteen months over Burma. I met him downtown in a restaurant an hour after we landed in Miami. I asked him that question which one always asks returning soldiers.

"Well," I asked him, "what do the states look like?"

And he gave the answer that any soldier gives.

"By God!" he said. "Over here they don't know there's a war on."

After all, there is no reason why civilians should know, since most successful wars are fought to prevent their knowing. But when he spoke, I was back again with my own memories, in the shed of a Jersey City pier, in November, 1918, with a customs inspector going through my locker trunk and bedding roll, examining my other pair of britches and my other suit of underwear, and my maps and papers just as though there had never been a war. Then I was at the Hotel Biltmore. You get queer ideas about what you are going to do when you get back home. Now that I was there and able to do them, none of them seemed attractive. It was still too early for many soldiers to be back from overseas. I was suddenly not adjusted to any civilian sight or sound. It did not even seem like the city I had left. The people in the streets, those sleek, well-fed civilians, those bellboys, those waiters in the dining room, did not seem to realize that there had been a war. They had been living happily and complacently in their own world, which had grown while I was gone. The war was over and already they seemed to have forgotten it. There were more automobiles than I had ever seen before, more furs, more orchids, more money. Everyone at home had been growing rich while I was there in France. I can still remember an old sensation that was close to bitterness, as I listened to people I had known talking about this and that, as though there had never been a war. It was impossible for a long while to exchange ideas with them, for our senses of values were so different. It was better to turn the page, better to forget the whole business and to live in that curious, shifting present. A good many of my contemporaries were not able to achieve that living in the present. It was not easy for it was a very different America from the one we had left. Manners and attitudes change very quickly in a war.

America, when I had left it, had been an orderly place, and now it was seething with all sorts of restive discontent. In a wave of emotional relief that came with peace, everyone was spending money very freely, from new millionaires to factory workers. There was a sort of recklessness which seemed to bring no lasting satisfaction. In every walk of life there was an undercurrent of discontent. In Congress the Republicans were fighting the Wilson Administration. Labor was striking to maintain its social gains. There were hints of new, dangerous ideas bred of the revolution which had occurred in Russia. There were the walkout of switch-yard workers, the great city strike in Seattle, the strike of the Boston police force. There was the riot in the Union Club beside St. Patrick's Cathedral in New York when elements of the Irish population tore down the British flag. There was the endless debate about the League of Nations. British propagandists were suggesting that we scrap a portion of our fleet; and later there was the inflation in

Germany and with it the strange suspicion that Germany had never been beaten.

It all adds up now in my memory to maladjustment and discomfort, disbelief in old tradition and suspicion of the present and the future that was reflected in all our manners. Moreover, there was a weary sense that no one could do much about it, which found expression in a desire to take what there was and to forget the rest — a feeling that nothing had come out the way we'd hoped. And finally there developed an almost universal wish to put this confusion of thought and the world's insoluble problems as far away from us as possible. In the election of 1920, Warren G. Harding put this backlog of discomfort into words when he spoke of getting back to normalcy. Even then this had an awkward sound and anyone who thought about it must have known that the normalcy of the old days was impossible to achieve. Yet we contrived to approximate an illusion. We did so because of the years of prosperity which followed the last war, because of the materialism derived from a desire for consumers' goods, because of a demand for things, such as tangible comforts. Out of this sort of spiritual confusion came that great growth of the tangible that changed the whole face of our country — automobiles in quantity production, the radio, the washing machine, the gadget civilization, the airplanes. It seemed in that illusion of prosperity, that the world was settling down. At least nearly everyone liked to think so, although logic might speak differently.

There began to be a new type of hero in this postwar world, which was so tired of soldiering. He was the businessman, who was making all these wonders possible. He became the hero of magazine fiction. He gave advice to young men in newspaper interviews, telling them how to behave, how to invest their money, how to speak to their employer so that they could get a raise.

That, roughly, was the postwar world of this country — the world in which you spent your childhood and from which most of you have derived your most impressionable memories. You may even feel, as do many older than you who were active in it, a furtive wish that it may return. And something like it probably will, not the same sort of thing, but something with its general shape, simply because human beings become weary after a time of strife and ideology.

This is an oversimplified discussion of political theory and international events. I am only trying to give, very briefly and superficially, a picture of the forces which my generation encountered when we came back from the last war, which developed into a stability that was not wholly destroyed by the depression of the thirties, a dangerous stability.

We can see now, as many of us saw then, that it was more a temporary balance of a great many conflicting stresses as opposed to any sort of long-term quiet. We can see it the more clearly now that the era is ended. It is plain now that we were all in a barrel, momentarily held motionless in some back eddy just above Niagara Falls. In fact that simile was used by someone in the 1932 elections. "Don't change barrels," someone said, "when going over Niagara Falls."

Those two decades, from 1920 to 1940, in which my generation spent its early manhood and its early middle age was a time of excesses, a time of futile beliefs, a time of many strange delusions. Through it all, our nation was in the throes of spiritual and physical changes which have not been completed yet. Without attempting an appraisal, there is one phase of it which both interests and puzzles me from the point of view of a writer of fiction.

It would seem on looking back, that those twenty years should have been a most unpropitious time for the practice of any sort of creative art. My teachers used to tell me, as perhaps yours do today, that the arts — particularly literature — flourish best in a period of confidence. As examples of such periods they cite the golden age of Pericles, the Renaissance, the Elizabethan and the Victorian eras and in our country, the flowering of New England. These all were times of economic prosperity, and of reasoned calm. They were times when people had a breathing space, and when there was a tolerably universal belief that most of men's problems were solved and that humanity could look forward serenely to a further uninterrupted progress, since everything was for the best in this best of worlds. Against such static and established backgrounds, the writer had the leisure to look about him, and to view from a logical perspective the values of his society and thus to form a sensible estimate of life and of faith. Certainly the last years in which we have been living have gone quite far from fulfilling this prescription. In them we have suffered panic, disillusion and heartache. In hardly one of those years have we been able honestly to believe in an undisturbed future. And yet, out of them, curiously enough, I venture to say that there has evolved something closer to a national literature than anything that has ever appeared in this country. It is, of course, too close to the present to give any adequate evaluation, and it may turn out that such a statement is a brash whistling in the graveyard. Yet it still seems to me that the time in which I have lived has been recorded for posterity by some distinguished exponents of my profession. They have recorded its sadness and its shallowness, and indirectly something of its amazing vitality and optimism. They have made it possible for posterity, if it cares to do so, to examine true portraits of the men and women who lived in my generation, to form a judgment of their fallacies and their manners. For some reason, for almost the first time in our history, the American writer broke away from the European tradition and became definitely conscious of America. He was aware that America in itself was a vital, moving scene, and the shiftings of that scene intrigued his thought. I don't think, on the whole, he liked any of it very much. He was uncomfortable and discontented with most of it. He hated the complacencies around him, he despised the social injustices, and the aridity of provincialism, but at any rate he saw what was going on around him and he set it down on paper. He was aware, if often incompletely, of the relation of parts to the whole American scene. He was able to create living characters, who epitomized vital aspects of that scene. He contrived further to evolve a literary technique of a highly superior quality.

It seems to me that our teachers and our critics have not been as keenly aware of these achievements as they should be. I think perhaps the reason is that criticism has not flourished as successfully as creative art in this time of change.

I don't think that a writer of fiction is ever good in this field, but I should like almost at random to point out a few plays and books which were produced in this period and which illustrate in a measure what I am trying to say. I don't know whether any of you have read them, but if you have not, they might help you to understand that other postwar world in which your fathers were brought up — and it may be more worthwhile than you think that you should understand it.

The plays of Eugene O'Neill come very close to the life and problems of that world. There are also some of the plays of Sidney Howard — notably *Silver Cord* and *Lucky Sam McCarver*. In the twenties, particularly, the theater was very much alive, but perhaps the novel has less of the limitations of the stage. A novel is never as exact or as formalized as a play. It can be full of unevenness and of technical mistakes and yet its final result may linger much longer in the memory. There were a surprising number of good novels written in the twenties and the thirties. Of course it is quite impossible to tell whether any of them will become great novels, but they were executed by competent craftsmen. I suppose perhaps that time has dated many of them already — in your eyes more than mine — but I believe that most of them still have vividness and an accuracy of construction. If you should care to know how we felt about war and how we analyzed war's disillusionment, there are *Three Soldiers* by John Dos Passos, *The Enormous Room* by E. E. Cummings, and Hemingway's *The Sun Also Rises*, and his greater novel, on which perhaps his reputation as a novelist must stand or fall, *Farewell to Arms*. The characters in these rather diverse books are not admirable people as one considers the conventional fictional hero, but they are indubitably people of their time, struggling with its discontent. If you want to know what youth was like, and what it thought about in that postwar period, there are the two novels of Scott Fitzgerald, *This Side of Paradise*, and *The Beautiful and Damned*, uneven novels written by a young man of extraordinary talent, sophomoric in parts but filled with the shifting, hopeless sort of restiveness which you also will experience when this war is over. Booth Tarkington, an older man, who already possessed a literary reputation, also wrote on this same theme and his *Alice Adams* is a sadly beautiful story, of the fallacious ambitions of a middle-class girl in a midwestern town. Sinclair Lewis, I think, still remains the greatest and most stable literary figure. If you want to find what was wrong and indirectly what was right with your fathers' America, you can still turn to *Main Street*, or *Babbitt*, or *Dodsworth*. The crime and the restiveness of our days still lies between the covers of Theodore Dreiser's *American Tragedy*, and in a different and more finished way, there is again F. Scott Fitzgerald with his story of the genteel bootlegger, *The Great Gatsby*. Then there is Thornton Wilder's *Heaven Is My Destination*, that picture, half hilarious but wholly sad, of the religious bigot. And there is John Steinbeck's uneven but powerful portrait of the forgotten man in *The Grapes of Wrath*. If you turn to our short stories, you will find that this difficult form reached a high level of technical perfection. Ernest Hemingway was, and still is, the master of it. Those of you who are writing now or who will try later, doubtless will endeavor to imitate his style, which seems on superficial examination so facile and easy. Hemingway has painted an unforgettable gallery of American types, but close beside him comes that sardonic master of humor, Ring Lardner, who has left us his professional athletes, gamblers, tired old men and noisy women.

It would not be difficult to go much longer with this list. There are many equally important names and works which I have omitted, not intentionally but only because I have mentioned those which have come most readily to my memory. At any rate, I have given enough to indicate that the art of drama and fiction was actively practiced at what would seem an unpropitious era.

Now that this era has been completely closed, and is already relegated into history with the advent of World War II, it is possible to indulge in a few smaller generalities. What was the main characteristic of most of this writing? I think it was largely a spirit of revolt, or at least profound malaise or discontent. It was the sort of discontent that manifested itself in a general dislike for the economic and social pattern under which we lived. It added up to a destructive criticism of the very sort of normalcy which the average citizen of this country so ardently desired. We produced very few integrated, contented characters. We were a maladjusted lot — but then perhaps all writers are. We flourished on our restlessness, since most of us were well rewarded for throwing bottles at the umpire. We were in revolt against conventional expression; we hated the smug complacency of business; we hated the illusion of order which covered so much disorder; we hated the platitudes of our politicians, and the advertisements in the *Saturday Evening Post*. We saw what was wrong with the lives we lived. We saw no way to improve them, but at any rate we lived our lives more fully and more freely and more completely than our fathers. We never adjusted ourselves to that postwar world, nor did we want to adjust. In that refusal lay both our weakness and our strength. Finally, I do not believe that any of us would have missed those years, for, taken all together, they added up to the greatest show on earth. The curtain is falling on them now and the scene is being shifted for another act and you are going to be the ones who will be on the stage. There is going to be a new sort of thought — a new sort of writing, and what this will be, what form it will take, neither you nor I know yet. I venture to guess, though, that your postwar life will be somewhat the same as ours. It is like that story of the pigeon — nothing changes quite as much as any of us think it will.

When I was your age I, and a great many of my contemporaries, frequently found myself annoyed by the efforts of older gentlemen, usually from school or college faculties, to understand and to be one of us. I can perceive now that there was a pathos and an eagerness in their effort to which I was completely blinded then. I can realize that they were offering us their companionship and their sympathy in the hope that we might profit from their experience. Of course I still do not believe that there can be any great mingling of the generations. I believe that one of the great tragedies of living is that experience gained by one's elders cannot be passed on by word of mouth.

"Boys," we used to chant in a mocking chorus, when they had left us and when we were safely alone with our own age group. "You'll let me call you boys won't you? I used to be a boy once myself."

It surprises me no little to find myself standing here making the same sort of effort as those misguided gentlemen. I find myself very anxious that you should realize that the existence which my generation led and the problems which it faced, may not be so very different from what you will encounter. I rather think that your fathers resemble you more closely than my father, for example, resembled me. My father and your grandfathers were brought up in a Victorian era where standards of behavior were set in simple molds of definition. They could look forward to certainties — and measured rewards and measured punishments. For every action then, there was a certain and predictable reaction. Our own lives contained none of this. The precepts we were taught in our teens no longer worked smoothly in our twenties. Our lives were not like the lives our fathers spent in their youth, but they add up to something which you can grasp more readily.

We suddenly found ourselves, just as you, projected into a world war, placed in uniform and clamped under a captious military discipline, jammed into ships and sent across the sea, to an odd country where farmers had manure piles in their front yards right by their bedroom windows and where there were mademoiselles from Armentières who did not understand very well what we were saying. We bickered in pubs with our English cousins just as you will bicker. We made jokes about our generals just as you will make them. Death and wounds became ordinary phenomena. The hard realities of life and death taught us our own peculiar language and set us as a generation apart. We came back into an incomprehensible sort of existence. We moved into years of inflation, into countless days of trying to forget, and into a long effort to achieve normality. We never achieved it and I doubt if you will either. We had our race riots, our conscientious objectors, our Bolsheviki and the IWW. You will have your Communists and other organizations that begin with initials. We had our hyphenated Americans and our little group of willful men in the Senate. You are faced with your isolationists and interventionists. We had our ragtime and later our jazz age. You have jive and swoon clubs and Frank Sinatra. Our girls wore sweaters which we used to call petting shirts. Your girls, as far as I can gather, are just called "sweater girls," and you have added to them "pin-up girls," an innovation but not a very great one. You don't know what you're going to do when this war is over or how you're going to earn a living, if any, any more than we did. Furthermore, there is nothing much you can do about most of this, any more than we could. You are entering, as we did, a world you never made. It has been the fashion of late years to blame certain undesirable conditions on certain groups or even on certain individuals. This is usually an oversimplification, for most of the things that happen in times like these are the result of very complicated combinations which often defy any accurate analysis. Circumstance evolves pressure groups and leaders and these groups and persons seldom alter circumstance. I think this may explain why so much we wrote had a superficial quality and possessed an atmosphere of bewilderment. It is hard to draw definite conclusions in a time when conclusions themselves are undergoing constant change.

In one way this puts you in a rather fortunate position. When we were young, many persons felt free to give us specific advice on many subjects, and now advice is hardly possible. I certainly should consider myself impertinent if I were to try to give you any and yet I think you might learn something if you read some of the books we wrote. The mere fact that I do not believe we successfully solved a single one of our problems may give you a certain consolation. You are going to attempt, I think, to solve the same ones all over again, but you are in a position to see that many of your difficulties are not new. There is no necessity for you to overdramatize yourselves as so many of us did. There is no need for you to take the extremes we took of revolt and of self-pity and of elation, for we have supplied you with an interesting library of textbooks on postwar behavior. Though there is little constructive you can learn from them, you can see quite clearly if you peruse their pages many of the mistakes we made and many of the sophistries which we committed. You may learn, as we did not, the danger of too frequently making a hysterical discovery of the obvious. More than that, in the light of our experiences, you may learn to cultivate two qualities which few of us possessed. It was not our fault entirely since they do not come easily with youth and the pattern of our lives may have been newer and stranger than yours will be to you. Few of us were patient. Few of us were tolerant — rightly so, perhaps, since there are times in which tolerance and patience do not fit. Yet I believe that they are important virtues now if only because of their rarity. You may learn to cultivate them if you can realize only partially that so much you are facing has been met before. The circumstances may be different — more vivid and more intense — but if you realize that others lived through something similar, this realization may help you to evaluate them. This, I am afraid, is about all we have to offer you. It should have been more and it surely is not much, but it is valuable, such as it is, that opportunity we are giving you to live vicariously our own experience.

Perhaps in the end that is all that literature means, and we have given you, such as it is, a literature, and I don't believe it is such a bad one either. It may even be that parts of this uncertain legacy may in the end be more important than our gadgets and inventions and our strides in science. At any rate, our pages of experience are there for you to read and to them you may add your own pages, and I hope that they will be better, but I do not believe that any of them will be more vivid than those of Farrell or Thomas Wolfe. This is all I have tried to say, and I hope that I have said it clearly enough so that you can grasp my meaning. That soldier in the last war was tired of carrying that bird. It seems to me that we writers have been carrying a bird ever since with some sort of message tied to its leg. Well, gentlemen, it's your bird now. Its plumage may be different, its wingspread may be wider, but in the main I think I can recognize it. It's the same old bird!

M